know you two can sort things out," she often said. "I just can't understand how this could have happened."

For Ken the bad time was marked by panic. He couldn't sleep at night, which left him groggy with fatigue by day. Unable to settle in the bed they shared, he spent the nights on the living-room couch, sipping Kool-Aid and watching television until the small hours of the morning. The distraction of old movies kept him from reviewing the mess he had made of things. In the mornings, his body longed for sleep. He drove to work through snowstorms with the car window down, hoping the cold air would revive him, slapping his face to keep from dropping off.

Somehow the nightmare had ended better than he expected. Karen and he would survive the mess he had created. She had blown her stack, as he knew she would, but she was staying. Now all he had to get through was the misery on Sunday of telling his grandmothers—and facing Barbara and Denis.

On Karen's return from work that Saturday night, he tentatively advanced to hug her and she accepted his embrace. They found to their mutual relief that the peace between them was holding.

He took her handbag from her and dropped it on a side table. She asked, "How's Melissa?"

Five-month-old Melissa had been reacting to the tension in the household by crying hard for long periods of time.

Ken replied, "I had trouble getting her to go to sleep. She didn't settle down until about nine o'clock, but she's all right now."

"Did she take her bottle?"

"Yeah."

Karen stood in the living-room, uncomfortable and not sure what else to say. Neither wanted to reopen discussion about the gambling and the missing money.

"Would you like a cup of tea?" Ken asked, his voice soft. It was an olive branch, one of the signals between them that meant a return to normalcy. Karen, English-born, could never resist a cup of tea.

"Sure," she responded with a warm grin, appreciating that he was making an effort.

In the kitchen he poured himself a glass of Kool-Aid from a pitcher in the refrigerator and put on the kettle. After a guilty hesitation, Karen cut herself a slice of fruit-and-nut bread. She was trying to stick to her Weight Watchers regime, but she felt a need for something sweet. To compensate, she put skim milk in her tea.

To fill in the silence she chattered about events that evening at the supermarket, but there were awkward pauses. Karen abandoned the pretence.

Her voice full of sympathy and concern, she said, "Tomorrow's a big day."

"Yeah," he nodded, "but it's something that I've gotta do."

They moved to the living-room and sat on the rumpled couch, pushing aside Ken's blanket and pillow to make room. He had been sleeping there, banished from their bed since Thursday when Karen had learned about the forged cheques and realized he was gambling again. *Saturday Night Live* was on television, a favourite of theirs. Karen watched a while, ready to be amused, but she was too tired. She got up and stretched.

"I think I'll go to bed," she said. He stood up, looming over her, and tentatively bent to put his arms around her. "Goodnight," he said wistfully. She studied him. He was a shambles, with bloodshot eyes and a two-day growth of reddish beard on his exhausted face. She gave him a brief forgiving hug and stepped back.

On the stairs she hesitated and turned. "You can come up to bed if you want," she offered.

"No," he answered quietly. "Not until I get back on the right track. Not until you can trust me again."

She nodded, feeling a stab of pity and love. She checked on the sleeping baby, undressed, read a few pages of a book by her bed, and dropped off to sleep.

The last thing Ken remembers clearly that night is watching the rest of *Saturday Night Live*. He knows he saw the end of the show and the beginning of something else, he doesn't remember what, and then he was overtaken by deep sleep. After two sleepless nights in a row, he had never been so worn out in his life.

He awoke from a disturbing dream. He saw the face of Barbara Woods, his mother-in-law. Her mouth was open in an expression of horror and her eyes seemed to be pleading with him for help. In the distance, he heard screams, the voices of Karen's sisters. Where was he? He seemed to be at the home of his in-laws.

Next he was at the top of the stairs outside the children's bedrooms. "The kids are in trouble," he was thinking. "Better see what I can do." He called, "Kids.... Kids!" No reply. He stood in the upstairs hall but there was no one around. That was strange. He'd better get help. Something terrible seemed to have happened.

The next part of the dream—was it a dream?—is spotty. At some point he may have picked up a telephone. Perhaps he didn't. Maybe the thought of a telephone came to his mind because he heard the noise a phone emits when it is off the hook. He ran outside, using the basement door to the underground garage where his car was parked.

Next he was at the wheel of his car. This was no dream, but he couldn't understand how it could be real. He saw in his right hand a long knife. Aghast, he threw it to the floor of the car. Next he was at the police station a block away. He opened the main doors leading to an office. A woman was seated behind a counter. He became aware of his hands, from which blood was pouring, and found he couldn't move his fingers.

The woman approached him. He leaned on the counter, taking his weight on his elbows with his bloody hands high, and said, "Oh my God. I think I just killed two people."

CHAPTER TWO

"My God, I've Just Killed Two People."

The Woods' townhouse in Scarborough is number 85 in a complex at 25 Brimwood Boulevard. The front door opens on a park-like lawn, the nearest street a block away, so it rarely is used by people arriving in cars. Family and visitors usually enter the premises through a basement door that opens on underground parking.

The basement floor contains a laundry and furnace area and two finished rooms, one used for television viewing and the other a bedroom where Karen's parents slept. On the main floor are a combined living-room and dining-room, foyer, powder-room, and kitchen. Four bedrooms and a bath are clustered around a hallway on the top floor, sleeping quarters for the five Woods children who still live at home.

Denis Woods, forty-five, and Barbara Woods, forty-two, had enjoyed a sound marriage for twenty-three years, amiably raising six children: Karen, then twenty-two, Samantha, twenty-one, Emma, twenty, Jonathan, seventeen, Prudence, fifteen, and Nicholas, twelve. On the night of May 23, 1987, Denis spent the evening reading quietly while Barbara did some typing. She talked for a while on the phone to a friend and then announced she was packing it in for the night. As she was preparing for bed around midnight, Denis discovered that Jonathan had fallen asleep in front of the television in the downstairs den. He sent him upstairs to bed, then he too retired. Prudence was asleep in her room. That made four people in the house. Emma was with her boy-friend, Jimmy Sotirakos, and would be returning late. Samantha was spending the weekend with her boy-friend and wasn't expected home at all. Nicholas, the youngest, was in Philadelphia that weekend for a soccer tournament.

Denis turned off all the lights except for a striplight at the top of the basement stairs to help Emma find her way when she returned home. A careful man, he checked that the outside doors were locked and that the sliding door to the patio was braced with a bar. Before getting into bed beside Barbara, he closed their bedroom door. He didn't want them to be disturbed when Emma returned.

He wakened in pitch darkness to feel hands around his throat. Someone very heavy and strong was crouched on top of him, choking him. He called out to his wife, "Help me, Bobbie! Someone's trying to strangle me!" There was no reply. He thrashed out with his leg and encountered something that didn't move. He couldn't tell if it was his wife or his attacker. Then he lost consciousness.

He roused to find that he was lying diagonally, face down, across the bed. His shocked mind registered panic. Where were Bobbie and the children? He rolled over and almost fell, landing on his knees on the floor. He struggled to his feet and made his way to the open door of the bedroom, grasping it for support. He saw a bar of light under the door at the top of the basement stairs.

Weariness overcame him. He thought dizzily that he might pass out. He sank down on the stairs and leaned his head against the wall. Something was wrong with the left side of his head; it was hurting. As he slipped into unconsciousness, he heard a strong male voice calling, "Police!"

Heidi Edith Turner, a civilian clerk with the Metropolitan Toronto Police, was working in Scarborough's 42 Division at the corner of Brimley and Finch. At about a quarter to five on the morning of May 24, the station was quiet; most of the police officers were finishing a snack in the lunch-room down the hall. Suddenly the double doors leading from the main entrance were thrown open, and a tall blond man, crouching over, lurched through and put his elbows on the counter. Turner was aghast to

9

see that his hands were pouring blood in such quantities that a puddle already was spreading on the counter.

She thinks he said something like, "I just killed someone with my bare hands."

The clerk whirled to call the sergeant, Henry Flavelle, who was on duty that night as road sergeant. Flavelle had just entered the station and was strolling to his office. Her agitation caught his attention. He turned and hurried towards her. She gasped incoherently, pointing at a crouched figure in a windbreaker. "There's a man, there's a man."

Flavelle, a twenty-year veteran with the force, approached a man leaning on his elbows on the counter with his hands in the air and his head bent. The man looked up and said, in a tone of amazement, "I've just killed two people." When the man straightened, the sergeant was startled by his size.

"My God, I've just killed two people with my hands," the man said, looking stunned. The sergeant shouted for help. No one responded.

There are several versions of what Ken Parks said as he stood at the counter of the police station. The sergeant isn't certain himself. Maybe the man said, "My God, I've just killed two people," then noticed the blood gushing from his wounds and said, "My hands!"

Sergeant Flavelle shouted again and five officers came running from the lunch-room. All were so flustered and excited that their accounts of the scene differ. One of them later explained apologetically that police are accustomed to going to the scene of a crime and were not prepared when "The scene came to us."

Heidi Turner heard the man repeat, "I've just killed someone," several times as the officers crowded around him. She thought he also said, "Oh God, I've just killed someone." Constable Cecil Gerrard has the most colourful version. According to Gerrard the man said, "I just killed my mother- and father-in-law. I stabbed and beat them to death. It's all my fault."

Sergeant Colin Arthur Ashton, who was in charge of the 42 Division station that morning, agreed. He heard, "I just killed my mother- and father-in-law. I beat and stabbed them to death. It's all my fault."

Another officer, Constable Brian Russell Penwarden, had a different recollection. He thought the man said, "I killed two people. I killed them."

Flavelle and Gerrard led the man, who didn't resist, into the Community Services operations room. Another officer ran for the first-aid kit, hastily scooping up all the bandages he could find. While someone telephoned for an ambulance, the police tried in vain to control the bleeding. The wounded man was asked his name. He said, "Ken Parks." Then he was asked who had been killed. The reply was, "My mother- and father-in-law."

The officer asked, "Did you beat them? Did you strangle them? Did you stab them?"

Ken's head jerked at the word "stab".

"The knife," he gasped. "The knife's in my car. There's a knife in my car."

The sergeant concentrated on getting the address where the killing had taken place. Ken said, "In the basement at twenty-five Brimwood, number eighty-five." The police were puzzled. Finally it was sorted out that the address was 25 Brimwood, unit 85. Flavelle raced for the door, followed by two constables.

As they were climbing into a cruiser, another constable came running. He said, breathlessly, "He says you'll need these to get in," and handed over a set of bloody keys on a key chain.

Constable Gerrard remained with the heavily bleeding man. "Where do you live?" he inquired.

Ken answered, "Sixteen fifty-five Geta Circle, unit thirteen, in Pickering."

The constable remembered the rules. He put on his official voice and said, "I am placing you under arrest for murder. You have the right to speak to a lawyer without delay. Do you understand that right?" Ken said, "Yeah." Then the officer told him that anything he said would be taken down in writing and could be used against him in evidence.

Ken was crying. According to the constable's notes, Ken moaned, "I don't know why I did it, but I killed them."

The constable asked, "How did you kill them?"

"With a knife."

"Where is the knife?"

"In my car in the parking lot, the red Capri."

The police were appalled by Ken's hands, from which blood continued to flow heavily through the wadding of bandages. Sergeant Ashton decided not to wait for the ambulance. At ten to five that morning, only five minutes after Ken's sensational entrance, he was placed in the back seat of a squad car. Ashton climbed in beside him, and Gerrard drove the car to Scarborough Grace General Hospital, only minutes from the station. Ken wept throughout the trip and kept saying, "Why did I kill them? Why did I kill them? Why did I kill them?"

At the hospital, a doctor on duty in the emergency department looked at Ken's mutilated hands and decided they needed more than simple suturing.

Ken was placed on a stretcher bed against the wall of a room away from the general traffic while Ashton called for help to guard him. Constables Eric Puusa and Murray Grills, on patrol duty in a marked scout car on the midnight shift, were not far from the hospital when they heard the summons on the cruiser's radio. Ashton and Gerrard met them in the hospital. Ashton, lowering his voice, said there had been a murder in a townhouse behind the station. "A stabbing, a messy situation," he said tersely. The accused person—he indicated Ken Parks— was charged with murder of one and possibly two persons, a man and a woman.

Puusa was impressed by the size of the man as the officers assisted nurses to help Ken undress. Puusa showed presence of mind. Realizing that the clothes would be produced in evidence, he handled the bloody garments carefully to prevent matting them. He noted blood-soaked grey track pants, a light-blue T-shirt, size extra large, with a few bloodstains, a blue nylon Adidas zipper jacket, also extra large, and blood-splattered Nike running shoes, size thirteen, partially laced. The big man, still sobbing, wore no socks or underwear.

The jacket was difficult to remove because the elastic cuffs dragged over the prisoner's mutilated hands. The injured man tried to assist, but it was clear that his hands were useless. The officers then removed a watch from Ken's wrist and spilled out the contents of his pockets—a pen flashlight, a blood-stained yellow envelope, a hairbrush, and a key chain carrying a jack-knife and three keys. When asked about them, he said they were his car keys and the key to his house.

Scarborough Grace hospital staff waited for two hours for a decision about whether Ken would be admitted there or sent to another hospital for very tricky plastic surgery needed to repair his hands. During the delay the patient police guards took up positions, one near Ken's head and the other by his feet.

By the luck of the draw, Constable Puusa remained with Ken for some five hours. In his notebook he recorded much of what transpired over that long period. He rarely spoke to the prisoner, but he made notes of everything Ken said to him, including the time of each comment.

He reported that the first thing Ken said was, "I killed her parents. I don't know why."

Then Ken said, "I had a problem gambling. I woke up in the middle of the night. I don't know why."

The constable asked chattily, "Do you work?"

Ken replied, "No. I lost my job gambling. I'm on bail now for fraud."

Ken was weeping and appeared to be in a state of fright and disorientation. If the prisoner was going to ramble on disconnectedly, Puusa wondered if anyone had remembered to read him his rights. It wouldn't hurt to do it again. Puusa took a laminated card from the back of his memo book and read: "I am arresting you for murder. It is my duty to inform you that you have the right to retain and instruct counsel without delay. Do you understand?"

Ken, still crying, didn't appear to be paying much attention. He said, "I know."

Constable Puusa decided to continue.

"You are charged with murder. Do you wish to say anything in answer to the charge? You are not obliged to say anything unless you wish to do so. Whatever you say may be given in evidence."

Ken nodded, watching blood seep through gauze wrapped around his hands. "I know," he said dully.

The officer finished, "If you have spoken to any police officer or anyone in authority, or any such person has spoken to you in connection with this case, I want it clearly understood that I don't want to influence you in making any statement."

And Ken repeated, "I know."

A few minutes after five, Ken held up his mittened hands and groaned, "What the fuck did I do?" The officer shrugged. Ken lay still, breathing heavily, his eyes closed. Then he asked Puusa, more urgently, "What happened?" The officer indicated he didn't know.

"I was sleeping on the couch," Ken went on, as if talking to himself. "I just woke up." A long pause followed. "I had a dream. I had a knife in my hand. I was killing them. I choked them, then I went to the police station."

Several minutes passed quietly, the only sound Ken's hoarse breathing. The clatter of the hospital emergency area seemed very distant. Ken said suddenly, "Don't worry about me, get them."

The officer didn't know what to make of that but wrote it down.

Ken held up his hands. Panting heavily like a runner, he gasped, "The pain is starting to come."

The officer called a nurse. At 5:12, Ashton came into the room and urgently beckoned to Constable Grills. Puusa heard him say something in a low voice about a man in the next room. After that Puusa was alone with Ken except for intermittent visits by hospital staff.

The prisoner appeared to be in agony but didn't complain. His eyes full of tears, he blurted, "I can't face my wife."

A doctor arrived to examine the damaged hands. Ken was growing more distraught. "Oh my family," he said. "What did I do?... Oh my poor wife.... Somebody help me.... Those poor people. I want to go to jail. I need help. I hope I didn't kill them."

Constable Puusa dutifully wrote it all down, checking his watch to get the times right. A nurse took the prisoner's blood pressure and, when he complained of thirst, brought him ice chips to suck.

The medication, Demerol and Gravol, was given at 5:30, by which time Ken's face was contorted with pain. He swallowed the pills gratefully but his agitation increased. He gasped, "I killed the poor people.... Is someone helping them?... Can someone tell my wife?... Why did she marry me?... What about my mum? She's going to die.... I don't care about my dad.... They won't phone my wife, will they? They'll go and see her?"

Puusa, writing the time—6:12—answered briefly, "Yes." He had no idea if the police would show such consideration, but he hoped so. A nurse brought in more ice chips and spread a blanket over the shivering prisoner.

Dr. Ernest Arnold Trevelyan Salmon, a vascular and thoracic surgeon at Scarborough Grace, arrived to examine Ken's hands. The left hand had severe cuts to two fingers, and the right hand had such deep lacerations to three fingers that the flexor tendons were severed, exposing bone. The doctor asked Ken if he could bend his fingers. The man tried, but couldn't. Salmon tested for sensation in the fingertips and found none. The doctor concluded that the nerves were severed as well.

Grace Hospital had no one available to perform the long delicate plastic surgery that would be required. Accordingly, the doctor made arrangements for Ken to be transported by ambulance to Sunnybrook Hospital.

The doctor thought there was something strange about the big man with the lacerated hands. He spoke fairly calmly but he had the appearance of a man in a severe state of fright. His eyes were wide open, the pupils tightened down, and he moved restlessly. According to the doctor, "It was a funny appearance. He had that stare about him."

Around 7:00, Constable Puusa put Ken's belongings in three brown paper bags. The big man was quiet and seemed almost asleep. At approximately 7:22, Puusa recorded that Ken suddenly said in a loud clear voice, "How come I drove there and not know?"

Karen Parks wakened that morning around 7:30 to the sound of someone knocking on the front door from within the house. Melissa had been stirring but was not yet demanding attention, so Karen had burrowed under the covers to doze as long as she could. The knocking was followed by the sound of people moving around in the house. A man's voice called from downstairs, "Police."

What now? she thought, hastily getting into her housecoat.

At the foot of the stairs to the bedrooms she saw two men in the uniforms of Durham Regional Police.

One of them said, "Where's your husband?"

Karen was confused. How had they entered? She and Ken were always careful to lock the door.

She answered, "Isn't he on the couch?"

"No."

She descended into the living-room and saw that Ken was gone. "What's going on?" she asked.

"Your mother has been killed," said one of the police officers. "It appears that your husband is responsible."

"No way," she replied coldly.

Karen picked up the telephone to call her parents. After one ring, a man answered, announcing himself as a police officer.

"I want to speak to Denis Woods," she told him.

"Who's this?" he said curtly.

"His daughter," she answered, fear beginning to crawl in her throat.

"Which daughter?" the man asked.

"Karen," she told him stiffly. "Put my dad on the phone."

He said, "Are police officers with you? Can I talk to them?"

She handed over the receiver. From what she could gather, the officer in her living-room was being rebuked.

He was saying defensively, "Well, she asked us what was going on, so what could we do?"

Karen thought, *my mother's dead*. She's dead. The police in her living-room were real; the abrupt, official manner of the policeman on the telephone had been convincing. This wasn't a prank or a misunderstanding.

Protected by shock, she was unmoved. She was only perplexed. Where was Ken?

Police on their way to investigate what had happened before dawn in the Woods townhouse were confused only momentarily between 85 Brimwood and 25 Brimwood. Sergeant Flavelle quickly determined that 25 Brimwood was a complex of townhouses in which number 85 was a unit. As the cruiser roared into the back lane, police received a call from unit 87 that there was a burglary next door, at 85.

"Each of the units has in the underground what I would describe as the back door," Flavelle explains, "so when you enter the underground along the walls there is a series of doors. You park your car and you go into your home via that door."

Because both parking spaces next to number 85 were occupied, the police stopped their two cruisers in the middle of the driveway and piled out. They tried the basement door of 85, found it locked, and knocked loudly. No one responded, so they used the keys Ken had provided. After several attempts, one of the keys worked.

With Flavelle in the lead, the three men went up a short flight of stairs and found themselves in a laundry/furnace room. Ahead of them, slightly to the left, was a door open on a brightly lit sitting-room. Flavelle called out, "Police!" and waited: not a sound. He shouted again, more loudly, "Police. This is the *police!*" and heard a groan.

They stepped into the sitting-room and saw that the far wall was smeared with blood. Beside the blood-stained wall was the body of a woman dressed in a red, white, and blue striped cotton night-gown. She was in a twisted position on her back, her eyes and mouth open and her face covered with blood. Her stiffened arms were raised with the fists clenched.

Someone moaned nearby. The police followed the sound to the stairway leading to the first floor. They found a man in pyjamas sitting on the steps, his head covered in blood.

"Is there anyone in the building?" Flavelle asked urgently.

"My wife and children," the man replied weakly. "They're upstairs."

One officer stayed with the injured man while the others drew their guns and raced up the stairs, noting a trail of blood on the left-hand wall. The rooms on the main floor were deserted.

Braced for the horror of finding more bodies, they followed streaks of blood on the wall of the stairway to the top floor. A quick search showed that the bathroom and four bedrooms were empty. Three beds evidently had been used but the occupants were gone. In one of the bedrooms a window was wide open with the screen pushed out. Flavelle stuck out his head to look at the lawn one storey below, but saw no one.

The officers returned to the basement just as ambulance crews arrived to place the bleeding man gently on a stretcher. Flavelle, intending to call for help to search for the missing children, looked around for a telephone. In the basement bedroom, he saw a telephone almost under the dishevelled bed, the receiver off the hook. He concluded that it had been knocked off the night table next to the bed.

He picked up the receiver but there was no dial tone. He studied the bed, which was covered with blood. When he lifted one of the pillows by the corner, he was surprised at its weight. He saw the reason: it was completely saturated in blood.

He went upstairs in search of another telephone and found one on the wall of the kitchen. He tried to call, but the line was dead. He remembered the burglary call from the next-door unit, 87, and knocked there. The door opened on terrified faces. When he learned who they were, the sergeant breathed a sigh of relief. The teenagers quaking before him in their pyjamas were three of the Woods children, unharmed. They had escaped through the upstairs window and taken refuge with the neighbours.

About twenty minutes after Ken Parks arrived at Scarborough Grace hospital, Denis Woods was delivered to the same hospital by ambulance. Constable Grills, summoned from Ken's side, was assigned to stay with the injured man. Grills found Denis bathed with blood from wounds to his head and face.

Dr. Salmon went directly from examining Ken's hands to inspect the older man's wounds. He was startled by the amount of blood Denis Woods had lost. The man's head and shoulders were covered in it and one wound was still pouring blood.

"What happened?" the doctor asked.

"Someone came into our bedroom," Denis replied, appearing dazed and confused. "In the dark. I don't know who it was. I don't know what happened."

The doctor made an examination. Denis had five sharp, clean cuts to his head. The one still bleeding was a deep gash in front of the left ear. Three other cuts were on his forehead and another, a slice that exposed bone, was above his ear. A wound at his throat had just missed the carotid artery, a close call. The doctor then spotted another injury, a puncture wound that penetrated to bone at the back of Denis Woods' left shoulder.

Karen told herself in the hours that followed her mother's death that very soon she would have to think about it. She couldn't continue in this numbed state, but meanwhile she was in no hurry for the pain to begin.

Subdued by the scolding, the Durham police officers no longer were volunteering information. One of them said with exaggerated politeness, "We'd like you to get dressed and come with us."

She nodded. Her movements were aimless, her mind a blank. Melissa made sounds of distress, so Karen collected herself. She put a bottle to warm in the microwave oven and went upstairs to change the baby's diaper. She carried her into the kitchen, ignoring the police, who sat patiently in the living-room. She fed the baby and took her back upstairs to dress her. Then she strapped Melissa in a tilted bucket chair while she went to her bedroom and dressed herself.

Karen went through the familiar routines without much awareness of what she was doing. She can't remember, for instance, what she wore that morning or how she dressed Melissa. She's sure she prepared the baby's formula and poured it into bottles, but she felt herself in a dream state, disconnected from the robot performing those tasks.

She suddenly realized that there had been no mention of her father.

"Where's my father?" she asked, turning wildly to the police. "Is he all right?"

One of them replied uneasily that her father was in hospital with serious injuries. Karen felt the shock of that news. Was he dying? Was he dead? She felt light, porous, dizzy. The police became restless with impatience. One of them said, "We have to go. Don't you think you'd better get a baby-sitter?"

"I don't have one," she answered, only vaguely registering what he was asking. Her mother had been her only baby-sitter. She turned her mind from that thought.

"A friend, maybe?" he suggested.

Karen considered a moment and then called Connie Sullivan, who lived near Scarborough Grace hospital. They had been in high school together. When she identified herself, Connie was startled. It was eight o'clock on a Sunday morning, an unusual time to call, and Karen had never before asked her to care for Melissa. Karen offered no explanation. Connie, alert to the odd tone in Karen's voice, asked no questions. She said, "Sure. Bring her over."

The police ushered Karen to the back seat of their cruiser but she balked at getting in.

"What about Melissa?" she asked. "Where is she going to be?"

An officer said. "It's a short ride. You can hold her on your lap."

Karen protested. It wasn't safe, she told them indignantly. It wasn't even *legal*. At her insistence, they opened the trunk of the cruiser to push through a seat-belt that she buckled around Melissa's sturdy car seat.

Karen was beginning to emerge from shock. The officers had a strange attitude when they first saw her, she thought, almost as if they were relieved. Much later she reflected that they had been prepared to find her dead. Their fears would have been sharpened by finding her front door standing half open. It was reasonable for them to think that a man who had killed his mother-in-law and almost killed his father-in-law might first have slain his wife and child.

She handed the baby to Connie, who looked at her sharply. Karen said simply, "My mother's dead." Before Connie could speak, Karen gave hurried instructions about how the baby should be fed and when she napped. Then she backed away. "I'll talk to you later," she said hurriedly. "I've got to go now."

As the police drove her to the Scarborough police station, 42 Division, for questioning, Karen asked to be taken first to her father. The police were evasive. "Maybe later," one said. Her thoughts turned to Ken. Where was he? The officers said they didn't know. She wouldn't accept that. By insistent prodding she learned he was in custody.

She tried to put the crazy pieces together: Ken arrested, her mother killed, her father injured. What was Ken doing in the middle of the night at her parents' place? Maybe he had suddenly decided to talk to them. That didn't make sense—he would be seeing them the next day at the barbecue—but suppose that's what he'd done. Maybe an argument had broken out.

Her imagination could take her no farther. Ken was not a violent man. He was aggressive on the rugby field, but in all the years they'd been together, even in the heat of their worst fights, he had never lifted a finger against her.

She was escorted down a hallway in the police station to a room where one of her brothers, Jonathan, and two sisters, Prudence and Emma, were waiting. They were still trying to reach Samantha, they said. Karen looked for Nicky, the youngest Woods child, and then remembered that he was in Philadelphia for a soccer tournament. She recognized the next-door neighbours who lived in unit 87. Two strangers came forward and introduced themselves. They said they were with the Salvation Army's victim assistance program.

"What happened?" Karen asked, looking from one strained face to another.

No one really knew. Prudence said she had been wakened by the sound a telephone makes when it is off the hook. She had dozed off and then heard a woman scream and some grunting noises. Her first sleepy thought was that someone was watching television with the volume too loud. Then she realized in fright that the sounds were coming from the basement and the woman screaming was her mother. She went down the stairs a short way and called, "What's going on? What's happening?"

Her sister Emma came out of her bedroom. They shouted together, "What's happening down there?"

The screams and grunting stopped abruptly. There was an ominous silence; Pru retreated fearfully to the upstairs landing. Emma called, "Mum, are you all right?" Emma's memory of the horrifying events differs slightly from Pru's. She thinks the sound of the telephone off the hook happened during the screaming and continued afterwards, and she doesn't think Pru went down the stairs.

They agree with what occurred next. The grunting noises started again and with them the sound of heavy feet racing up the stairs towards them, two at a time. They fled in terror into Emma's room and shut the door. Emma jumped on her bed. Pru stood with her back against the door and then, realizing how ineffective a barrier that would be, ran to huddle behind Emma. Someone stood on the other side of the door in the upstairs hall, panting and walking around. After a paralysing minute, they heard footsteps retreating down the stairs and then the familiar metallic slam of the outside door in the basement. After that there was silence.

They ran across the hall and turned on the light in Jonathan's room. He wasn't fully awake, but the sounds of screams and banging had penetrated his sleep and he was beginning to stir.

Frightened and shaking, they had a quick low-voiced conference about what to do. Jonathan, sixteen, bravely volunteered to go downstairs to investigate. As he looked around for a weapon, his sisters followed him into the hall. They were aghast to see bright bloodstains on the frame of the bathroom door.

Jonathan whispered, "Maybe he's still down there."

They decided to call for help and bolted into Samantha's room where there was a telephone. Jonny's recollection is that the basement door clanged shut as they lifted the phone and found that the line was dead.

Panic swept them; their one thought was to escape. They decided to jump out a window. They picked Emma's room and pushed out the screen. Emma grabbed shoes, a jacket, and her purse as Jonathan jumped first. Pru followed, and then Emma. They knocked on the door of unit 87 and eventually aroused their neighbours. The words tumbling over one another, they said there was someone in their house. The neighbours called the police and reported a burglary.

"I want to die," Karen wept. "I wish it had been me instead. Why couldn't it have been me he killed?"

Pru and Emma threw their arms around her. "No, no," they cried. "We need you, Karen. We need you now to be our mother."

CHAPTER THREE

What Happened?

The lawn below the window from which Pru, Emma, and Jonny Woods had jumped was an unforgiving surface on which to land. Emma twisted her ankle and Pru wrenched her back. Karen was relieved to find that, apart from those minor injuries, her siblings were physically unharmed in the slaughter that had befallen the family.

"How's dad?" she asked them.

"We don't know," they answered, weeping. "We can't find out anything."

Anxiety for their father crowded out every other thought. The horror of their mother's death was more than they were ready to face while there was still a possibility that they would be left with no parents at all. They cried, hugged one another, then broke apart to pace the room. They begged the police for information. The answers they received were vague and unsatisfying. The children tried to put together the pieces of the puzzle for themselves. They had assumed in the beginning that a burglar somehow had gained entry, a maniac who attacked Barbara and Denis when they wakened and discovered him. That theory was coming unravelled. In the fragments of unguarded conversation overheard among the police officers, the children learned that someone had been arrested, and that person seemed to be Ken Parks.

Ken!

It couldn't have been Ken, they thought—but also, it could. The intruder was big and heavy, judging from the sounds on the stairs, and he seemed to know the house. Also, Ken would have a key.

Still, they couldn't believe that Ken was the killer. It made no sense. He was as close as a brother to them all, someone they looked up to. Only a few weeks earlier, he had taken Jonny to a hockey game and out to dinner. Besides, it was impossible that he would harm their parents. They had a hundred memories of Ken at their dinner table, laughing, exchanging affectionate banter with Barbara and Denis. None of them had ever heard a hostile or even unfriendly word pass between Ken and their parents. Even with hints in recent weeks that Ken was in some kind of trouble, neither Barbara nor Denis ever spoke ill of him. Their mother, they knew, thought Ken was just about perfect.

And yet it seemed that Ken had just killed her, and maybe killed their father as well.

Samantha arrived with her boy-friend, her face white and wet with tears. Karen sat dry-eyed, wondering why she couldn't cry. If her dad also died, she thought she would not be able to bear the grief. Her life had been blasted; the disaster was of such magnitude that she couldn't think about it. She concentrated instead on praying that her dad would live. Whenever a police officer came into the room, the children pleaded to be taken to see their father. Finally, around nine that morning, an officer told them it was being arranged.

"However, there are a lot of media people outside," the man said. The children looked at one another in consternation. To avoid exposing the young people to cameras, microphones, and reporters, the officers escorted them through a side door into a closed garage. The children climbed into two cruisers and slid down so that their heads were below the windows. The garage doors opened and the cruisers swiftly left.

Anger boiled out of Karen. She turned to Emma and said harshly, "Why didn't you help them? Why didn't you help when you heard the screaming?"

Emma answered, miserably, "I was too scared." Karen, ashamed, squeezed her hand in apology.

She couldn't stop thinking of her mother dying in agony, and the terror her parents must have suffered. "I want to kill Ken," she cried out suddenly. "I want to kill him."

To avoid the reporters waiting at the main entrance of Scarborough Grace hospital, the police guided the family to another door. The children were relieved. "The last thing we needed," Karen reflected later, "was to be a side-show. We were all in shock."

Police were taking a statement from Denis Woods, so the children were instructed to wait. While they sat in a drab lounge area, too numbed to speak, a nurse came to report on their father's condition. He was fine, they were assured. Denis Woods had some cuts to his head, but he was in no danger. Though Karen remained tearless, the others sobbed in relief. An officer who came to the waiting-room confirmed the good news. He had just left their father, he said. Denis had lost a good deal of blood, but he would be on his feet in no time.

The officer looked at Karen, a dignified small figure holding herself together with obvious effort, and said gently, "Your husband has been arrested for the murder."

She asked, "Where is he?" and he replied, "He was injured. He's been taken to Sunnybrook Hospital."

She nodded. She heard him, but she made no connection to the information. She would think about Ken some other time. She marvelled at her calm. It was as though some force was protecting her, she reflected. Almost as if her mother was watching over her. *Her mother!* The conviction grew until she was certain of it. Her mother was somewhere near, worried for her and hovering around to make sure she was all right. Karen felt a flood of gratitude so intense that she told her sisters about it.

"That's crazy," Samantha responded tersely.

A half-hour later, the police officer stood in the doorway again and said they could see their father, two at a time.

By unspoken agreement, Karen seemed to have been designated as the stricken family's leader. They turned to her and she organized them sensibly in teams, using exactly the tone and manner of their mother. She decided that she and Emma would go first; no one objected.

They gasped at their father's appearance. Denis seemed small, fragile, and broken, almost unrecognizable as the solid, decisive person they knew. His face was ghastly pale, and dried blood was matted in his hair. One side of his head was swathed in thick, snow-white bandages, and another bulge of bandage was taped on his neck. His left eye was swollen nearly shut and beside it was a cut, bristling with fresh stitches.

He seemed to be dozing as they came in but opened his eyes at their approach.

"Howya doing?" Karen asked tenderly, her throat tight.

"Not bad," he answered in a frail voice. "Is your mother all right? Is everyone else okay?"

My God, Karen thought in dismay, he doesn't know. She groped for words but what came out was, "Sure. We're all fine."

Denis closed his eyes gratefully. Karen tiptoed out to consult with the others while Pru slipped in to take her place.

In the corridor outside, Karen told Jonny and Samantha, "He doesn't know that mum is dead. Someone has to tell him."

They looked appalled, but were speechless. "Who's going to do it?" Karen said, her voice shaking with her effort to keep her feelings under control. "I can't."

"Not me," said Samantha. "Not me either," said Jonny.

Emma and Pru, when consulted, also refused. None of the children wanted to be the one to bring their father such terrible grief. The Salvation Army's victim assistance people, listening to the discussion in quiet sympathy, offered to find a chaplain to break the news, and the children readily agreed. While the man was being summoned, Karen slipped back into her father's room.

Denis was saying querulously, "I don't even know what happened."

Karen moved to the bedside and took his limp hand. "Dad," she said. "It was Ken."

Her father winced and turned away. "I figured as much," he said bleakly. He had been thinking that the heaviness of the weight on him indicated that his attacker was a very big man. As big as Ken. He could think of no reason why it would have been Ken, but the likelihood had been growing in his mind.

27

The merciful detachment that Karen had been able to maintain abruptly shattered. She broke down and wailed. "It's my fault," she cried as Emma rushed to hold her. "I should have heard Ken leave the house. I could have warned mum. I should have known what he was going to do. I should have known what kind of a mood he was in." She was moving into hysteria. "How could I have married him? I'm the one who brought him into the family. If I'd never married him, this wouldn't have happened."

"It's not your fault," Emma said, her arms around her sister. "There, there." Despite the anguish that shook Karen, tears didn't come. A hard knot of sickness was gathering in her stomach.

The hospital rules were suspended to allow all the Woods children to be with their father for the grim news. The Salvation Army chaplain arrived quickly and introduced himself. He sat down beside the bed and softly told Denis that his wife was dead. Denis shook his head and his eyes filled with tears. "Poor Bobbie," he moaned. "Poor, poor Bobbie."

He lay crying, his eyes closed for privacy, but with an absence of shock that led Karen to suspect he had already guessed the truth. "He keeps asking about Bobbie," the police had said. Karen decided her father had deduced that his wife was dead from the officers' evasive replies. The whole family was developing a faculty for hearing what the police didn't say.

After a while Denis slipped into sleep, and the children left him alone with his sorrow. They returned to the dreary waiting-room, already almost as familiar to them as their home, and talked about the family's future. They could not imagine how their father would manage without his Bobbie, the family's centre, the peacemaker, the organizer, the ballast, the one who steadied them all, the housekeeper with an almost obsessive need for perfection. Everyone in the Woods family depended on Barbara. Only Barbara could find their missing gym shoes, or whip up dinner single-handed; only she knew what to say when their hearts were broken.

Denis Woods was an uncommunicative man who kept apart from the family's rivalries and upheavals. His life revolved around his spotless and smoothly run home, where Barbara could be depended on to be good company when he wanted it or to protect his need for seclusion when he didn't.

What would happen to him? the children wondered. They were certain he couldn't manage without Bobbie. He had never bothered to learn where utensils were kept, or how to operate the appliances, or how to manage the finances. Barbara was a faultless housewife and dedicated mother. Possessed of an orderly mind and a gift for administration, she had taken complete charge of the household, and Denis had been pleased to leave it that way.

Like many long-married couples who find their needs compatible, Barbara and Denis had fused. They were two separate people with very different personalities, but in fact they had become over the years an entity, like Siamese twins with one heart.

The children couldn't picture him without her. Denis should return to England, they decided, because he had family there to give him support. Certainly they wouldn't be much help to him around the house. Barbara had not even allowed her children to learn to cook, preferring to do everything herself. The more they discussed it, the more it seemed to them that England was the solution to the loneliness Denis faced. Only Karen was doubtful. She couldn't see her father uprooting them all again; but, on the other hand, she agreed it wasn't possible that he could run the household alone.

With fear for their father's life at rest, the Woods children were left to contemplate the loss of their mother. Grief for her came in waves. One moment they were talking about the possibility that their father would move to England and the next they were sobbing for their lost mother. Sometimes all but Karen were crying hard, standing in the hospital waiting-room with their arms around one another. Karen, dry-eyed, gave comfort but asked for none.

She thought about Ken, the cause of their pain. Her anger against him had vanished, exhausted in the single wild outburst in the police car when she had said she wanted to kill him. Karen probed tentatively at her frozen feelings to discover if she hated her husband; she could find no emotion at all. She was waiting, she realized, to find out what had happened. Her sense that her mother was watching over her was very strong. Karen was sure that Barbara wanted her to proceed slowly and carefully, to make sure that she was doing the right thing.

The killing was so out of character for Ken that there had to be an explanation. Ken was not a murderer; of that Karen was certain. Violence was completely foreign to his mild, passive nature. Besides, she knew better than anyone that his fondness for her parents was genuine. She didn't doubt that he loved Barbara, and she knew he had great respect for Denis. Still, the police said he was the killer. What could have happened?

She remembered that the police officer had said Ken was injured. Maybe he had tried to kill himself, she thought. That was likely, given Ken's capacity for remorse, but that still left unanswered the question of how the killing had happened. Karen shook her head in confusion and despair.

In part to divert them, she decided to tell her brother and sisters the whole story of Ken's gambling and the embezzlement. They listened in fascination to the account, grateful for the distraction and the explanation of why Ken had stopped dropping by. Looking for a link between the gentle Ken they knew and the madman who had killed their mother, they were full of questions. Had she and Ken fought last night? Was Ken mad at mum and dad? Unknown to them, was Ken a violent man who was in the habit of blowing up and hitting her? No, no, and no.

They turned to the same plausible scenario that had occurred to Karen, picturing Ken impulsively deciding to have it out with Barbara and Denis in the middle of the night. Maybe Denis had been hard on him and the men had exchanged hot words, leading to a fight that Barbara got between. They could picture that: she was certain to try to break them apart. Then they remembered that Denis hadn't known who his attacker was, and they slumped back in their chairs, that line of speculation ended.

Karen was developing another possibility. Perhaps Ken temporarily had lost his sanity. She ticked off all the pressures on him in recent months—the gambling losses, the theft, the arrest, his joblessness, his lies. The strain might have unbalanced him, she thought. The others nodded approvingly. That made more sense than anything else they'd been able to imagine.

From time to time Karen called her friend Connie to ask about Melissa. Connie always assured her that the baby was fine and considerately kept her curiosity in check. No trouble at all, don't worry, and I'm so sorry about your mother.

As noon approached, the Salvation Army's victim assistance people were concerned that the Woods children hadn't eaten that day. Since Samantha's boy-friend lived only a few blocks away, it was decided to pick up hamburgers at a fast-food outlet and have lunch at his place. The others chose to drive the few blocks, but Karen wanted to walk, needing time alone to sort out her thoughts. She plodded along the sidewalks and across intersections oblivious of her surroundings and unable to keep her thoughts coherent. By the time she arrived, everyone had plunged hungrily into the food, but it looked repulsive to her. She was certain that if she tried to eat she would vomit. She felt like someone in the early queasy stages of flu.

None of them thought to call anyone, not Barbara's mother in England, not her friends, not even the youngest Woods child, twelve-year-old Nicky, who was playing soccer in Philadelphia that day and still didn't know that his mother was dead.

Ken's first coherent memory of that bloody morning is the police station. He was aware of being led into a room where he was seated while a police officer wrapped bandages around his hands. Police in uniform asked him questions—his name and address, the address where the killing happened. His answers must have been blurred because it was some time before they understood that when he said "eighty-five Brimwood" he was referring to a unit at 25 Brimwood, not a street address.

He was trying to understand what had happened. The thought he had was that something terrible had happened to Barbara and maybe the kids. Barbara had had that "help me" look on her face, and the kids had been screaming. What was he doing in the house anyway? How did he get there? Where was Denis? Who cut his hands?

Ken was aware of driving to the hospital and waiting there on a bed, but everything seemed to be at a hollow distance. He remembers being transferred by ambulance to Sunnybrook Hospital. News of the crime seemed to have preceded him. The plastic surgeon assigned to examine him refused, fearing that Ken was too dangerous to approach. Ken marvels at this, since two police officers were inside his room to guard him, two stood outside the room, and two others were posted down the hall.

At the surgeon's insistence, a psychiatrist was dispatched to make an assessment of the wounded man. After half an hour with Ken, the verdict of the psychiatrist was that the prisoner was not psychotic and posed no threat to medical personnel. With that assurance, the plastic surgeon agreed to examine Ken's hands.

Ken's mind was reeling. He thought maybe Barbara and Denis were dead, but he didn't know how he knew that. Who could have done such a thing? Could he have done it? Why didn't he remember anything? How come he didn't know what had happened to his hands?

After the psychiatrist left, a police officer in plain clothes came into the room, his manner that of someone accustomed to command.

Ken said, "Are they both dead?"

The officer, Staff Sergeant Bobby Burns Adair of the elite Metro Toronto Police Central Homicide Squad, hesitated. Ken asked insistently, "Did I kill them both?"

The officer, writing the remarks in his notebook, replied, "Wait a minute."

Bobby Adair had been wakened at five that morning, May 24, 1987, and ordered to open a homicide investigation into a killing in Scarborough. At about seven he was inside unit 85 of 25 Brimwood, having noted with a seasoned police officer's care that the weather was cloudy and cool, with no rain. He talked to the coroner, looked at the blood on the stairway walls, noticed that Barbara's kitchen was neat and tidy except for a smear of blood on one partially open cutlery drawer, and then went into the basement, noting disapprovingly a welter of shoes of all sizes on the floor of the laundry room.

Barbara Woods' body was still in the television room where police had found it two hours earlier. There was a great deal of blood on her face and around her head, but the only obvious injury he could see was in the area of her left eye. She was dressed in a red, white, and blue striped night-shirt that was twisted to show she was wearing white panties. On her feet were white socks.

The adjoining bedroom showed signs of a great struggle. The amount of blood on the pillows and sheets was startling, and the covers were wildly dishevelled. The homicide sergeant went from there to 42 Division to check on the progress of the investigation and at about eleven that morning arrived in Ken's room at Sunnybrook Hospital. He was required to wait while the psychiatrist completed his examination. Constable Eric Puusa was on guard inside the room, and another constable stood at the door outside.

At 11:38 the homicide officer saw Ken Parks for the first time, a huge man lying on his back with his thickly bandaged hands raised above his chest. Ken appeared agitated and in great pain.

The sergeant decided to postpone answering Ken's questions. He had an investigation to conduct. He brusquely asked the man's name—"Ken Parks"—and age—"twenty-three". He then asked if Ken would object if he used a tape recorder to take a statement. Ken replied that he didn't care.

The tape was filed as evidence, together with a transcript because Ken's replies were almost inaudible. His normal speaking voice is soft and people strain to hear him, but on the tape it also was uneven, his breath coming in shallow gasps broken by sobs.

Only when the tape was finished did the homicide officer tell Ken that he had killed Barbara Woods but not Denis Woods.

Ken asked, the words dragged out, "How's my wife? Did I hurt her?"

The sergeant said Karen was fine. Ken heard him but wasn't convinced. The answer had been given somewhat evasively. He began to cry again.

During the long wait for the surgery, police continued to question him. At one point Sergeant Adair said he wanted to take another statement on tape.

"You have the right to call a lawyer," he informed Ken.

Ken groaned, "I can't afford a lawyer. I have nothing more to say. I've told you everything I can."

He and Karen had been shocked at the fees they had been charged by the lawyer retained to defend him on the fraud charges. Most certainly they couldn't take on any more legal expense. Sergeant Adair insisted, and the second taped statement was taken.

Though two policemen testified otherwise and there is no reason not to believe them, Ken does not remember that anyone ever "read him his rights". He's not sure he would have remembered it if they had.

It has been understood since the beginning of provincial legal-aid plans that police will inform accused persons who say they are indigent of their right to a publicly funded lawyer. In fact, Ken Parks contributed to a Supreme Court of Canada decision on that very issue. On February 1, 1990, the Supreme Court in a unanimous decision by seven judges ruled that police failure to do so violates a person's constitutional rights to such a degree that all charges against that person could be dismissed. The precedent on which they depended was written by Judge David Watt when he barred from the Parks trial the second tape, the one made after Ken had said he couldn't afford a lawyer.

A judgment written by Mr. Justice Antonio Lamer noted that "The right to retain and instruct counsel, in modern Canadian society, has come to mean more than the right to retain a lawyer privately. It now means the right to have counsel free of charge where the accused meets the financial criteria set up by the provincial legal aid plan."

In Ken Parks' case, as police admitted in the trial, there was a failure to advise him that a legal-aid lawyer could be called, an oversight that was particularly grave since his charges were so serious and his state of mind incoherent.

In fact, Ken's statements on the two tapes are strikingly similar, so the issue was mainly one of law rather than content. His replies are consistent and direct, but it is evident that he was in the grip of powerful emotions. From time to time he groans.

When he speaks, his voice is hoarse and his breath rasping and uneven.

The police treated Ken with courtesy and kindness, which increased his inclination to be co-operative, but he had little information to give. Despite persistent and expert police questioning during the twelve hours before the surgery on his hands, Ken was unable to unearth any memory of the actual killing or the attack on Denis. He could not explain the appalling cuts to his hands. No, he didn't remember driving the fourteen miles from Pickering to Scarborough.

He repeated on both tapes his only clear recollection: "I woke and saw my mother-in-law's face." The police took no note of the curious verb "woke".

For their part, police interrogators found it impossible to believe Ken's insistence that he couldn't remember anything.

At eight o'clock that night, Ken finally was taken to the operating room. The delicate plastic surgery to repair nerves and tendons lasted for four hours and was only partially successful.

Some time after midnight he awakened from the anesthetic and recognized that he was back in his room. The first people he saw were two uniformed police officers. Seeing that Ken was regaining consciousness, one of them pressed the button for a nurse.

Sergeant Adair appeared early the next morning. "Your father's here," he said. "He wants to see you."

Ken was astounded. His father, Jim Parks, was a mysterious figure in his life. Ken's parents separated when he was three years old and Ken had seen or heard from his father fewer than half a dozen times since, usually to exchange only a few impersonal sentences.

Jim Parks came into the room, a dark-haired man almost as big as his son. There were tears in his eyes.

"Are you okay?" he asked huskily.

Ken, still overcome with astonishment, was so touched he began to cry. "I'm fine," he stammered.

"I'm going to get you a lawyer," his father said. "Don't say anything until I get you a lawyer."

Ken, thinking of the legal expenses already incurred with the lawyer who was defending him on the fraud charge, shook his head emphatically. "I don't want a lawyer," he said. "I've already told the police that."

His father stared at him, uncertain what to do. "No lawyer," Ken repeated. The police guard indicated that the visit was over, and his father, after a long sorrowful look at Ken, turned and left.

Ken's family heard the news by degrees. His favourite blood relative, his maternal grandmother, Lilly Hodge, had just returned to Scarborough on that cool Sunday from the trailer home at Balsam Lake north of Toronto where she vacations for most of the summer. She had a telephone call from Tyrone Manuel, a Newfoundlander who has been living with her daughter Betty, Ken's mother, since 1972.

"Ken's in terrible trouble," Tyrone told her. "I can't tell you about it on the phone, it's too serious. Can you come to Oshawa right away?"

Her son, Glen Hodge, arrived with his wife, Diane, to drive her the twenty miles to her daughter's tiny red-brick home perched on the edge of rail yards in Oshawa. She remembers the trip as a nightmare of terrified apprehension. Lil is scrupulously impartial in her treatment of her brood of grandchildren, insisting that each is perfect and she has no favourites, but Ken was her first grandchild and she prizes him. In 1980, when Tyrone landed a well-paid job on the truck-assembly line of General Motors in Oshawa, Ken was sixteen and reluctant to follow his mother. He wanted to stay in Scarborough to finish high school, and his grandmother Hodge solved the problem by inviting Ken to live with her. The arrangement worked smoothly for them both. Ken was grateful for his grandmother's generous disposition, and Lil was glad to have Ken's amiable company. Ken stayed with his grandmother for four years until his marriage. She gave him the mothering for which he was starved.

As Tyrone greeted her at the door, Lil noticed that two of Betty's four children, Robby and the teenaged Tammy, were there. Tense faces turned towards her. Robby was the first to speak. "Ken killed Karen's mother," he said.

Lil was incredulous. "I can't believe it," she said, feeling faint. "Not Kenneth. Not Kenneth. He couldn't do it, it's impossible."

Tyrone and Glen assured her that it was true. The Scarborough police had phoned Ken's brother Darrin at Ken's request. Darrin promptly called his mother but got Tyrone, who explained that Betty was out with a friend. "Ken's killed Karen's mother," he blurted out. Ty couldn't believe it. He checked with the Durham police and asked if there was a mistake, but the police confirmed Darrin's account. There was no room for doubt that the Ken Parks who had been charged with murder was the one they knew. He was in a hospital somewhere, Ty was informed, arrested and under police guard.

Ty then called Glen, Lilly Hodge's second son, a plumber, who picked up Lil. Tammy, eighteen, the youngest of Betty's children, was also summoned and arrived just before the three from Scarborough. Mavis, Lil's youngest, was married to a draftsman in the northern Ontario town of Dorset. She was on her way.

When Betty, Ken's mother, came through the door, she stopped in amazement to see so many of her family. "What's this?" she cried merrily, pulling up a chair. They all spoke at once. Betty doesn't remember who gave her the gist of it, but once she realized what they were saying she started to scream. She jumped up and bolted out of the house, throwing herself into the arms of the woman next door, a neighbour accustomed to hearing her woes.

After a while Tyrone fetched her. Darrin Parks had arrived and right after him Lil's other son, Ronald, an electrician in the town of Port Perry, and his wife, Susan. The family tried to deal with the incomprehensible nightmare. It wasn't possible, they kept saying. They had known Ken all his life. In many ways, he was the most easy-going and gentle person in the family. As Tyrone kept saying, with his Newfoundland lilt, "He wouldn't hurt *any*body." It had to be a mistake. They dispatched Tyrone and Glen to drive to the Scarborough police station to get more information.

The men returned unsatisfied. "Ken walked into the police station and said he killed two people," they told the others. "Then they found Barbara dead and Denis with his head cut. And Ken's hands are all cut. That's all we can find out."

The house that Ty and Betty occupy was too small for them all, but the stunned family didn't want to be separated. They got into their cars and pick-up trucks and drove to Lil's immaculate house in Scarborough to regroup.

"Please excuse the house," Lil apologized mechanically, as she always does. "I've been up north." It's a family joke that she always feels her home is not tidy enough, when in fact Lil's house has a permanent shine, nothing an inch out of place.

Like Karen and her siblings, the Hodge–Parks family was trying to find an explanation that would fit with the unlikelihood that Ken was a killer. They turned over possibilities. The only theory that made any sense was that Ken was trying to protect Barbara and Denis from an attacker. That explained how his hands got cut. His confession to the police was an attempt to shield the real killer. That sounded like Ken, a very protective, loyal man.

It occurred to them suddenly that Ken would need a good criminal lawyer. None of them knew one experienced in murder charges, so Glen Hodge volunteered to make inquiries from the lawyer he used. "Don't worry about the money," Lil Hodge said grimly. "I've got some stock I can sell."

Tyrone cautioned, "It's going to be expensive." Glen Hodge said quickly, "We'll worry about that when we get to it. The first thing is to get Ken a good lawyer."

The Parks family is no stranger to legal difficulties. Ken's two brothers, Robby and Darrin, have had trouble with the law most of their lives. "They were full of mischief," their grandmother Hodge explains loyally. She's being kind. The mischief includes bar fights and burglaries.

Oshawa is a lunch-bucket automotive city of some 200,000 people where couples go out for the evening in matching windbreakers covered with bowling crests. The tough, macho tone of the high school was a disaster for the Parks boys. They arrived in the city as youngsters who did occasional shop-lifting but very soon were accomplished thieves. Because of their youth, judges usually sentenced them to serve terms of probation and community service. For a while, though, Darrin was kept in a detention centre. Betty and Ty, heartsick, grew accustomed to police calls in the night and bail hearings in the morning.

Glen Hodge called his lawyer friend at home and was given the names of what were described as "the three best criminal lawyers in Canada—the tops". When he left the phone, he read the names to the others: Clay Ruby, Morris Manning, Edward Greenspan.

The family decided that nothing more could be done until the next morning, so they went their separate ways. The men took Monday off work and met again at Lil's neat house. They looked up the telephone number of the first lawyer on the list, Clayton C. Ruby, a name familiar to them all. They had seen Clay Ruby many times on television news clips, dressed in black robes and standing outside some courthouse, his hair tousled in the wind and his dark eyes burning with conviction as he spoke of the justice of his case. Glen Hodge, who placed the call, was dismayed when a secretary explained that Mr. Ruby was away on vacation.

Mr. Ruby's partner, however, might be available to assist until Mr. Ruby returned. Would they like to speak to Marlys Edwardh?

The name was unknown to them, but they reasoned that she must be good if she worked with Clay Ruby. When Glen described to her what had happened, she said she would see Ken at once.

Betty Parks went with Tyrone and her mother, Lil Hodge, to Sunnybrook Hospital. They were allowed into Ken's room and they found him weeping.

"I can't believe the things the police are telling me," he said. "Is it true that I hit Barbara with a tire-iron?"

Betty hadn't heard anything about a tire-iron, she said. To comfort her son, she told him about the lawyer.

"I don't want a lawyer," he protested. "I don't want you spending your money on me."

"We're going to help you as much as we can," Betty told him. "We're all here for you."

Betty turned to the guard standing inside the door.

"Can I hug him?" she asked. He nodded, so she put her arms around her son. Ken burst into tears.

Marlys Edwardh, then thirty-seven and already rated as one of the country's leading criminal lawyers, is a small, slender, erect woman with a cap of hair the colour and gloss of chestnuts, cool grey eyes, and a warm, impish face. She arrived at Sunnybrook Hospital soon after she was retained, and was accompanied by a big, bearded man, Delmar Doucette, thirty-two, her articling student. She had two imperatives. One was to insure that her client made no further statements to the police unless she was present; the other was to get her name on the chart as Ken's lawyer so she could have access to him.

They introduced themselves to Ken as lawyers his family had retained until Clay Ruby could take over. Ken liked them both on sight. Marlys impressed him when she requested, her manner pleasant but firm, that the officer in the room withdraw and the man did so.

When the door whispered shut behind the officer's back, Marlys settled down to ask Ken what had happened. Ken replied miserably that he didn't know. She had expected to encounter someone of tougher disposition; the youth before her was distraught, frightened, and confused. Marlys thought, "This man is a teddy bear."

She said to Ken, "You've given the police your explanation and nothing more needs to be said at this stage. You have a right to remain silent, and you should exercise that right from now on."

Ken mumbled, "There wasn't much to tell them. I don't remember anything after going to sleep on the couch. I woke up and saw my mother-in-law's face...."

Marlys asked carefully, "How did you get along with your mother-in-law?"

Ken answered with tears in his eyes, "I really cared for her. We got along great. We were pretty close."

"And your father-in-law?"

"I like him a lot, and I think he liked me."

She had more questions about the events of that night, but Ken could remember nothing. He had no comprehension of what had happened; it was inexplicable to him.

Marlys believed him. She has interviewed many people newly arrested for murder but never one like Ken Parks. His profound remorse and horror conveyed powerfully to her that she was hearing his truth. The real question was what his truth meant. Was he mentally ill? Was it psychogenic repression? Why didn't he have access to his memories?

Whatever the explanation, Marlys was convinced that Ken was being honest when he said he couldn't remember the killing. It remained for her to find a defence that would explain Ken's inability to recall what had happened. Her husband is a noted psychologist, Dr. Graham Turrall, so she would start by asking his help. The defence would require neuro-pathologic or psychiatric sleuth work of a high order, and Graham had the contacts to find the help she needed.

The range of psychiatric defences available in modern criminal law is wide and subtle. Marlys Edwardh happens to have amassed as much experience in that arcane field as any criminal lawyer in the country. Defences that involve some element of insanity in the plea have become almost her specialty. She's familiar with a world-wide network of experts on whom she can call for help, and they, in turn, respect her grasp of their labyrinthine field.

She said to Ken: "Tell me everything you did the day before this happened."

Ken retraced his activities. When he mentioned that he had played rugby on Saturday morning, she made a note to order tests to see if he had sustained a head injury that would cause his memory blackout. She was also thinking, *it might be a brain tumour*.

She checked Ken's chart and was shocked to see that a psychiatrist had already examined him. Her defence almost certainly would rest on psychiatric testimony and she didn't want doctors she didn't know dipping into Ken's mental state and sharing that information with the Crown. She wrote across the chart in a firm hand, "No psychiatric tests."

As she left, she politely notified Sergeant Adair that her client would be making no more statements in her absence. The sergeant nodded, content with what he had. The long delay over the surgery and Ken's insistence that he didn't want a lawyer had combined to give Adair uninterrupted access to his prisoner, something rare in modern police experience.

When Marlys left, the police guard stepped back into the hospital room, regaining his turf. Marlys hurried to a telephone and placed a call to a Sunnybrook psychiatrist, Dr. Ronald Billings.

"My client, Kenneth Parks, will need a psychiatric assessment," she said. "I'd like to retain you for the defence."

Billings agreed and said he would order whatever tests of Ken's brain were necessary. Marlys hung up, much relieved. A measure of control had been restored. With Ken's consent, his medical records would be her property, part of a private file, and the Crown could get access to them only by means of a search warrant. Soon after, Billings, trailing a resident, Dr. Hersch, bustled in to start his assessment of the patient.

Ronald Billings is a distinguished member of the profession. He is a psychiatrist on the Sunnybrook staff who is also the assistant head of the department of psychiatry at the hospital, associate professor of psychiatry at the University of Toronto, and co-author of a textbook on psychiatry. Significantly, he has expertise in the field of forensic psychiatry: Ron Billings sits on the regional review board that examines people sent to Penetanguishene's Oak Ridge institution because they have been found to be criminally insane.

On the way to the room, Ron Billings had a brief outline of the situation from his resident. The patient's inability to remember was puzzling, he thought. Probably a schizophrenic episode. Maybe a paranoid state, or a delusional state. Or it could be a deliberate act and the patient had a self-induced amnesia. Or possibly a fugue state, a form of hysteria caused by emotional stress. If the person turned out to have a personality disorder with antisocial tendencies, it could have been episodic discontrol syndrome, where people with minor provocation over-react and do something violent.

Del Doucette, who had lingered out of concern for Ken's distress, got up to leave when the doctors came into the room. He suggested that the police officer also withdraw. "The doctors should have privacy to examine their patient," Del told him. The police officer demurred, saying that his instructions were to the contrary. Though Del protested, the man was unmoved. Del left, but the officer remained and conspicuously scribbled in a notebook as Ken spoke to the doctors.

Dr. Billings began by asking if Ken had ever experienced blackouts, seizures, or memory loss. "No, never," Ken said. Dr. Billings then probed Ken's state of mind in recent weeks. Ken told him that he hadn't been sleeping well, and that he had been despondent. Was his memory of the event returning? Could he recall anything more, anything at all?

Ken had thought of little else in every waking moment, but he couldn't picture anything beyond the scattered fragments he had described, over and over, to the police: Barbara's pleading face, something about the telephone, the kids screaming upstairs, himself running up the stairs, himself in the car with the knife, then the police station. That was all. Ron Billings was puzzled. How could this man drive fourteen miles, kill someone brutally and attack a second person, cut his hands to the bone—and yet not remember *anything?*

Yet Billings had the impression that Ken was rational and sane. His immediate concern therefore was the condition of his brain. He decided to order some tests, a brain scan and an electroencephalogram (EEG). He was dismayed when he was advised that Ken was leaving soon for the Don Jail.

"The tests will have to wait, then," he said, "but I want that neurological assessment done. I'll send Dr. Edmeads around right away and we'll make the appointments."

Before leaving, Ron Billings paused to write on Ken's chart an order for a full examination of Ken's brain. A number of possibilities had to be studied, among them complex partial seizures, temporal lobe epilepsy or limbic seizures, malfunction related to drugs or alcohol, or post-concussive or post-ectal confusional state. He worried about a tumour. If Ken's memory loss was caused by a tumour it was a big one, almost certainly of fatal dimensions.

Dr. John Edmeads, the neurologist, had the same concern. He concurred that a CAT scan and EEG were imperative.

CHAPTER FOUR

Two Prisons

On the day of her mother's death, Karen was almost too demoralized to have a coherent thought. She found it impossible to reconcile the two parts of her life: her beloved mother had been murdered and her beloved husband was the murderer. Ken must have had a crazy spell. Television was full of plots about people who went berserk. She had read about murder trials where ordinary, decent people pleaded temporary insanity. It seemed to happen. It was the *only* way it could have happened.

She couldn't believe that Ken would deliberately and coolly set out to kill her parents. For one thing, he cared too much for them; for another he simply wasn't a violent man. She had been with him almost daily for six years; she couldn't be wrong about something as fundamental as that.

Karen seized on a crumb of information dropped by a police officer, who said that Ken couldn't remember anything. That sounded to her like a man who had killed in a fit of mental breakdown.

Her sisters and brothers, she noted, were taking the view that they were lucky that Ken hadn't killed them too. Karen didn't want to get into an argument about it. The fact was that they didn't know what had happened any more than she did.

The day of the disaster was endurable only because none of them could quite believe it. The six Woods children had never been in such pain and confusion in their lives. In their keening grief, what hurt most bitterly was that they didn't have the support of either parent. Nothing had ever happened to any of them that Barbara hadn't tried to soothe and make better. The worst part of their agony was that their mother wasn't there to give comfort.

They spent most of the day at the hospital. They had no place else to go, since their house was cordoned off to allow police forensic teams to complete their investigation. Samantha clung to her boy-friend, who looked bewildered. When Emma's boy-friend, Jimmy Sotirakos, turned up she threw herself into his arms.

Karen watched, feeling nothing. Later that day she left the waiting-room and walked to Connie Sullivan's to see how Melissa was faring.

She couldn't avoid the questions in Connie's eyes. Keeping her voice under control and not embellishing the story, she said that Ken had killed her mother and attacked her father. Her father would survive. Connie's reaction was incredulity. "That's not Ken!" she gasped. Connie's boy-friend wasn't so certain.

"I'm not surprised," he commented. "He's deep. You never know what's really going on with him."

Karen said stubbornly, "We just don't know what happened. Apparently even Ken doesn't know what happened."

"He's lying," the other insisted. "He's just bullshitting."

Karen was hurt. Her loyalty to family, a deep force in her nature, was aroused, and she found herself defending her husband.

"You can't say that," she said indignantly. "We have to wait and see what the police turn up."

Connie agreed to keep Melissa a while longer, so Karen went back to the hospital. The young people took turns sitting quietly with their father, who slept most of the time. They watched him breathe raggedly, and when he wakened his face was twisted with his suffering. They held his hand. There wasn't much to say.

That evening Barbara's closest friend, Linda Taylor, came to the hospital in a distraught state. She had seen a report on the television news that Barbara Woods of Scarborough had been murdered.

"Why didn't you call me?" she asked Karen.

"I'm sorry," Karen said lamely. "We just didn't think of it. We haven't called anyone."

Linda Taylor collapsed in a chair in the waiting-room. "I can't believe that Ken did this," she said. "He and Barbara were so close. Barbara thought the world of him. Remember, she called him 'teddy bear'? She used to say he wouldn't hurt a flea."

"She used to call him 'the gentle giant'," Karen said, her face twisted. "We're trying to find out what happened. I think Ken just went nuts."

Linda shook her head in disbelief and went to visit Denis. Denis told Linda that he was worried about Karen. The rest of the family would find some way to go on, but how could Karen survive such a double blow? She loved her mother deeply, and he knew she loved Ken too. He feared that she would be torn apart. Linda assured him that Karen appeared calm. In fact, she was the most collected of all the Woods children.

He asked if Nicky had been notified. Linda checked with the other children, who were aghast that they had forgotten. He was expected home the following night with Linda's son, Robert, another member of the soccer team. Karen volunteered to pick up Nicky when he arrived back.

Karen suddenly remembered that she was supposed to work that night at midnight to enter price changes in the supermarket computer. She called the store to explain that she wouldn't be there. She gave as a reason, "There's been a death in the family." She couldn't trust herself to keep her composure if she had to say, "My mother has been killed and my husband did it."

The shattered Woods children clung together. When night fell, they considered where they would sleep. They agreed that they didn't want to be scattered to the homes of friends and neighbours. Karen suggested that they all drive to Pickering and sleep at her house. There was plenty of room—a queen-size bed in the master bedroom, a couch in Melissa's room, the living-room couch, and bunk beds in the third bedroom where Nicky and Pru were accustomed to sleeping when they came for weekend visits. Samantha's boy-friend drove some of them in his car, and Jimmy, Emma's boy-friend, took the others.

Karen prepared something for them to eat but found she couldn't get down a bite herself. To her dismay, her sisters and brothers were apprehensive for their safety. They asked nervously, "What if Ken gets away and comes here?"

Karen dismissed their fears as nonsense. She pointed out that Ken was under arrest somewhere and under police guard. He couldn't escape; and if he did, they should know that Ken wouldn't hurt them. That, in fact, was exactly what they did fear. Ken wanted to kill everyone in the family, they said, and could be expected to come after them if he could get away.

They jumped at sounds in the street. To distract themselves, they decided to flick around the channels and watch the television news. Maybe there would be something about the killing, and they could pick up some information. Three news clips showed reporters standing in front of the Woods house describing the murder of "Barbara Woods, Scarborough mother of six". While the camera panned over police cars parked in the garage around the rear door of the townhouse, reporters described the crime as a domestic dispute between Kenneth James Parks, twenty-three, of Pickering, and his mother-in-law. They confidently offered the opinion that the two had a long-standing conflict.

A fourth channel, Toronto's enterprising and brash CITY-TV, gave them a shock. The camera showed two men carrying a stretcher out of the house and on the stretcher was Barbara Woods in a body bag. The children screamed and burst into tears. For the first time, Karen was able to weep too.

After that the young people were too shaken to sleep. They resisted going to bed until around two in the morning. Karen settled them in the various available beds, taking thirteen-year-old Pru into bed with her. Pru dropped asleep, but none of the others could settle down. Karen found them in the living-room where they had arranged themselves on the couch and on the floor. One of them was staying awake for guard duty, they told Karen, in case Ken turned up.

"That's stupid," Karen said disgustedly. They stared at her with stony faces until she turned and went back to her bed.

In the morning the family bought the three Toronto newspapers at coin boxes and read the terse facts of the murder and subsequent arrest. They learned nothing new. The police still had no details apart from the obvious facts that two people had been attacked and one was dead.

Karen was driven to the Scarborough supermarket where she worked. The manager had read the morning paper and was sympathetic when she explained that she wouldn't be coming to work for a while. "Take as long as you like, Karen," he said kindly.

Emma and Samantha called their employers and asked for leaves of absence. Karen dropped Melissa off at Connie's again, and the Woods children spent the day at Scarborough Grace hospital, taking turns at Denis's bedside. Their father was more coherent and was beginning to make decisions. At his suggestion, it was agreed that Barbara's funeral would be postponed until Denis was well enough to attend. Several times that day Karen went to Connie's, an easy walk from the hospital, and rested herself in the tranquil presence of the baby.

She would need transportation, she realized. Her car, hers and Ken's, was in the hands of the police, so she asked her father if she could use his. He agreed and told the police that his keys could be found in Barbara's purse or in his pants pocket. An obliging police officer went to the Scarborough townhouse and fetched the keys, leaving them at the police station.

That night Karen and Linda Taylor drove to a drop-off location to meet the soccer team returning from Philadelphia. They found the players and their parents milling around a litter of equipment and baggage. Karen located Nicky in the throng. "Where's mom?" he asked immediately, when he saw her.

Karen had been rehearsing her answer to that question. "There's been a terrible accident," she explained. "Come over here, I have to talk to you."

They found privacy in the hubbub by standing near a wall.

"What kind of accident?" he asked.

Karen avoided that question. "Dad's okay," she said. "He's in hospital, but he's okay."

Nicky asked, "But where's mom?"

"She's gone to heaven," Karen told him.

"What happened?" said Nicky, looking perplexed.

"A terrible accident," Karen repeated.

She drove him to the hospital, noting that the twelve-year-old appeared very natural and unconcerned. Wise now in the way of shock, she kept an eye on him. He remained poised during a visit to his father. He decided he would spend the night with his friend Robert, and it was there that Linda Taylor filled him in on the details, telling him that Ken had killed his mother. Linda's grief had turned into rage against Ken. She told Nicky that Ken Parks was a vicious murderer and the law would punish him.

The Woods children, with the exception of Nicky, slept a second night at Karen's. Despite Karen's protest that they were being unreasonable, they again huddled together in the living-room with one of them posted as sentinel to warn the others if Ken turned up. To relieve their anxiety, Karen called the Durham police.

Explaining who she was, she said, "We're all a little nervous and it would make us feel better if you would keep an eye on us tonight. Do you think you could drive by every now and then?"

When the police agreed to send a cruiser past the house at intervals throughout the night, the children sighed with relief.

The telephone kept ringing. One caller was one of Ken's colleagues from Revere Electric, his former employer. She said she couldn't believe that Ken would kill anyone. What had happened?

Karen said, "We don't know."

Ken's aunt Mavis phoned to see if Karen was all right. "We're in shock here," she said. "We can't believe it. What happened, do you know?"

"No," Karen told her tersely. "Not exactly."

She doesn't admire herself for it, but Karen wanted Ken's family to suffer. "We think what happened was that he came in the house and tried to strangle my dad and then he went upstairs and got a knife out of the kitchen and killed my mother, and then he went back and used the knife on my father's head, and then he went upstairs where my sisters and brother were hiding, and then he ran out."

"That's awful," said Mavis weakly.

"Yes it is," said Karen in a bitter tone.

When she hung up she was appalled. She didn't believe that Ken had acted deliberately, so why had she been so mean? She faced herself and didn't like what she saw. She'd lashed out at Ken's family out of pure spite.

The next morning Emma and Jimmy Sotirakos drove Karen to the police station to pick up the keys to her father's car. The officer asked for identification and Karen exploded.

"Just give me the keys," she snapped, her pent-up feelings finding release.

"Would you expect me to hand over these car keys to anyone who comes in?" asked the officer.

Karen, red-faced, shouted, "Who else would know they are here? Just hand them over!"

Her father's car was parked near the rear door of the townhouse, which was still under police guard. Karen avoided looking at the basement door. She didn't want to think about what had happened behind that door. As she unlocked her father's car, she saw a trail of blood leading from the back door. She called her brothers and sisters and they followed the trail. It went in one direction towards a visitor's parking spot and then veered and went to another, as if the person wasn't sure where the car was parked. The bloody trail ended in the parking space behind Number 77. Close to it, as though Ken had tripped and almost fallen, was a partial handprint in blood on the concrete, a large handprint.

Karen tried to remain detached. She listened as her brothers and sisters gave instructions to a police officer who was bringing them fresh clothes. Despite her anguish, she was amused at the officer's exasperation as her siblings gave their full attention to their wardrobes. They were being fussy: "No, not that one, the *light* green one." "The sweater in the bottom drawer on the left side." "No, those are Nicky's shoes. Mine are in the laundry room. No? Try the closet in the room near the bathroom."

She noted that the Woods children were too shy to ask the police to bring underwear.

"You have enough," Karen protested several times, impatient to get back to the hospital.

"No, no," one would say. "I haven't got my beige shirt!"

"And I need my jeans," another would say.

At noon that day, Tuesday, police asked the Woods children for statements. The interview with Karen lasted for two hours and was mutually unsatisfactory. The investigating officers had expected that she would provide them with a motive, but Karen insisted that Ken loved her mother and father and bore them no ill will. On the other hand, she could get little information from them.

"How's Ken?" she asked.

"He's fine," she was informed. "He's had an operation on his hands. They were pretty badly cut so it isn't certain how much movement he'll get back."

"Where is he?"

"At Sunnybrook Hospital."

"What does he say about what happened?"

"He says he doesn't remember."

"I'd like to see him," she said.

The police exchanged glances.

"Later," she was told.

The other children trooped in for their interviews, one after the other throughout the day. Afterwards they pooled the information they had gleaned from the officers. They concluded that the police were still baffled. The consensus seemed to be that Ken was lying or insane.

Karen still couldn't eat, though it was the third day since her mother's death. She was coaxed on all sides to have something, but the sight of food revolted her. On Tuesday morning, when she didn't touch her breakfast, her family was frantic. "You'll make yourself sick," Emma protested. Karen shrugged.

When she went to Connie's later to check on Melissa, her friend made a tuna sandwich and insisted that Karen eat it. She tried a bite, apprehensive that she would vomit, but it stayed down, so she gulped the rest of the sandwich.

That afternoon police called a family meeting of the six Woods children to show them photographs. The first was of a carving knife. "Is this yours?" they asked Karen. "Is it from your house?" She shook her head. Emma looked at the picture. "Yeah, yeah," she said excitedly. "That's our knife." All of them then identified it as one their mother kept in a protective sheath in a kitchen drawer.

She was asked about a tire-iron. Did Ken have one? Yes, she told them, sickened. Maybe he had two. Ken kept one under the passenger seat of his car.

Karen asked urgently when she could see Ken. Ken would be leaving the hospital soon for prison, she reasoned, and probably wouldn't be allowed to touch Melissa once he was behind bars. It was only fair that she take Melissa to him while he could still hold her. Most of all, though, she wanted to end the painful indecision over how she felt about Ken. She had to see him to know if she hated him.

Staff Sergeant Adair said he would take her to Sunnybrook to see Ken at one o'clock the next day, Wednesday.

Karen decided not to tell her sisters and brothers. They were ranting about Ken and what they would do if they ever saw him. During their tension-relieving tirades she kept silent. It would only upset them to know she wanted to visit Ken.

Her father asked if she had any money. Karen had to confess she didn't. It wasn't necessary to remind him that Ken had taken all their savings. Denis wrote her a cheque for $500, and she used the funds to replenish food supplies, seriously depleted by her siblings, and to buy gas for the car.

Denis was regaining his strength rapidly and with it came burning anger. "I don't care what Ken's reasons were," he told Karen with flashing eyes. "I'd like to kill him. If I had a gun and Ken was standing in front of me, I'd shoot him. I'd be able to pull the trigger."

Karen didn't speak. Her father was entitled to his feelings. She just didn't happen to share them. Not yet, anyway.

On Tuesday night the other Woods children slept at the home of a friendly school teacher. They explained to Karen that they hated being in the house where Ken had lived and, besides, it was too scary. At the same time, they didn't want to abandon Karen, whose silence and air of remoteness frightened them. They insisted that she have Connie stay with her.

When Karen and Connie were alone in the Pickering house, Karen confided that she would be visiting Ken the next day.

"Why?" Connie asked in astonishment.

"I want to see him and find out why he did it," Karen explained.

"I'll come with you," Connie said loyally.

Now that the meeting was scheduled, Karen was impatient to get it done. One look at Ken, she thought, and she would have some answers. Ken had gone crazy and maybe still was, but she needed to see that madman in him for herself. Maybe it would be clear to her that he had had the potential all along to be a killer. If so, she could get over feeling stunned and confused. It wouldn't be easy to accept that she'd been wrong about him for six years, but she could begin to deal with that. Anything was better than her present bewilderment.

Marlys Edwardh was working on the Sinclair Stevens inquiry when the call came about Ken Parks. It was alleged that Sinclair Stevens as a federal cabinet minister had misused his office to salvage his personal finances. Marlys Edwardh had a suggestion that dramatically altered what had been a plodding inquiry that was long on conjecture and coincidence and short on evidence. Sinclair Stevens probably had a crackerjack secretary, she thought. Such a woman, under oath, could supply all the information the inquiry needed.

Her hunch proved astute. Shirley Walker sat in the witness-box for almost two weeks and provided the commissioner, Chief Justice William D. Parker, with incriminating evidence, some of which Walker had stored in paper bags in her closet. Chief Justice Parker subsequently found that Sinclair Stevens indeed had put himself in a conflict-of-interest position.

The first call to Marlys was made by Glen Hodge, Ken's young uncle, who asked her to take the case until Clay Ruby returned. She agreed, her ego unruffled. Many clients have come to her by that route. To date, none has ever switched to Clay Ruby when he became available.

Soon after, a man who said he was Ken's father came unannounced to see her.

The lawyer recalls Jim Parks as a sad and listless man who sat on the couch in her office looking mostly at the floor. He explained that he didn't know his son very well, but it was hard to believe that Ken was a murderer. He offered some money and said he would get more.

Marlys Edwardh was not concerned about the money. She had been raised in an environment steeped in concern for social causes. Her parents, Melvin Edwardh and Catherine Muir Edwardh, are conscientious, hard-working, erudite people with deep convictions about social justice. Marlys, the youngest of three, was born in 1950 and was raised in Alberta until she was seven, when the family lived briefly in Colorado while her father got his Ph.D. and her mother an M.A. In 1958 they moved to Toronto where Melvin Edwardh took a position as president of Gage Educational Publishing, a respected publishing house specializing in textbooks, and her mother taught high school English.

Later when Seneca College, a community college, opened, Catherine Edwardh taught English there until her retirement. She and her husband then went to China, where she taught school in Shanghai for a while.

Marlys doesn't know where she got the idea to be a lawyer, but it was firmly fixed in her mind from the age of thirteen, at which time in her life she had never even met one. Possibly the impetus came from her family's devotion to social causes and a link Marlys saw between the law and the protection of civil liberties. She comes from a long line of people who care about such matters. Marlys' maternal grandfather had to flee the United States when his efforts to organize a railway union outraged the authorities.

Dinner conversation in the Edwardh household boiled with discussion about current events. In the sixties civil rights movement in the United States, Marlys' sister, Joanne, known as Joey, was active in the struggle to permit blacks to register to vote. Her father kept bail money in the house in case she was arrested at an inconvenient time when banks were closed. Since those tumultuous years Joey has worked consistently in the Third World, her field the aged; she now lives in Santiago, Chile.

Marlys Edwardh is imbued with the same drive to live a purposeful life. "I think I see the law as an instrument for social change," Marlys comments.

She obtained an undergraduate degree in sociology and political science at Carleton University in Ottawa and then was accepted at Osgoode Hall Law School. In study week of her first year she went to Ottawa to visit some friends, who introduced her to Susan Reisler. Susie Reisler, who has been Marlys' closest friend ever since, is best known in recent years as a commentator on CBC television's *The Journal*.

That week Susan Reisler had a young lawyer, Clayton Ruby, staying with her. He was in Ottawa to defend a young Puerto Rican, Hernandez Pagan, who had escaped to Canada after an attempted assassination of the head of the police riot squad in San Juan. Clay Ruby, though very new as a lawyer, already had a public reputation through his efforts to help young drifters, known then as hippies, who were drawn to the gaudy, raunchy Yorkville area of Toronto. With another young lawyer, Paul Copeland, he had authored an impertinent law book, *Law Law Law*, which could fit into the hip pocket of jeans and provided the bearer with useful information about such matters as the right to remain silent.

Though Clay Ruby was the son of an exceedingly wealthy man, it was a matter of intense pride with him that he relied solely on his own resources. Accordingly he was cutting costs by sleeping on the living-room floor of Susie Reisler's apartment.

"Maybe Marlys can help you," Reisler suggested. "She's in law school."

Clay was not inclined to believe that a first-year law student could be much use, but the situation was desperate. He had some fifteen witnesses who were arriving by air from Puerto Rico to give testimony, and all of them needed to be sorted out and interviewed before the trial. He didn't see how he could do it by himself. He met Marlys and put her to work.

They divided the witnesses roughly in half. Almost at once Clay discovered that Marlys was as astute as she was pretty. He puts it simply: "She has judgement."

They have been colleagues ever since. The Pagan case dragged over two years, during which time Marlys continued to assist Clay. When she was finishing her third year in law school, Clay suggested casually that she article with him, though at that time criminal law, his field, had known few women lawyers. When she finished articling, he asked her to come into practice with him.

"It's been a very straight path," she notes with a grin.

They work in tiny quarters on the second floor rear of a handsome Victorian-era house near the Bloor Street–Avenue Road intersection of Toronto. Their long association and friendship accommodates itself smoothly to the succession of dogs, all of them named Berkman, that Clay brings to the office, and a period of maternity leave in 1984 when Marlys gave birth to a bright and charming son, Kyle, whom she adores. She and husband Graham Turrall, a psychologist, live in a handsome rambling house in an upper-middle-class area of Toronto.

While Marlys and Clay usually work separately on important and difficult cases, some of which result in landmark decisions at the Supreme Court of Canada, they almost always consult with one another and sometimes share the work. Their most notable collaboration was on the inquiry into the failure of the justice system in Nova Scotia that led to Donald Marshall, a Micmac teenager, serving eleven years in prison for a murder he didn't commit.

One of her cases that attracted much public attention was the appeal on behalf of Mahmoud Issa Mohammad, a convicted Palestinian terrorist ordered deported from Canada.

Several times, more than she can count, Marlys has defended people accused of murder. The question most frequently asked of criminal lawyers is, "How can you help a killer?"

Her reply to that perennial query is: "There is a vast range of responsibility to be assessed in those cases. When someone causes the death of another human being, our law makes many distinctions in determining what level of criminal responsibility, if any, ought to be applied to that death. Causing death may lead to a complete acquittal, because if you accidentally cause death we don't punish. We don't find criminal liability. If you intentionally, deliberately, plan and carry out a homicide, that is first-degree murder."

She continues. "Part of any defence lawyer's job is to ensure that the state mounts a case that proves the charge. Every single one of us is entitled to rest assured that a conviction will occur only on the basis of proper evidence.

"That's my first answer. My second is that because there is this gradation of responsibility, one looks to a range of defences. Perhaps the death is not purely accidental and therefore might be manslaughter, or perhaps the person is mentally ill and there ought to be a defence of not guilty by reason of insanity. We're trained not to make judgements. We're trained to look exhaustively at the range of possible defences that should be put forward."

She explains, "If you believe in a system that focuses responsibility only on those who are truly blameworthy, then our job is to make sure that the state proves its case and people aren't sent to prison on the basis of either the Crown not proving its case or there not being a proper defence."

When she left Ken Parks' hospital room on Monday, Marlys was thinking of all the defences open to her. She was convinced that Ken wasn't a man who would kill deliberately, so the options were narrowing to a plea of not guilty by reason of insanity or some evidence of a damaged brain. If it turned out that the defence would be insanity, Ken would be sent to the prison-like hospital for the criminally insane at Penetanguishene, to be held there indefinitely—"at the pleasure", as the warrant reads, of the lieutenant-governor.

By coincidence, Marlys Edwardh was soon to challenge the constitutionality of such warrants. In February 1990, she and Clay Ruby appeared before the Supreme Court of Canada to argue the fundamental injustice of lieutenant-governor warrants, which hold people in custody for an indefinite time when the courts in fact have found them innocent.

Marlys wondered about Ken's wife. Karen Parks wouldn't be testifying against her husband, since the law does not place that obligation on spouses, but she would make a formidable witness for the defence. No jury could fail to be moved by a young woman speaking in favour of a husband who had killed her mother.

On the morning of Wednesday, May 27, 1987, Marlys heard that "the wife", Karen Parks, was on her way to Sunnybrook Hospital to see Ken. To the lawyer's dismay, she was informed that Staff Sergeant Bobby Burns Adair, the homicide detective assigned to the Parks case, was bringing Karen to her husband's side. It would seem that Karen Parks had lined up with the Crown. Sergeant Adair would witness and record the scene when the wife confronted her husband. Karen's accusations most certainly would be repeated in court as evidence against Ken.

"I thought the occasion was being used for forensic police work," Marlys later related with a tight smile. "It wasn't to give two people an opportunity to be together."

The lawyer was unable to leave her office to avert the impending disaster. She would have to rely on the good sense of Delmar Doucette, her articling student, who was at Sunnybrook Hospital. Marlys had learned that Ken was about to be sent to prison and she had sent Doucette to the hospital to try to get a delay until Dr. Edmeads, the neurologist, could complete the brain tests. She didn't know how to reach Doucette, but Marlys hoped he would be able to do something about Karen Parks.

Del Doucette at that moment was in an elevator on his way to Ken's room to tell him that he had been unable to stall the order to have him taken to prison. The best that could be done, Doucette discovered, was to ensure that Ken went to the Toronto Jail, which has a hospital range staffed twenty-four hours a day, rather than to the Metro East Detention Centre, where medical facilities are more primitive and the attention Ken needed for his hands would not be available.

Doucette noticed two women, one of them holding a baby, getting off the elevator at the same floor he did. They went to a nursing station, apparently to get directions, while he headed for Ken's room.

As Karen, carrying Melissa and accompanied by Connie, got off the elevator, she had an attack of panic. She had been demanding to see Ken but, as the moment neared, she wasn't sure how to conduct herself. So much depended on how she felt when she saw him. She trembled with trepidation. A nurse gave her instructions, pointing back the way she had come. Karen hurried, anxious to get it over, and in her haste sped past Ken's room.

Ken's room was equipped with an observation window on the corridor, and he saw Karen go by.

"My wife is out there," he told Doucette.

"Your wife!" Doucette gasped. He went out to intercept her just as Sergeant Adair and Constable Higgins arrived to escort Karen into the room.

"Are you Karen Parks?" Del asked.

"Yes I am," she replied.

"What are you doing here?" he said, stalling for time.

"I want to talk to Ken."

Doucette, his heart pounding, said, "I'm Del Doucette. I'm an articling student with Ken's lawyer. I'm not sure you can go in there. I'll have to think about it."

Karen was astounded. She had given no thought to Ken's legal situation. She knew he was charged with first-degree murder, but it had a distant sound, a mere phrase, a piece of television drama. She had a sense of matters slipping out of her control. Normally she would have been part of the decision to hire a lawyer.

"Why not?" she retorted sharply, glaring at the big, dark, bearded man. Doucette couldn't tell her the real reason, certainly not in front of Sergeant Adair, so he suggested lamely that "it wouldn't be a good idea" for Karen to go in.

Karen regardly him coldly, as one would an obstruction to go around or through.

"He's my husband," she declared stiffly, "and I have a right to see him."

Karen's moment of dread was over, and the delays had sharpened her impatience. Three days had passed since the killing, and she was still in a state of numbed confusion. It was profoundly unsettling not to know how she felt about Ken. She had loved the man for six years—it was strange to feel nothing but emptiness. Maybe he was a monster she would hate for ever, but before she started down that path she had to *look* at him. She owed that much, at least, to herself, to Melissa, and to him.

"Please wait," Del asked her. "I have to talk to Ken's lawyer."

He called Marlys, who was appalled that Adair was with Karen. Meanwhile a jurisdictional dispute was emerging. Ken's prison guard told Karen that she couldn't enter the room without permission. Staff Sergeant Adair assured him that it was all right, but the guard wasn't so sure. He too went to a telephone and placed a call.

Del returned with instructions from Marlys to keep Karen out if possible. She told him to advise Ken that he shouldn't see Karen under those conditions. At that moment the guard had word that Ken could see his wife if he wished. The guard accordingly asked Karen for identification, which she produced without her customary protest about unnecessary bureaucracy.

As Karen, flanked by Sergeant Adair and Constable Higgins, moved towards the door of Ken's room, Del Doucette stood in her way.

"You can't go in there," he told her.

"I'm his wife," she insisted. "I have permission to see him."

Doucette turned to the police. "She can't see him," he said, with some agitation. "My client hasn't agreed to this. It's an invasion of his rights."

Karen began to understand the objection. The lawyer feared that there was going to be a scene that would be damaging to Ken in court. Maybe, she thought shrewdly, that's what Sergeant Adair expected too.

"How about my rights!" she said heatedly. "He's my *husband*."

"It's not in my client's interests...," Doucette began.

"It's in *my* interests," she retorted, "and I have police permission to see him."

"Just a minute," the lawyer said desperately. "I need to talk to my client about this."

Through the window in the hospital room, Karen glimpsed Ken standing by his bed. She thought he might be returning from the bathroom, but in fact he was watching his second guard put shackles on his ankles in preparation for taking him in a wheelchair to the shower room.

Ken was stunned that Karen was there. He had never expected to see her again, but his first reaction was relief that she apparently was unharmed. He had been groggy with sedatives in the two days since the surgery, but the question that had burned in his mind was Karen's safety. Had he hurt her too? He asked anxiously about her, but no one seemed to know. Police guards told him she was fine, but their tone lacked conviction. When prison guards arrived to take over from the police, they had even less information.

Relief was replaced by amazement. Obviously she had come to tell him she wanted a divorce, but he had not expected her to do that in person. Better than anyone, he knew that the woman who had been killed was not only Karen's mother but also her dearest friend.

Ken got back into bed to await Karen. Through the window, Karen watched Doucette talking to him and noted the lawyer's urgent, alarmed body language. When he emerged a few minutes later, he was dejected. He reported candidly that he had advised Ken that he should refuse to see Karen but that Ken had rejected the advice.

"I don't care what she says to me," he told Doucette. "I want to talk to her."

Doucette, his face worried, repeated this to Karen. "I told him not to see you," he told her, "but he won't listen. Wait a minute while I talk to the police."

Del turned to Sergeant Adair. "Where do you intend to be while Karen is having a conversation with her husband?" he asked.

"We'll be with her in the room," the homicide detective replied.

"If you go in there and Sergeant Adair goes in and Constable Higgins goes in there, so do I," Doucette said.

Karen was steaming. "Look, I don't want a whole room of people when I see my husband. I'm his wife and we want some privacy."

"That's completely unacceptable," Del told her. "I'll have to call Marlys about this."

Marlys told him that under no circumstances were the police to be in the room when Karen met Ken. Doucette put down the phone thinking that he just might have a heart attack.

"It was the typical confrontational situation," he explained later. "You put someone dear to the accused into the room so he will say everything that's on his mind. Then you write it all down and produce it at the trial."

Del consulted with Ken, advising him that it would not be in his interests to have police in the room. Ken didn't want the police there either. He said it was bad enough that prison guards would be present.

That raised a new issue for Del. He asked the guard what his position would be about whatever he overheard during the meeting. The guard said he wasn't sure. He made another call to his superior, who said that Ken's wishes could be respected with regard to the police presence and the guards would take no note of what they heard. It is correctional policy that guards do not testify, though it is always open to the Crown to issue subpoenas to require them to tell what they know.

Staff Sergeant Adair was unhappy with the decision, but the correctional system had charge of the prisoner.

"All right," he agreed, scowling at Karen, "but remember that you're not to touch him."

Karen suddenly decided that her initial meeting with Ken might be so emotional that it would be better for Melissa to stay with Connie. She handed over the baby and stepped through the door.

After all the fuss she expected to be alone with Ken, but one of the prison guards stayed in the room, companionably drawing up a chair near the door where he could keep both in sight. She turned to Ken, who was propped against pillows with both hands in thick bandages like a child's mittens. She noted cuts on both his beefy forearms.

Ken said quickly, "If you want a divorce, I won't fight it." Then he burst into tears. For a long time he sobbed without being able to speak.

Karen, disarmed, stood by the bed helplessly. She said, "Don't cry. There, there, Ken, don't cry."

A nurse, checking Ken's vital signs on a monitor in her station, noted that he was hyperventilating and hurried into the room. She and Karen tried to calm Ken, but it was almost ten minutes before he got himself under control. In a strangled voice, he said, "Karen, I don't remember anything."

"There, there," Karen murmured again, her emotions swimming. This was the same Ken, the one she had loved for six years. Something appalling had happened, but this was no monster; this was her husband, a sweet man.

Connie was watching them through the observation window. She later reported to Karen that the minute she saw Ken she felt the same way. Ken was not a mad beast responsible for a revolting crime, but a broken and bewildered man.

"I have Melissa with me," Karen said gently.

Ken shook his head.

"Don't you want to see your daughter?" she asked, as one would a child who needed comforting.

He nodded, weeping again. She stepped out of the room and took Melissa from Connie. She returned and put the baby on Ken's chest.

Melissa burped and spit up. Ken grinned for the first time and said, "Gee, she hasn't changed, has she?" Karen laughed.

He had a feeling of unreality. Karen's tone with him seemed unaffected by the events of Saturday night. She was her usual self, wry and affectionate. Awed at the wonder of it, he chose his words carefully for fear he would break the spell.

The baby gurgled on his chest, making a bridge of normality between them.

"How's your father?" he asked.

"He's just fine," she replied.

"Karen, I'm so sorry. I'm so sorry."

She said, "I know."

He drew a ragged breath. He said again, "I can understand if you want a divorce. I won't fight it."

"I don't know what I want right now," she said. "Let's not talk about it."

"Did I hurt any of your brothers and sisters?"

She was taken aback. She had been expecting to get information from him, but instead it was going the other way.

"No. They weren't touched," she told him. "How are your hands?"

"They're sore," he confessed.

In defiance of her instructions, she bent and kissed him on the lips. As she straightened she saw the police officer and Delmar Doucette standing at the window, watching them. Both looked perplexed. The scene they were witnessing was one of perfect domesticity: a man and woman talking quietly and lovingly, with a baby dozing in the man's arms.

"The lawyer didn't want me to see you," she said to Ken.

"Yeah," he said. "I said that whatever happens, I had to talk to you."

She said, "I'm glad. That's how I felt too."

When she left, they embraced and she kissed him again.

When she came out of the room, the lawyer smiled broadly at her. "Thank you," he said, with fervency in his voice, handing her a business card for Marlys Edwardh.

She looked steadily at him, not liking his assumption that she was friendly to the defence. Her hostility flared and she replied coldly, "You're welcome."

But she took the card.

Sergeant Adair stepped into the room. "What did they talk about?" he asked the guard.

"I don't know," said the guard blandly. "I didn't hear a thing."

The next day Karen awakened with a sense that something profound had shifted. She was confused for a moment, and then she realized what it was. Her mother's spirit had left her. She didn't have the feeling any more that her mother was keeping her safe. Now she was on her own. Karen didn't feel abandoned. It was as though her mother had been worried about her and had waited to leave until she was sure Karen could manage.

Ken was moved from the hospital soon after Karen left his room. After many discussions between Del Doucette, Marlys Edwardh, Dr. Billings, Ken's surgeon, and correctional people, the decision to send him to Metro East Detention Centre had been revoked. He went instead to the Toronto Jail, which everyone calls "the Don". With both hands effectively out of commission in the heavy casts and bandages, Ken would need help to eat and wash.

The Don Jail is a grim building high on the banks of the malodorous Don River in a neighbourhood of densely crowded Chinese grocery stores and narrow streets jammed with old brick houses that in recent years have sprouted skylights and timber porches. He was transported in chains by taxi, wearing clothes supplied by the jail, and was put in the medical range.

Karen decided not to tell her family that she had seen Ken. It would only hurt and bewilder them. Her sisters and brothers, once as fond of Ken as of one another, had turned against him with a vengeance. They seemed to enjoy saying that Ken would spend his life in prison or, better still, be executed.

The country had just entered into a debate about reinstating capital punishment. Parliament would decide in an unusual way, a free vote. The Woods children were solidly on the side of the death penalty. Karen, feeling isolated from the family solidarity that had developed, decided to keep silent. She still hadn't made up her mind what she would do, she reminded herself, so there was no point in ruffling feelings already raw.

She saw her father later that day. He was taking charge of his motherless brood. "How are you going to manage, Karen?" he asked anxiously. "You must have mortgage payments to meet."

She didn't want to depend on him, especially not if she was seeing Ken. It wouldn't be fair. "I'll be fine," she assured him. "You've got enough to worry about. Don't think about me, I'll manage."

That Wednesday night she called Ken's maternal grandmother, Lil Hodge, and was invited to drop in. Others of the Hodge family were there and the visit went badly. Karen's anger boiled up again and she was helpless to stop herself from sounding tough and unforgiving. When Lil Hodge was stiffly defensive of Ken, it only fuelled Karen's bitterness. She told them about her visit to Ken but she didn't say that her heart had gone out to him.

They asked if she knew what had happened on that night of horror. "We still don't know," she admitted. The family talked of little else. The earlier version Karen had given Mavis was full of inconsistencies. For instance, how did Ken get such terrible cuts on his hands and arms? Karen had concluded that it must have been her mother who got the knife from the kitchen drawer. Assuming that the first attack was an attempt to strangle Denis, it made sense that Barbara would run to get a weapon to protect him. Perhaps she had cut Ken's arms, and he cut his hands when he took it away from her. Then he killed her.

"He stabbed her with the knife, and the police think he also hit her with a tire-iron," Karen told them.

A dismal silence fell on the room. Karen left feeling triumphant at their misery but immediately afterwards was sorry and ashamed of herself. What was making her act like that?

That night Ken called her from the Don Jail. He was in pain. The staff had refused him medication, and it worried him that his dressings hadn't been changed.

Karen consulted the business card Delmar Doucette had given her and called Marlys Edwardh.

"I'll take care of that," said Marlys warmly. "We should get together."

"I don't think so," Karen said firmly. She still hadn't made up her mind where she stood, but she wasn't yet ready to line up with the defence.

Marlys recognized the tone of a woman who couldn't be pushed.

"Whatever you like," she said mildly. "I know the doctor who is in charge of the provision of medical care through the whole provincial correctional system, Dr. Paul Humphries. He's a good person, and I know he'll do something about Ken's hands."

"Thanks," said Karen, hanging up abruptly.

The two major components of Karen's life, her family and her husband, no longer fit together. So many questions about the crime were unanswered. Maybe when she had the whole story she could decide, but meanwhile she resented being pulled two ways, the police on one side and Ken's lawyers on the other. She wanted time to consider. If she sided with Ken, it was becoming clear that her father and her brothers and sisters might be lost to her.

She had no one with whom to share her dilemma. A dozen times a day she had an impulse to talk to her mother; each time the impulse was followed by a wash of grief. When the phone rang, her first reaction was joy that it would be Barbara. The desolation that followed was so deep it was difficult to claw her way out. Sometimes, absent-mindedly, she went to the phone and started to dial her mother's number, and then sobbed.

Karen suspected that her family knew from the police that she had visited Ken in Sunnybrook Hospital. They said nothing, and she appreciated their tactfulness. Both sides hesitated to mention Ken. Out of consideration for her, her brothers and sisters no longer discussed the death penalty, at least in her presence, and Karen never referred to her contacts with her husband. Like Karen herself, the Woods family was waiting to see what she would do.

Denis pressed Karen into service as his agent. She spent the rest of the week doing such errands as using his bank card to withdraw money for the family's daily living expenses. The children, who still were staying with friends, needed pocket money.

Emma and Pru and Jonny continued to sleep at the home of their teacher, while Samantha moved in with her boy-friend. Nicky was the only Woods child who retained a semblance of normal life. He was staying with his friend Robert and attending school.

On Thursday Karen paid her first visit to the Don Jail to see Ken. She was revolted by the clang of metal doors as she submitted her request to a man behind bullet-proof glass. The venomously ugly room where she waited was full of weary women and cranky children crowded along hard benches that lined the walls and stood back to back in the middle of a dingy, smoky room. She was assigned a number and found a place to squeeze in, where she waited what seemed an interminable time.

Her number was called and she went through a door to find a line of people standing with telephones at their ears, each one facing a man through a thick glass wall. "You have fifteen minutes," an attendant told her sternly. She looked at Ken in prison clothes. He was holding a phone clumsily to his ear with a hugely bandaged hand.

"How are you?" Karen asked.

His voice came back, distorted by a poor connection.

"I'm all right," he said. "They're going to give me my pain medication today and they've said they'll change the dressing. I think Marlys called them about it."

"That's good," said Karen. She was touched to see that he was struggling not to cry. She changed the subject and talked about Melissa. The baby was neutral ground and he welcomed the diversion, plying her with questions about where the baby was staying and if she was sleeping well.

Then Ken remembered that Marlys had warned him that the phones were bugged. He explained to Karen that he was supposed to be cautious.

"I don't care about that," he said earnestly. "It's more important that I be straight with you and tell you everything I know."

"Well, what happened?" Karen asked.

"All I remember is waking to see your mother's face. That's all, I swear. I don't remember driving there, I don't remember Denis, I don't know how I cut my hands."

He was having nightmares, he said. He kept seeing Barbara's face, her mouth open and her eyes begging him to help her. He couldn't escape the memory even when awake.

Karen left with a burning need to talk to someone about the turmoil inside her. She ached for her mother, and her heart twisted again at the enormity of her loss. She considered confiding her dilemma to her father, who always was sensible and rational, but she had to reject that. He could not be expected to have any sympathy for Ken and she couldn't ask it of him. This struggle was hers, and hers alone.

She wished, as she had a hundred times, that Ken had killed her instead of her mother. *Why not me?* It made more sense for him to have an attack of insanity and kill her, who had been taunting him about his shortcomings, than to drive to Scarborough and kill Barbara, who had never offended him.

When the madness overcame him, why hadn't he simply come up the short flight of stairs to her bedroom and killed her? Then she wouldn't have to face her grieving family every day and see the accusation in their eyes.

She wished for oblivion, for an end to pain. If she were dead, there would be the relief of nothingness. She roughly pulled herself back from that temptation. It had its attractions, but she could not leave Melissa without a mother. She simply couldn't do that to a helpless baby.

Her financial problems needed immediate attention. She was penniless and deep in debt. Since she had decided against taking money from her father, how would she and Melissa survive? She decided to confide in the attentive Salvation Army officer from the victim assistance program.

"Our taxes and the mortgage payment are due," she said, "and I don't have a dime. We're about three thousand dollars in debt."

"We can help you," the man said. "That's what we do."

The Salvation Army provided $1,500, which paid the monthly mortgage instalment, and he coached her through the steps to apply for welfare.

Melissa was having a thoroughly miserable time. The tiny girl, bewildered at having her normally stable life shattered, fretted in Connie Sullivan's care. Connie was as unaccustomed to caring for a baby as Melissa was unused to her. She made frantic calls to her mother. "She keeps crying," she wailed. "What do I do?"

In the first week after Barbara's death, Karen was only dimly aware of her daughter's distress. She moved her from Connie's care after the first two days, and for two nights, Thursday and Friday, Melissa stayed with the school teacher who was providing shelter for the Woods family. Another time Lil Hodge, Ken's grandmother, took her.

Karen sank into a depression so deep that her family was alarmed. Her most frequent comment was that it was her fault. She should have known that Ken was about to crack. She could have prevented the tragedy if she hadn't pushed him so hard. If she had wakened after Ken left she could have telephoned her parents and warned them. How could she have slept while her mother was being killed? And so on....

Karen's brothers and sisters worried that Karen would kill herself. They were insistent that she should not be alone at night. When Connie decided to return to her own bed, they prevailed upon Karen to sleep at Connie's house for a few nights.

"We don't want you to be alone," Emma said. "Please, Karen, stay with Connie."

Karen agreed. Her normal bubbling energy had vanished, to be replaced with exhaustion. When she wakened from fitful sleep, there was an instant of blessed forgetfulness, followed by a wave of despair that crashed down and left her sobbing.

She couldn't bear to think of her mother's suffering before she died. Barbara had screamed in her agony and terror. Karen didn't want to think about it, but her wandering thoughts kept fastening on the screams. If Ken had killed her instead of Barbara, it would have worked out better. Her mother would have raised Melissa lovingly, and the baby would be fine. Samantha, Emma, Pru, Jonny, and Nicky would still have their mother; Denis would have his beloved Bobbie.

They would miss her, but Karen Parks was dispensable in the family; Barbara Woods was not.

It was some time after the killing before Karen saw Ken's mother. Betty Parks and Tyrone had been dreading the moment.

"We didn't know what to say," comments Tyrone. "Like, 'Sorry about your mom,' is kinda...I dunno....You don't want to say anything the wrong way, but what can you say?"

"We thought she'd be bitter and maybe mean," says Betty, "but she wasn't like that. She couldn't believe that Ken had done it."

"There was a lot of tension, though," Tyrone recalls. "No one knew what to say. Actually none of us said much."

On Friday, May 29, five days after the slaying, police forensic teams finished in the Woods house and said the family could move back. None of the children could bear the thought. On Sunday, when Denis was released from hospital, he too found it intolerable to return. Linda Taylor hospitably made room for him in her house.

Though still weak from his ordeal, Denis Woods purposefully went about making funeral arrangements. He went straight from the hospital to Pine Hill Cemetery to pick out a plot and on Monday consulted a funeral director. Emma, Karen, and Melissa went with him, along with a sympathetic colleague from his company.

They had to keep in mind Barbara's disdain for expensive funerals. "A waste," she often said. "When I die I want to be buried in a plain wooden box. Don't you forget. Promise me, right? Promise."

In deference to her views, Denis asked to see the cheapest coffin available. They were shown a cloth-covered box that he, Emma, and Karen agreed was repulsive. The compromise was to buy the least expensive wooden coffin in the display, at $800, but Emma and Karen thought it left something to be desired.

Denis said firmly, "That's what she would have wanted. We'll have to do what she wished."

The funeral directors prepared the body for viewing on Tuesday night. Someone in the coroner's office had advised the undertakers that Barbara's injuries were such that an open casket would not be desirable. Denis and the children protested, and the Salvation Army came to the rescue again. An officer explained to the funeral director that it was important for the grieving family to see Barbara, that it would be very traumatic for them to have a closed casket.

Since Barbara Woods had been dead for ten days, the family was enjoined not to touch the body. They stood around the casket and were shocked at what they saw. Barbara's nose, which had been crushed by the tire-iron, had been repaired with plastic. Some rebuilding was done as well on the side of her head where the skull had caved in under blows. Her hair was curled and combed and there was make-up on her face.

"They did their best to make her look all right," Karen says in her fair-minded way. "But it didn't look much like her."

Still, the Salvation Army people were right. The children had been yearning to see their mother a last time; they had needed to make a final farewell. It gave them a measure of peace to look at her even though they wept inconsolably afterwards.

Karen doesn't usually feel comfortable about open coffins. When she goes through the ritual of a funeral home visit, she avoids looking at the casket for as long as she decently can. When she finally approaches the casket, she gives it only a hurried glance. With her mother, however, she stood beside the coffin and couldn't tear herself away. Much was wrong about the repair and make-up, but it *was* Barbara and she found it difficult to stop looking.

Denis and his bereaved children were surprised that so many people sent flowers. The family thought of itself as somewhat insular, but their gregarious mother apparently had made friends wherever she went. Most touching were the flowers from clerks in the Zeller's store in the mall where Barbara went for breakfast tea with her mother.

Ken's grandmother, Lil Hodge, bravely came to the funeral home, accompanied by her daughter Mavis. Both women were apprehensive.

"I didn't know how I would be received," Lil Hodge says with dignity, "but I wanted to pay my respects."

She was touched when the Woods family recognized her and even greeted her with hugs. "Towards the end the girls were treating me a bit coolly," she comments, "but everyone was polite."

The saddest moment came when the family was left in the viewing room to say goodbye. The children stood around the casket sobbing and then withdrew to allow Denis a final moment alone with his Bobbie.

The service was conducted by the same Salvation Army officer who had been so kind to them throughout the ordeal. The family had no other connection to clergy, and they trusted him. He spoke simply of the suddenness of the death and what a loss Barbara was to her family.

The next day Karen went to see Ken and told him the funeral was over. Ken said wistfully, "I wish I could have seen her. Not when you and your family were there, of course, but maybe after everyone was gone. It's hard for me to believe she's dead."

Ken was allowed visitors twice a week, for fifteen minutes at a time, and Karen filled his quota. She found it painful to see him, but it didn't feel right to stay away. Ken's mother and Lil Hodge mildly resented that Karen left no space for them, but they didn't rebuke her. Ken's family satisfied themselves with telephone calls that Ken was allowed on a pay phone in the jail. Ken was apologetic that the visiting slots were filled, but he explained that he and Karen had a lot to work out. That much was obvious to all.

Ken's family developed a new explanation for the awful events of that night. They decided that someone must have telephoned Ken in the night to come to the Woods house. When he got there, Barbara and Denis were being attacked. Ken tried to stop the assailant by grabbing the knife, which was how he cut his hands.

The police were no help. They had nothing new in the baffling case. It seemed no one ever would find out what had happened. Ken was still searching his memory in vain. Only Barbara knew, and she was dead.

Karen and Ken no longer discussed it. On static-ridden telephones, they talked of household matters. Poverty was pinching Karen, making her anxious. She was juggling the creditors, she told him. Melissa had a cold. Her family had moved back into the house.

"How are they?" he asked cautiously.

"Okay," she replied laconically, though it wasn't true. The Woods family was staggering through a painful adjustment as father and children tried to cope with the unfamiliar territory of the kitchen and laundry.

Karen was lending a hand when she could, but she said little to Ken about this. It worked both ways. She didn't talk about Ken with her family, and she wasn't discussing her family with Ken.

Once Karen and Ken had a row reminiscent of the ones that preceded the ghastly night of the killing. It began with a mysterious bill from a kennel. When Karen telephoned the kennel to say there was a mistake, she was informed that weeks earlier a Ken Parks had placed a puppy there to be boarded. Karen was stunned until she remembered that Ken had brought home a puppy that she wouldn't let him keep. The times tallied: another deception.

When she confronted Ken angrily, he explained, "I thought I had a friend to take the dog, but he changed his mind. I didn't

74

know what to do. He was such a cute little puppy and I was afraid that if I took him to the Humane Society, maybe he would be killed."

"That's all very well, but what am I supposed to do now?" Karen asked with some of her old fire.

"I'll find someone," Ken promised. "Maybe one of the guys in here wants a puppy."

Someone did, a man who was being released. To Karen's relief, he paid the kennel bill.

A few weeks after leaving the hospital, Ken returned to Sunnybrook Hospital to have the casts removed. To his dismay, he found it impossible to move any of the damaged fingers. Physiotherapy would help restore function, he was told. "Fat chance of that," he thought.

Marlys Edwardh was delighted. Getting permission for Ken to return to Sunnybrook for treatment to his hands was a victory. The next part would be trickier—having the brain tests done at Sunnybrook. She was expecting that at any moment the Crown would move for a remand to send Ken to Penetanguishene's locked hospital for the criminally insane for a pre-trial assessment. That would be a disaster because the examination would be routine and conservative of outlook, with all the results available to the Crown. "In effect, the client is served up to the Crown," she comments. Maybe, just maybe, she could wangle to have the tests done at Sunnybrook instead and keep the medical evidence within her control.

The business with Ken's hands was an important precedent. She started to work on that.

At first Karen was grateful for the welfare income of about $700 a month, but as the summer progressed she discovered as all poor people do that welfare is a trap. When Karen, always enterprising, considered helping herself with such initiatives as part-time employment or subletting part of her house, she was informed that her welfare income would be cut accordingly. She couldn't afford to lose her welfare payments in case the sublet or temporary job fell through, so she concluded with exasperation that welfare intends its recipients to be passive.

She thought of moving but could find nothing cheaper to rent. Monthly mortgage payments were $460, and with utilities, condominium contribution, and taxes the total was $700, approximately the cost of a small apartment. She concluded that she might as well stay where she was. She didn't attempt to pay her condominium charges or the Pickering taxes. She assumed that she wouldn't be evicted, given the circumstances. Her telephone and utilities bills she paid only when she had to in order to prevent the service from being cut: one month she would catch up with Hydro, the next with the television cable.

When she was desperate, Lil Hodge helped out. Ken's grandmother was standing by with infinite loyalty, stripping her savings to help Karen and to pay Ken's legal bills.

CHAPTER FIVE

Kenneth Parks

The first impression a stranger receives of Kenneth James Parks is his size. He's six foot five—or what used to be six foot five before metric conversion—and his normal weight is 275 pounds. Until recently his thick, straight hair was the colour of a wheat field and in summer would bleach almost white, but it has darkened to a strawberry blond. When he grows a beard, it's red.

He's blue-eyed, with fair skin that turns a bright pink when exposed to the sun, and he holds his body loosely, his shoulders slouched. His physical movements are slow, those of a man perpetually not in a hurry. He takes little interest in clothes and usually is dressed in jeans, sweat-shirt, and zippered jacket.

With people he doesn't know well, he has an embarrassed, diffident manner and cracks his knuckles nervously. His friends, however, find him easy-going, seemingly carefree, and full of comic, good-natured comments. The side his wife knows, the brooding sadness at the heart of him, is not seen by others. He seems free of any degree of introspection or existential wonder. More than two years after the killing, his mother said of him, "He's beginning to be his old self again. You know, always kidding around."

Ken's appetites are simple: uncomplicated food—steaks and pie being favourites—washed down with pop. He has never been interested in such young-male rituals as having a beer with the boys—or, for that matter, in drinking anything alcoholic except an occasional glass of wine—and he doesn't smoke. In high school he tried drugs, but he found that scene unpalatable. Instead he turned to the heartiness of team sports, rugby and soccer, which he plays with such dedicated fierceness that in the process he has broken his nose twice and each of his fingers at least once.

His colouring comes from his Norwegian heritage, and his size from his father, who is of Ukrainian stock. His complex, private nature, screened by geniality, is his own construction. Ken Parks comes from a turbulent background and learned early to retreat to the safety and anonymity of good behaviour.

His maternal grandmother, Lilly Lokken Hodge, in her early seventies, is the family favourite. She's a woman gifted with common sense who wears her heart on her sleeve. Erect, firm-bodied, vigorous, and well groomed, she wears pretty colours and likes to be tanned. Her parents came to the North American Midwest from Norway and she was born in Minnesota on Christmas day in 1917, the second-youngest in a family of eight. When Lil was very young the Lokkens moved to Canada and took up mixed farming near Broomhead, a fragment of a village in southern Saskatchewan.

Her childhood was bitter and hard. Lil's mother died when she was small, and her father, a severe disciplinarian, ruled the household with little patience or skill for the nurturing of children. Lil endured the searing depression of the thirties, which fell most severely on south Saskatchewan. A drought brought winds that blew away the topsoil and then clouds of ravenous grasshoppers descended from the sky and ate the fields bare. Women went mad; the mental hospital in Weyburn was said to be full of farm wives driven crazy by the wind and grinding poverty.

Lil Lokken left school in Grade 8, as many farmers' children did, to help with the chores. She was twenty-two years old and working in a jewellery store in Weyburn when Canada declared war in 1939. Soon after, she married a young soldier, Stanley Hodge, a happy-go-lucky twenty-year-old of English and Scottish heritage. Stan had enlisted in the South Saskatchewans, an infantry regiment. He was sent overseas in 1940, leaving her pregnant. A daughter, Betty Irene Hodge, was born on June 24, 1941. Betty Hodge would be Ken Parks' mother.

Betty Hodge was a pretty little girl, blonde and blue-eyed like her mother. When she was only two, the child simultaneously developed scarlet fever and measles, either of which can lead to serious complications. In her case, it was deafness. Betty still remembers the day sound stopped for her. She was playing outdoors when a sudden silence fell. No wind, no voices, no traffic sounds. She could hear nothing.

Betty became unresponsive and irritable, and she stopped speaking. Lil suspected from the beginning of the change that her child was deaf, but the local doctor insisted that her ears were fine. The doctor explained to Lil that the child was "backward".

In August 1942, Stan Hodge's regiment had the misfortune to be part of the disastrous sacrificial beach landing at Dieppe, where about 1,000 Canadians died and 2,153 were seriously wounded or taken prisoner. Some 60 per cent of the men involved became casualties, the highest rate of losses in any major Allied operation of the entire war. For present generations, Dieppe has come to symbolize the ill-conceived battles that have dotted history, where young men are slaughtered because of the vanity and stupidity of their leaders.

Stan Hodge was among those Dieppe survivors who spent the rest of the war, three years, in a German prisoner-of-war camp. The diet and strain almost destroyed his health. He developed such severe ulcers that on his return to Canada half his stomach had to be removed.

The country that welcomed home the troops in 1945 was innocent of any understanding of the emotional trauma that wars can cause. The scars don't show, but many Canadian veterans of the Second World War came home emotionally crippled. In old age some became derelicts, drunken men in rags who swelled the ranks of the homeless, but in the simpler age immediately after the war their pain went unacknowledged. Veterans were expected to pick up their lives where they had left off—and most did, as seamlessly as if they had not killed, or seen friends die, or lived in terror for long stretches of time, or been penned for years in a prison camp. It wasn't until the seventies, when Americans confronted the post-traumatic stress disorders of Vietnam veterans, that society began to have any appreciation of the lifelong emotional havoc that combat can inflict on those who seemingly survive it.

The Stanley Hodge who married Lilly Lokken in 1939 was a pleasant youth, sober, affectionate, and full of cheer. The Stanley Hodge who returned from prison camp in 1945 was a man who was morose, bitter, and hard-drinking. In the final years of his life he was an alcoholic and a violent man as well.

Betty was four when her father returned to Canada and saw her for the first time. He decided he didn't like her. She was a stupid and stubborn child, he thought, and he said so. In truth, he was still a very young, unsure man, unprepared to share his wife's attention with an entrenched rival.

Lil Hodge was distressed by his rejection of the child, but she is an optimist and she counted on his changing his mind. Betty was appealing, she thought, and would win him over. In order to avoid his wrath, she was careful not to show the child any affection while he was around. If she cuddled the child or consoled her when she hurt herself, Stan would erupt in fury. Getting along with Stanley became the ruling principle of their relationship. Lil tried endlessly to please him, but even so, Stan was edgy, nervous, and quick to take offence.

Stan's sleep was lacerated by nightmares that left him drenched with sweat. Often he would sit up in bed, crying out hoarsely, or jump out of bed and walk around, wildly waving his arms. He would breathe with deep, grunting noises, like a man who had been running hard, and his eyes would be open and staring, almost bulging out of his head. If she tried to speak to him or nudge him awake, he would push her away roughly and continue his mutterings. In the morning, Lil would say, "You walked in your sleep again last night," and he would glare at her, amazed, with no recollection that his sleep had been disturbed.

When Betty was five the Hodges decided there was no future for them in Saskatchewan, a province still so poor that main highways were unpaved. They moved to St. Thomas, a pleasant town in southwestern Ontario, where Stanley had some friends who rented them a second-floor apartment in their big house. Stan held a job briefly as a security guard but soon became restless and moved his family to the Toronto area, settling first in a cousin's house on the northeastern outskirts. Then he moved to Scarborough, a sprawling community on the city's eastern flank.

Five more children were born, but two died in infancy, leaving them with four children, Betty, Ronald, Glen, and Mavis. With the birth of Ronald, their first son, Stan lost all tolerance for Betty. He blamed her for mishaps the other children caused and treated her with open contempt. Lil endured in silence his tirades against the little girl, and when he was out of the house she tried to make it up to the child with comforting hugs.

Lil's life was a round of toil. In addition to raising four small children and running the household, she had to cope with a meagre budget and a husband who frequently flew into rages. She accepted her hardships without complaint: they were the familiar stuff of her childhood. Besides, she was part of a generation of women who lived by a code of silence. Like others in her situation, she took it as a personal shame that her husband had a mean, judgemental nature and an explosive temper, and that he rejected one of his children. Women in the fifties counted their blessings—a roof over their heads, a man who was a good provider, the children they had welcomed. The rule was to maintain a stoic pretence that their marriages were perfect in every way. Friends and neighbours might guess otherwise, might *know* otherwise, but none would be so callous as to intrude on the family's privacy and pride by offering sympathy or help.

Lil hadn't given up her conviction that Betty couldn't hear. In the years that followed Betty's illnesses and her sudden loss of language, Lil and Betty developed their own means of communication. The child seemed to have a vestige of hearing and could understand if someone got her attention and shouted, but her speech was reduced to making sounds that only Lil understood. Mostly they got along amiably by pointing and making other broad gestures.

Lil stoutly argued with Stan that Betty had had normal intelligence before her illnesses and the consequent ear infections, but Stan's view was that Betty simply was stupid.

Matters came to a head when Betty was six and started school. When her hearing was tested, she was found to have a type of nerve deafness. She was equipped with hearing aids, huge cumbersome devices she loathed, and her Grade 1 teacher attempted to teach the child to speak again. Within a few weeks the effort was abandoned, and Betty was transferred to a special school for the deaf and hard-of-hearing.

She has no pleasant memories of her childhood. Other children taunted her about the hearing aid apparatus she wore prominently on her chest. "They teased me a lot," she says. "I can't remember what they used to call me, but I went through a rough time." Her response was to cry. She doesn't remember anyone being kind except her mother, and then only when her father was absent.

Incalculable damage was done in that bleak childhood to Betty's confidence in herself. As an adult, she's an uneasy person. Her eyes slide away in conversation, and she seems a woman whose feelings are readily hurt.

While Betty was growing up, Stan Hodge had found steady work as a carpenter with the Toronto Board of Education, a job he held until a year before his death in 1984. With the assistance of Stan's veteran's grant, the family bought a small three-bedroom brick bungalow in Scarborough, at 28 Par Avenue, and Lil blissfully threw herself into the task of keeping it shining clean. She discovered in herself a passion for growing flowers, and she started a remarkable garden that became the pride of the neighbourhood.

Meanwhile Betty was bussed to her school each day, increasing her isolation from the children on the street. She finished Grade 6 and was placed in a three-year hairdressing course. Because she failed a year, she didn't graduate for four years and then, at seventeen, found work in a salon. Her income wasn't sufficient for her to establish a place of her own, so she continued to live with her parents, though her father still belittled and berated her without mercy.

She had grown to be a pretty woman, but her loneliness robbed her of sparkle and she was awkward in social situations. As happens with many people with hearing difficulties, her voice lacks modulation and she has a tendency to mishear or mispronounce some words. With progress in technology, however, her hearing aids became unobtrusive, hidden behind her ear and covered by her hair. Though she didn't have to tell anyone about them, she made it a point of honour to inform her dates that she wore hearing aids.

At a school dance in the spring of 1963, when she was twenty-two years old, she met James Parks, a tall, skinny, pleasant man, and was drawn to him at once. His background was Ukrainian, and he worked as a shipper. They became lovers and she discovered she was pregnant. Her father, who had accepted Jim grudgingly, then turned against him and ordered her not to marry. He argued that Jim was a social inferior, not nearly good enough for his daughter. Despite Stan's heated opposition, Betty and Jim Parks were married in June 1963, in a United Church ceremony, and the wedding was followed by a reception in the back of a restaurant.

The young couple lived first in the basement of Jim Parks' parents' house. Betty hugely enjoyed that period of her life because the Parkses, Albert and Janet, were affectionate people who treated her well. Ken was born on February 21, 1964; eighteen months later, the couple had a second son, Robert Albert. Because the basement was too crowded for four people, Betty and Jim moved to an apartment in Scarborough.

After that, Jim's behaviour changed. He went out every night, giving no explanation, and Betty grew more and more resentful. Their arguments increased in volume and energy. Jim showed himself to be a stormy man with a terrifying temper. One night there was a fight that frightened the children and Jim left, slamming the door behind him thunderously. Betty packed up the boys and went home for a few days, after which the couple, making mutual vows to improve, were reunited.

Lil Hodge liked Jim Parks through it all and feels warmly towards him still, but she's an open-hearted woman who usually sees others in a good light. Stan, however, detested him and directed the full force of his stormy disposition against his son-in-law. It is Lil Hodge's view that Betty's marriage might have lasted if Stan had not displayed such ill feeling towards Jim. In any case, Jim's nightly wanderings continued and remained a matter of contention between them until Betty decided on a separation and moved back with her parents. The arrangement was a difficult one so, very soon, she went hunting for space and found two rooms in a basement.

Her divorce lawyer advised her that a judge would look more favourably on granting a decree if she could demonstrate that she had tried reconciliation. Accordingly, Betty and Jim lived together again for a month. They found their relationship as untenable as before, but she became pregnant with their third son, Darrin. The divorce was granted in September 1967, the grounds of adultery supported by medical evidence that Jim Parks had gonorrhoea. Darrin was born in April the following year.

Jim Parks cut all communication with his family, though Lil believes he would have kept in touch with his sons except for Stan's blistering opposition. Betty, raising three small boys with no support payments from their father, was obliged to apply for welfare. The family was placed on the waiting list for a subsidized apartment, which became available in about a year. They moved into a three-bedroom unit on the sixth floor of a high rise in Scarborough occupied by other welfare families. By that time Betty was pregnant again from a liaison she regrets, with a construction worker who immediately disappeared from her life, and her daughter, Tammy, was born in 1969.

Kenneth James Parks, her oldest child, was a big handsome baby. As a first grandson in both the Hodge and Parks families, he enjoyed special status. His father adored the tow-headed young-ster. In Lil Hodge's view, Jim spoiled his first-born, indulging him in every whim and readily forgiving the boy for the mis-chievous pranks to which he was prone. Ken has no memory of such good times. He can't recall any warmth from his father, but he can't forget the time, when he was about three, that his father, at the height of a rage, slammed the door and caught the boy's big toe in it, breaking the nail.

Ken grew up a wilful youngster, quick to get into fights with his brothers, restless, easily discouraged, and with a short attention span. When he started school at Mason Road Public School, he was an indifferent student and a frequent truant. In Grade 4 he failed his year because he was absent much of the time and couldn't settle down in class when he did attend. Since school had no rewards for him, he much preferred to hang out with a gang of boys who also lived in subsidized apartments, boys who, like Ken, had distracted parents with little time to worry about their children's whereabouts or activities.

The boy-pack, all of them nine or ten years old, delighted in bold theft. A favourite target was the loading dock behind a Dominion supermarket where food was dropped at six in the morning and left unattended. The children rummaged through the boxes, taking cakes and pies and jugs of milk. They were never caught, even when they brazenly returned the milk jugs for refunds. Another productive activity was to offer to run errands for people in the building. If someone wanted a package of hot dogs from the store, for instance, the boys would steal the wieners instead and pocket the money.

One day a clerk caught them and called the police, who took them to the station and notified their parents. Betty grounded Ken for two weeks as punishment, but he wasn't chastened. He continued to steal whatever caught his eye and about a year later, when he was ten, he was caught again. A department store security officer saw him take a Swiss army knife, and police were summoned. Betty, her hands full because Rob and Darrin also were stealing, grounded him again for two weeks.

It didn't stop him from stealing, but he was never caught again.

Slowly but significantly, however, the wild, unruly boy was changing. He was beginning to like school, a transformation that began when he failed Grade 4. While he was humiliated to be kept back a year, he took consolation in the fact that his younger brother Rob, in Grade 3, also failed and therefore didn't catch up with him. That year Ken suddenly began to grow, and by spring he was the biggest boy in his class. On the next Hallowe'en, when he went door to door with friends of his own age, some people refused to give him candy, accusing him of being too old to be trick-or-treating.

His life turned around when he gained enough co-ordination to get involved in team sports. Success on the soccer field and volleyball court led to better school attendance, with the result that his grades improved dramatically and his disposition began to settle down into friendly co-operativeness.

He had another piece of luck: he encountered one of those gifted, caring teachers who can make a difference in a troubled child's life. Mr. Finley, a man in the grip of the prevailing hippie movement and its dreams of peace and mutual caring, was in charge of the school's remedial maths program. After class, he would put his feet on the desk, light a cigarette, and play his guitar, while his entranced students bent over their maths projects. Ken adored Mr. Finley, who in turn treated the boy with an affection that eased the child's hunger for fathering. As a side benefit, Ken developed a skill and interest in mathematics that never left him. In the computer age to come, he would be a whiz.

By this time Ken had a stepfather, Tyrone Manuel, an itinerant labourer who had moved in with Betty Hodge. Betty and Tyrone met soon after Tammy was born and two years later, in 1970, they decided to live together in a common-law relationship. The union has lasted; they find one another good company. Once Tyrone and Betty planned to be married and even picked out the church, but the plan fell through and it never seemed important to revive it.

Tyrone Manuel is a stocky, bearded man who was raised in a Newfoundland village, which he left at the age of seventeen to find work in Toronto. He's a rough and ready person, affable and bright-eyed, the sort to spend his leisure time with a beer in his hand. Betty has appreciated him for his solid support of her through stressful times as she struggled to raise her four children. Ken didn't warm to Tyrone, however. He didn't like the drinking. He hated the times that Tyrone and Betty argued. To shut out their voices, he would hide under his covers.

Betty's hearing impairment is a factor that her family takes for granted. The children have always known that their mother's hearing, even with a hearing device in each ear, is imperfect. To get her attention, they stand in front of her where she can see them. They aren't sure, of course, but they suspect that much of her ability to understand what they say depends on lip-reading. As the family has come to know, when Betty isn't certain what has been said, she has a tendency to bluff: She'll nod her head, smiling warmly.

Betty had remained in close contact with Jim Parks' parents after her divorce, and she took the boys to visit their paternal grandparents on a frequent and regular basis. Ken has fond memories of Janet and Albert Parks. Albert worked in a Loblaw's warehouse, with a second job on weekends with a nursery. In addition to their two children—Ken's father, Jim, and his younger sister, Mary—they raised three foster children taken from disrupted families. To their great credit, they were patient and loving with the unhappy youngsters, who eventually settled down contentedly.

Ken was struck by the warmth of that household, so different from his own experience. He never heard his paternal grandparents speak unkindly to one another, or to anyone. He was impressed by their spirit of charity and the volunteer work they did. When his grandfather Parks died in 1979, it was a dreadful blow for his grandmother, who never entirely recovered. In recent years she has suffered greatly from Parkinson's disease.

When the boys visited the senior Parkses, their father was never there. Sometimes, on a birthday or Christmas, a gift would arrive. Once it was a small pool table, another time a rocking horse, the gifts of a man out of contact with children and wandering in a toy store with his own wish list. Ken used to think about his father, yearning for him, especially when he was depressed. Other boys had fathers; it seemed that every other boy had a father who doted on him and took him to hockey games. When other boys talked of good times with their fathers, Ken suffered deeply.

Despite the unrelenting criticism she had to endure from her father, Betty visited her own parents at least once a week, bringing her children. From his grandfather Hodge, Ken received the dismaying opinion, firmly expressed, that his father was a worthless person. His mother was more close-mouthed on the subject, but something in her attitude seemed to confirm that his grandfather was right.

When he finished Grade 6 at Mason Road Public School, Ken moved to Bliss Carman Junior High School. By this time a robust athlete and a good student, his personality had turned sunny. He was playing soccer on school teams and organized volleyball as well. But he was also shy. He was convinced that he was a homely, dumb, oversized person who was unlikable. To show he didn't care, he developed a happy-go-lucky air, but he was a curiously affectionless youngster. Though he belonged to a large extended family who kept in touch with one another, he felt no real closeness to any of his relatives. He could not attach to anyone; there was no one he loved or could not do without, though he would have described his grandmother Hodge as the best of the lot.

In high school at Sir Wilfrid Laurier, where he played basketball, football, and rugby, Ken found a job weekends and after school doing maintenance work at Woodside Square Mall. In summer he worked full time, cutting grass. His best friends were the Ramanis, a swarm of fifteen youngsters, born in Austria, whose widowed mother was black. All the Ramani children were black too, in startling contrast to Ken's Scandinavian blondness.

Ken was fifteen when he met two of the Ramanis, the twins Richmond and Honif, who played soccer. Gregarious and fun-loving, they folded him into their huge, warm family. Unlike the boys Ken had hung out with before, the Ramanis had no interest in stealing. Instead, their idea of a good time was sports or horsing around at home.

That family had a profound influence on the young, lonely, socially unskilled Ken Parks. It was a fascinating household. The mother of the Ramani brood spoke thirteen languages, none of which was English, so her children spoke to her in German or an African language. The older children actually ran the family, paying the bills and supervising the household with a degree of responsibility that Ken had never seen before. All the older Ramanis had after-school jobs at the mall, and they divided up the chores at home with equanimity and fairness.

The Ramanis came into Ken's life at the right time. Betty and Tyrone had moved to a townhouse in a nearby subsidized housing project, a neighbourhood that housed a distinctly rougher group of teenagers. Boys his age were getting into serious trouble with the law, mostly for robberies and drugs; territorial battles were conducted with brutal weapons.

Ken was insulated from much of what was happening by his friendships with the Ramanis and with another soccer buddy, Gus Tsorkidis, the son of the coach.

Soccer had become Ken's obsession. He played goalie for Clara-Lee Westview in a minor soccer league and travelled with the team. Clara-Lee Westview had been a consistent loser when Ken first joined the team, but steadily its fortunes improved. When he wasn't playing or at a practice, Ken went his own way, conscious of his loneliness. If he came home late, or didn't come home at all, his mother asked no questions.

In the summer of 1980, just as Ken finished Grade 8, he separated from his family. Tyrone Manuel landed a good job in Oshawa working for General Motors on the truck-assembly line, and Betty Hodge was moving with him. Ken, fearing for himself if he lost the friendships that were propping him up, pleaded to be allowed to stay in Scarborough and go to high school there. Lil Hodge came to the rescue. Ken could live with them, she said. She would make a bedroom for him in the room next to the living-room.

Lil's hospitality was not without a personal motive. Her husband had become an alcoholic. Stan's verbal abuse of her, something she had learned to tolerate, had turned uglier. Often while drunk he would strike her. Though Stan had prided himself on his work record in the past, he no longer cared. His absences were causing his employer, the Toronto Board of Education, great concern. Lil hoped that the presence of their big grandson would act as a curb on her husband's violence.

Betty was agreeable and Ken was ecstatic. The boy was sixteen and not fully grown when he gathered up his belongings happily and moved in with his grandparents, to bask in Lil's solicitous care and a larder always stocked with his favourite foods. "You know what it's like to live with your grandmother," he once explained with a wide grin. "Cakes and cookies."

Ken's casual comings and goings were distressing to his grandparents, whose supervision of their own children had been more exacting, but they came to accept that he was accustomed to missing meals without explanation and to coming home when he pleased. They were less tolerant about his habit of sleeping in when he wished, going late to school or missing it altogether. His mother had never cared, but Lil wouldn't tolerate it.

Accordingly, Ken was a diligent student that year at Wilfrid Laurier high school and did well in Grade 9. After school and on weekends he worked in the mall, mopping floors, or in the Becker's store run by the father of his friend Gus. In the summer he worked full time at the mall in order to have money for rugby and soccer equipment and the travel costs of league play. Lil accepted room and board money from him when he offered it—and banked it in his name.

In the fall he started Grade 10 and promptly was caught up in the school's drug culture. The most dominant, popular group in the school, it seemed to him, used drugs. He joined a gang of teenagers who habitually cut classes to hang out on the Scarborough bluffs and smoke marijuana. Twice Ken took acid for its kaleidoscopic clarity. He liked being high: it made him feel sexually attractive and staved off the moods of depression that sometimes threatened to swamp him. Other boys his age bragged about their sexual triumphs, but Ken had never even approached a girl for a date. He yearned over the pretty young women in the school, but he was convinced that girls saw him as clumsy and dull.

"He looked like a druggie at that time," Karen comments, with a forgiving smile. "He wore his hair long, parted on one side and combed over. I wouldn't have looked at him twice if I'd seen him then."

Most of that reckless crowd drank beer in great quantities, but Ken didn't like the taste. Wine suited him better, but getting drunk never appealed to him. He was dismayed to find that he had a physical aversion to tobacco: it made him choke. If he persisted in trying to smoke cigarettes, he would have a coughing fit so protracted and severe that eventually he would vomit.

He realized in the spring, too late to catch up, that he was about to fail some of his Grade 10 year, and he did. Ken passed in five subjects and failed three; he would have to repeat geography. He took stock of himself and decided that the environment of Wilfrid Laurier would destroy his chances to have the kind of stable, productive life he wanted. The Ramanis were at nearby

Cedarbrae High School, so he decided to switch schools to be with them.

The transfer was not without a price. The geography he had missed was a Grade 9 subject at Cedarbrae. He was too embarrassed by his size—six foot five—to take the subject with smaller teenagers. That year he proved a brilliant student at maths, pulling down marks in the nineties, but he continued to be abysmal in English. The fact was, he read almost nothing; except for compulsory reading in English courses, he had never read an entire book in his life.

Ken developed an easy style of dealing with his grandfather Hodge. When Stan would launch into a drunken tirade, Ken simply agreed with him. He maintained a friendly manner that seemed to take no note of his grandfather's slurred speech or staggering walk. Stan drank beer steadily, beginning when he wakened, and fell into bed dead drunk early in the evening. Until he passed out, he was a mean man to cross. Lil was shocked the first time he hit her, but came to accept the blows as part of the price of what was otherwise a good life.

In his cups, Stan dwelt on the wretchedness of his prison-camp experience in Germany. It became almost his only topic; he couldn't get it out of his head. After nearly forty years, the memories of that bleak experience surfaced full force; the misery was fresh again and his grievances raw.

His memories of prison camp were dominated by the ravenous hunger he had endured. He talked about food—what he had to eat, what he dreamed of eating. His sleepwalking took a curious turn. He developed a strange habit of rising from his bed, sound asleep, and going to the kitchen to cook himself a meal. In the morning Lil would find the debris in the kitchen, steak and onions in one pan, fried potatoes in another. Stan protested that he couldn't remember a thing.

The mere act of cooking seemed to satisfy his unconscious needs: he never ate any of the food he cooked. He would turn on all four burners, get out food and bowls and pans, prepare something carefully, and then, satisfied, go back to bed to sleep contentedly the rest of the night. A few times when his son Glen attempted to waken him during these strange activities, Stan would whirl and strike him violently.

His daughter Betty remembers being roused one night by the smell of bacon. She went into the kitchen to find her father in his underwear, his regular sleeping costume, cooking a hearty breakfast. Many times when Ken came home late at night, he would interrupt his grandfather in the act of making scrambled eggs, his eyes open in a fixed, manic stare, his breathing hoarse and excited. The sound of the rasping breathing, in fact, became the family's alarm; it alerted them to the fact that Stan was headed for the kitchen.

Stan and Lil owned a trailer parked permanently in a park near Balsam Lake in the Muskokas north of Toronto, where they lived much of the summer. Their son Glen would visit with his wife, Diane, and the couple slept in an attached canvas room where the cooking was done. Many times Diane smelled propane and saw her father-in-law in his shorts heating up leftovers. If she spoke to him he would stare at her in bewilderment.

Occasionally Stan would dress himself in his sleep, go through the door of the extension room, and stroll into the park. Diane would waken Glen, who would pull on some clothes, chase after his father, and lead him back. Once Glen lost his father in the dark. When he returned to the trailer he found Stan crouched outside what the family calls the "adder room", trying to open the zippered doorway. Glen helped him and Stan went quietly through it and back to bed; the next day he denied hotly that any of it had happened.

Some mornings Lil found even more unsettling evidence of her husband's odd nocturnal roamings. In the night Stan would go into a closet to urinate, or would pull out a dresser drawer and defecate in it. She found it was no use to rebuke him or complain; Stan had no recollection of it at all.

Lil resigned herself to the morning clean-ups, since sleepwalking seemed to be a family trait. When her sister Minnie Lokken, four years younger, came to Canada from Scotland for a visit, the two women shared a bed during a pilgrimage they made to

Saskatchewan. Lil was disturbed almost every night by Minnie mumbling in her sleep. When Lil would nudge her, saying, "You're talking in your sleep!" there was no reply.

Another sister, Gladys, also talked in her sleep, shouting out with such urgency that the family would rush to her room to see what was the matter. One of Gladys' children, Arlene, walked in her sleep at the age of nine. The child went out of the house in the middle of the night, crossed the street to a neighbour's, and sat in a bucket to urinate.

Ron and Glen, Stan and Lil's two sons, also seemed to be afflicted. As a boy Glen used to walk around the house in his sleep, talking to himself unintelligibly, sometimes calling out. When Ron was about eight, he got up one night and ran screaming into the living-room, hiding himself behind the chesterfield. When his parents tried to reach him, he ran across the room, still yelling, and hid behind a chair. They captured the boy and took him to bed, but he was a long time calming down. He continued to leap up and yell, waving his hands wildly. When he was spoken to, he didn't appear to hear. Lil and Stan took him into their bed for the night; in the morning Ron could remember nothing of what had happened or even of what frightening thing he had been dreaming.

From the ages of about twelve to sixteen, both Ron and Glen went through an embarrassing period of bed-wetting. Lil tried to help by shaking them awake during the night to take them to the bathroom, but she found them exceedingly difficult to rouse.

As an adult Glen slept so heavily that his wife, Diane, found him almost impossible to wake in the morning. If she shook him, he would flail his arms, sometimes striking her heavily, so she learned to keep a wary distance and wake him by shouting. Once or twice a week he mumbled in his sleep, and sometimes a night terror seemed to sweep him, leaving him drenched in sweat.

Glen's two sons, John and Phillip, suffered the same difficulty. Until he was ten, John wet his bed two or three times a night; after that it tapered off until it ceased when he was twelve. Medical tests showed no physical cause, but doctors surmised that the reason for it was that the boy slept so deeply.

It was suggested that the parents wake the boy during the night and take him to the bathroom, but this proved of little help. Glen and Diane found that they couldn't wake him unless they shook him vigorously, and even then he didn't seem to wake up entirely. Sometimes Glen would carry the boy to the bathroom and prop him up in front of the toilet. Johnny would urinate but clearly wasn't aware of doing so; if his father loosened his grasp, Johnny would fall.

A few times John urinated in his closet. When his mother accused him of it the next morning, he would laugh, thinking she was kidding him. Similarly, he had no recollection of the times when nightmares seized him and he would shout loudly and then sit up in bed sobbing. When his parents attempted to comfort him, he would only stare, looking confused and uncomprehending.

Phillip repeated the pattern. At the age of ten he was wetting his bed two or three times a night and, again, doctors could find no organic reason for it. Often while Diane was changing the boy's bed, Phillip would go into the living-room and sit beside his father, mumbling. Other times he simply appeared in the living-room, staring at his parents. When asked what he wanted, he didn't respond.

The next morning Diane would tell him about it.

"Mummy," the boy would protest, "I don't do that!"

"Yes you do."

Ken Parks had similar experiences. At about the same age, he too was a bed-wetter and difficult to rouse. On one shocking occasion when he was eleven he was almost killed while sleepwalking. Betty went in his room one night to check on him and saw his legs just disappearing over the window-sill. She screamed for help and Rob and Darrin came running. They succeeded in pulling him back into the room, preventing a six-storey fall. The next day Ken was bemused at the story; it was news to him.

Sometimes Ken woke up sweating and with shortness of breath, as if he had been gripped by a terrifying nightmare. He could never remember the dream.

Ken's brother Darrin also wet his bed until the age of about ten, and often he disturbed the household by talking loudly in his sleep. On at least one occasion his sleep disturbance took the same form as his grandfather's. When Darrin was nineteen Betty found him, sound asleep, cooking a fried-egg sandwich. In the morning the sandwich was on the kitchen table, untouched, and Darrin denied knowing anything about it.

Ken's uncle Glen tells of a time when Ken fell asleep in the front passenger seat of Glen's car on the way to a fishing expedition. After snoring for a few minutes, Ken suddenly sat bolt upright in great agitation and seized the dashboard with both hands, eyes staring. He mumbled sounds that Glen described as "parts of words", and then slumped back, still asleep.

Lil's bedroom was next to Ken's, and two or three nights a week she could hear him talking in his sleep. She learned that it was no use to call him in the morning to waken him; he simply didn't hear her. Most mornings she had to go into his room and shake him awake.

Stan's behaviour made Lil increasingly anxious for their safety. Often he left pots on the stove until they burned dry. Once the house filled with smoke from something he had cooked and left. The couple no longer slept together—Stan had a bed in the basement—but she often woke to hear his panting as he moved along the hall towards the kitchen. She would follow him and watch while he would get a cup out of the cupboard, put tea in it, place the sugar and milk next to it, plug in the kettle, and then complacently go back to bed. Lil would wait until he was gone, then turn off the kettle and go to her own bed.

Ken, coming home from the mall after work, would find the lights on in the kitchen and all the stove burners lit. It was such a regular occurrence that he took it matter of factly. It was routine to turn off the stove and switch off the kitchen lights before going to bed.

One night Ken heard his grandfather shouting. He hurried to the basement and found him lying in a pool of blood and urine. He had fallen and cut his arm on a bottle and then wet himself. His grandmother came as Ken tried to lift Stan, who stared at them, panting like an animal, his eyes bulging. When

95

they spoke to him, there was no reply or movement. Ken carried his grandfather to the bathroom, where Lil took over the task of getting him into dry clothes and bandaging his bleeding arm. In the morning, Stan irately demanded an explanation for the bandages.

The difficulties of dealing with Stan's drunkenness and nightly excursions made comrades of Lil Hodge and Ken. He loved living with her; for the first time he had a family member with whom he felt secure. He could confide in her, he thought, though he never did. He was touched that she was unconditionally on his side. She seemed to think he was just about perfect. The shy teenager was in bliss. Lil's plight with a drunken husband wrung his heart. It hurt to hear Stan yell at her or refuse to drive her to the trailer, and he would try to soften his grandfather's mood by saying something to make him smile.

Lil Hodge was aware of Ken's loneliness and gave him what he needed most, praise and tender mothering. His presence was protection. Stan never hit her when Ken was in the house.

Ken rarely saw his mother and Tyrone, or his brothers and sister. He almost never thought about them, but he continued to fantasize about one day meeting his father. He had begun to believe it might never happen, that he would grow old and die without ever knowing his father. That appeared more likely than ever when his paternal grandfather, Albert Parks, died of a heart attack in the summer of 1979. Ken assumed that he would see his father at the funeral and was braced for it, imagining how the scene would go. Just before the service he was told that his father had left a note saying he was too upset to attend.

Ken was shocked. He appreciated that it would be uncomfortable for Jim Parks to encounter his three sons after an absence of twelve years, but he thought it callous of his father not to be a comfort for his grieving mother at the funeral.

Then, on Easter Sunday 1981, Ken and his father unexpectedly met. It happened when Ken dropped in unannounced to visit his widowed grandmother. Janet Parks said, "Your father's here," and indicated her bedroom down the hall where the television was located.

Ken was shaking as he walked to the partly open door. He pushed it open and saw a big man seated in a chair watching television, half turned from him. The man looked around. Ken said, "Hi." The man replied, "Hi," and turned back to the screen.

Silence hung between them. The man resolutely concentrated on the screen. Ken stared at the averted face of his father, undecided what to do, and then bolted from the house in tears.

The Ramani twins were waiting outside in a car with Ken's new girl-friend, Karen Woods. He told them about the encounter, his anger beginning to build. They had a solution: they all went roller-skating.

CHAPTER SIX

Karen Woods Parks

Woodside Square Mall in Scarborough on Toronto's northeast flank draws youth from miles around. Some are employed at the minimum wage in the mall's fast-food outlets and shops; others merely hang out in the mall's eating area amid the litter and midway din of stalls selling an international hash of fried rice, pizza, and perogi.

Shopping malls have a peculiar social ecosystem of their own: one element formed of the managers and owners of shops, another the employees, another the regular shoppers who move purposefully through the maze of strollers and potted trees, and another the loiterers, a group made up of house-bound mothers, elderly people looking for cost-free entertainment, the homeless who come for warmth, and dislocated teenagers, the most visible of all in their bright mating attire.

The young are drawn to modern shopping plazas for the same reason that their grandparents flocked to drugstore soda fountains. Malls are places where the young are certain to be found and where parents, usually, are not.

Young people flee to malls from homes that cramp them. They escape fond parents who can't bear their nest-leaving activities; they escape exacting parents who won't tolerate their messiness; they escape from vicious or drunken or crazy parents who hurt them, and from overburdened parents who are impatient for them to be gone, and from indifferent parents who don't care where they are or who they are, and from anxious, uncertain parents with sharp tongues.

The teenagers who hang out in malls care for one another with a degree of concern and wisdom that would astonish their elders. For the price of a cup of coffee, they join a social order as clannish, exacting, and complex as the Masons. The tribes they form provide a moral structure with well-defined rules, give comfort to the wounded, and offer conviction to the uncertain and distraction to the fearful. Malls can be sanity stations for a generation overwhelmed by a sense of futility. In the malls, the young can forget the ill omens of poor school records and harsh home experience.

Teenagers in malls are always falling into romantic love with one another. The malls are indifferent witnesses to the burning love affairs that blaze from adolescent loneliness and confusion, but those wistful and ardent spring matings have a timeless history: almost all dissolve by autumn.

A few survive. In Woodside Square Mall in the summer of 1981, Ken Parks met Karen Woods. Three years later they married.

One of the privileges most enjoyed by teenagers who worked in the Woodside Square Mall that summer was going to movies free. Ken, Gus, and the Ramani twins, with the collusion of cronies taking tickets at the door, saw every film that came to the Odeon theatre in the mall, and some of them many times. Movie-going was more than an entertainment: it was a scouting opportunity. The popcorn counter had a high turnover of teenaged women, and the men kept an eye out for promising newcomers. In the summer of 1981, when the love affair of Ken Parks and Karen Woods began, Ken, a boy who mopped the floors in the mall, was seventeen and Karen, the theatre's new candy girl, was sixteen.

Karen's friend Lorraine Fernandez also worked behind the popcorn counter and was dating Richmond Ramani, one of the twins. One night when Ken and Richmond were collecting Lorraine after work, she brought along Karen and introduced her. The men offered Karen a lift home in Richmond's car, but she refused, saying she lived only a short distance away and preferred to walk. Ken thought to himself, "She's scared of us."

After that Ken was aware of her bright, cheerful presence in the young crowd that worked at the mall. He liked her Australian accent, her smallness, and her quickness, but she seemed indifferent to him. That got his attention, even though he had just started dating someone else, a mall friend named Lisa who at that time was vacationing with her family in Florida. Somehow a comfortable foursome developed, with Lorraine and Richmond, Ken and Karen meeting after work to have something to eat and to talk about their lives.

Lisa returned from vacation but Ken had become enthralled by Karen. He behaved honourably, breaking off with Lisa by telling her he cared for someone else. That left him free to concentrate on his new crush, who continued to put out signals that he should keep his distance. The foursome came together daily in the mall through the rest of the summer, with Ken increasingly intrigued by Karen's determination to give him no opening to declare his love.

For a long time, Karen accepted the foursome as just another temporary grouping within the mall family of teenagers. She could sense Ken's growing interest in her but she kept a wall of reserve between them. One brief liaison with a school friend had been a disaster. He had broken it off without explanation after about a month, and she feared a repeat of that hurt. Still, Ken attracted her. He was almost painfully polite, his gallantry with her in marked contrast to the attitudes of the other males in the gang, and he was so blushingly unsure of himself that he aroused her maternal instinct.

Towards the end of August, the gang had gathered one evening as usual, but Karen drifted away from Ken and fell into deep conversation with another male. Ken watched them laughing together and felt the sting of jealousy. His worst fears were realized, he decided: Karen was lost to him. In his misery, he drank more than his customary one or two beers. Later, in the car, Karen told him that he was drinking too much and Ken, mortified and hurt, snapped back at her. Karen got out of the car and indignantly slammed the door. Looking back, she saw to her consternation that Ken was crying.

That night Ken shyly asked her for a date. Touched by his vulnerability, she couldn't refuse.

The next night over hamburgers she told him she was having an impossible time at home. Her parents, but especially her mother, were on her back all the time about the hours she was keeping. She was thinking of moving out.

He was aghast. She had seemed so sensible, a person from one of those solid, intact, affectionate families he admired and envied. Teenagers were always talking like that, he reflected; she didn't mean it. The next day when he was hanging out with Richmond at the mall, he heard his name on the page. The call was from a distraught Karen, her voice scarcely recognizable through tears. She wanted him to come and get her. She was leaving home.

Ken found her behaviour extraordinary, and so did everyone else who knew the Woods family. Both Karen's parents were conventional, duty-conscious, upright middle-class people who were raising their six children in what appeared to be a model environment of stability and benign discipline. Karen was the neighbourhood's first choice for baby-sitting; the oldest Woods girl was so dependable, people said, so good with children. Karen Woods was the most improbable runaway teen anyone could imagine.

Barbara and Denis Woods, Karen's parents, were born and grew up in England. Barbara Ann was adopted and raised as the only child of Albert and Constance Lancaster. Barbara's natural mother, it was said, was killed in a wartime bombing.

Albert Lancaster was an itinerant civil servant who attained managerial status in the municipal housing field and wound up in West Kirby, a small city near Liverpool. In that town a teenaged Barbara Lancaster met Denis Woods, twenty, the only son in a military family, and they fell in love.

It was a romantic courtship, spiced by vigorous opposition from Denis's parents. His father, a permanent army officer, and his austere mother shared a view of an orderly universe regulated by hereditary rank and privilege. Their concern was that Barbara, being adopted, came from an unknown genetic pool that might produce flawed grandchildren. In the hope that the young people would tire of one another, Denis's parents forbade him to marry Barbara for two years.

Denis is a logical, careful man who considers every alternative before making a move, calculating the degree of risk with mathematical precision. Concepts of rebellion or rashness were abhorrent to him even as a youth, so he agreed without resentment to his parents' ban. Barbara, a more impulsive and optimistic person, was hurt.

Denis was enchanted by Barbara's sparkle and prettiness. It was new for him, a cautious, reserved man raised in an environment of emotional distance, to give his trust so freely, but he was head-over-heels in love. Every morning he could be found leaning against the wall outside Barbara's home, waiting to walk her to school. They found they danced well together and went often to a favourite place, a club in Liverpool that featured an up-and-coming group, the Beatles.

At the time they started going together, Denis was working his way towards a degree in electrical engineering. Because his father wouldn't pay university tuition, Denis had enrolled in a painfully slow semester program in which he could work for extended periods to meet his expenses.

On January 25, 1964, when Denis was twenty-two and Barbara nineteen, they were married. He was still completing his education, so they began domesticity in an almost penniless state.

Barbara became pregnant a month after the wedding. Stung by her in-laws' continuing disapproval, she struggled to disarm their criticism by being the perfect wife: unfailingly supportive and loving of her husband, a splendid cook, and matchless in her ability to polish a table top.

She made little headway with the senior Woodses, and to add to her distress, her mother also had a fault-finding nature. Barbara went tearfully to Denis for emotional support and approval. The pattern of their marriage was formed in that crucible of mutual dependence: he needed her bounce and affection, and she needed his steadiness. Each was the major focus of the other's life; their disparities became the union's strength.

Karen Anne was born to them on November 29, 1964, exactly on the day she was expected. The infant had a thatch of spiky black hair that led the nurses to dub her "the Beatle".

Karen says Barbara was "just a natural mother, always wonderful with babies". Denis and Barbara took their small daughter home to a frugal flat. Their resources were so meagre that they couldn't afford to keep the place heated that winter. Barbara would huddle in bed with her baby all day to keep warm, turning on the heat in the evening just before Denis was expected home.

Barbara's mother and father helped with gifts of money, clothing, and even furniture, but little was forthcoming from Denis's parents.

Samantha Louise, their second daughter, was born December 11, 1965, eleven months after Karen, and Emma Victoria was born October 16, 1967. By that time the family income was more forgiving. Denis had graduated in electrical engineering and was employed at a respectable wage by English Electric. The family was living in a semi-detached house in Stafford that Barbara kept deliciously warm.

In the interval Barbara's father died. Karen has only one memory of him, that of a kindly man who carried her to the corner store in Stafford and bought her Smarties. Barbara's mother, widowed and with no other children, began spending a great deal of time with her daughter, and eventually moved in. Constance Lancaster had the compulsive nature of a perfectionist, but it was accompanied by missionary zeal for the improvement of others. Barbara tried to please her exacting mother, but she never seemed to get the house clean enough or raise her children well enough. Denis often returned home from work to find his wife huddled in their bedroom, sobbing.

In 1969 rumours swept Denis's office that English Electric was about to be sold. In great alarm, Denis and several other engineers sent out a blizzard of job applications to hydro companies in other countries. Denis received two offers, one from Ontario Hydro in Canada and the other from Tasmania Hydro in Australia. He chose Australia because he pictured the island of

Tasmania as a good place to raise children. Barbara protested in horror that it was too far from England, but Denis consoled her with a promise that they would move back in two years if she didn't like Australia. Karen was four when the family sailed on the *Fair Sky*, a voyage that lasted six weeks. She was seasick for most of it.

They settled in a big house in Hobart, the capital, and a few months later Barbara's mother arrived to live with them. The couple had three more children, Jonathan Leslie, born on August 17, 1970, Prudence Mary, born on September 14, 1972, and then Nicholas Lancaster, born July 1, 1975. Far from feeling burdened by the task of raising six children, Barbara seemed to thrive on doing everything herself and didn't allow her children to assist with the household chores. Karen, as the oldest, was not even required to help with the younger children. "I didn't have you because I wanted a baby-sitter," her mother would say, sending her out to play.

Despite her preoccupation with her growing brood, Barbara was intensely homesick for England. She hated the fauna of her new country: hairy spiders as big as her hand, snakes in the backyard, tarantulas under the porch. She didn't mind the rainy winters, but the hot, dry summers depleted her. She pined for England.

Barbara grew increasingly insistent that Denis should keep his promise to move them back to England. Whenever she felt blue, she reminded him of his pledge, but he always put her off. They had a big family, he pointed out, and Tasmania was far cheaper than England. She was unimpressed by his arguments. Finally, after eleven years in Tasmania, he suggested a compromise: Canada.

On May 17, 1980, the Woodses packed up and left Australia for Canada. Karen, fifteen years old, cried throughout the long plane ride. The change could not have come at a worse time for her. She was in Grade 10 in high school, hugely successful in her subjects and popular, part of a gang of friends who went camping and sailing together. The most important reason for her tears was that she had fallen in love with a school friend, Robert Hand. Their friendship, which began in Grade 8, had flowered in

Grade 10 and they were going steady. Robert was an easy-going, athletic youth who made Karen feel comfortable and valued. At fifteen, Karen had never been happier in her life.

She still believes that if she had remained in Hobart she and Robert Hand eventually would have married. She would have gone to university, as he did. She pictures their life together as secure, pleasant, and affluent.

She pleaded with her parents to allow her to stay in Hobart as a boarder at her school, but Denis and Barbara would not tolerate breaking up the family. With a distraught teenager in tow, they flew to Vancouver, changed planes, and went on to Toronto. For a few weeks all eight of them stayed in Mississauga with the Bowrings, the hospitable family of an engineer and former colleague at English Electric. On Karen's first night in Canada she cried so hard that Mrs. Bowring brought her headache pills and warm milk and endeavoured, without success, to console her.

Karen's parents had given up trying to soothe their outraged and desolate daughter. "They got to the point where they ignored me," Karen says, grinning at the recollection. She adds forgivingly, "There's no talking sense to a fifteen-year-old."

Denis Woods readily found a management job with a company that sold transformers and other major components used by hydro companies. He moved his family to a four-bedroom townhouse in Scarborough at 25 Brimwood Boulevard, number 85. After renting for a year, the Woodses decided to purchase the house. In time Barbara and Denis made themselves a comfortable bedroom and adjoining den in what had been an unfinished basement, so that the four top-floor bedrooms could be given to the children and to Barbara's mother, who rejoined them a few months after they settled in Canada.

Barbara had a strong sense of family responsibility concerning her mother and she drilled that into her children. Family, she often said, means that you take care of one another.

In the fall of 1980, the six Woods children were launched in Canadian schools. All of them adjusted happily except for Karen, who was still nursing a grudge about the move and writing long tear-soaked letters to Robert Hand.

Karen hated everything about Albert Campbell Collegiate, which conveniently was only a few blocks from her house and directly across the street from Woodside Square Mall. She was shocked at the tight jeans everyone wore, and alarmed that the school seemed to be full of drugs, which repelled her. Her peers had an air of sexual looseness she found disconcerting.

Because her academic credits in Australia didn't fit into the Ontario curriculum, Karen was given a scrambled timetable. She was placed in Grade 11, but took some subjects in Grade 12 and a few in Grade 13. The arrangement made academic sense but left her socially rootless. She was unable to attach to the groupings of classmates who spent the academic day together.

Another barrier, at least in her own mind, was her Australian accent. Sometimes she couldn't be understood at all, and would repeat words over and over. With a fierce determination much like her mother's, Karen set to work to eradicate every vestige of the hated twang.

Partly because of her disjointed schedule, and mostly because she was miserable and seething with resentment at being in Canada, Karen had poor grades. The teenager who had been a top student in Hobart got only average grades in Scarborough. She was skipping classes to hang out with other truants at the Woodside Square Mall's eating area amid the carnival atmosphere of booths selling fast food.

"I was rebelling," Karen comments now. "I was saying to my parents, 'Well, you made me come here, so now see what you've done.' "

Barbara and Denis were not aware that Karen had become an inferior student until the summer of 1981 when they saw her Grade 11 report card. They chastised her indignantly but with less steam than Karen expected. Her parents seemed to see the low marks as a temporary aberration caused by adjustment to a new country. They assumed that Karen would soon settle down and become her dependable self.

The truth was that Karen had become an openly defiant teenager. Her confrontations with her mother began only days after their arrival in Canada when Karen had her ears pierced, something Barbara had expressly forbidden. Other acts of mutiny were less overt. In March 1981, Karen got a job as candy girl in the Woodside Square Mall's Odeon theatre, working Monday nights and Saturday matinees. She became a full-fledged member of the mall gang and was enthralled. At her friends' urging she would sneak liquor from her parents' stock and share it at school dances. Sometimes, slightly tipsy and afraid to go home, she would spend the night at a girl-friend's home.

Collisions between Barbara and Karen became daily occurrences in the Woods household. In the summer of 1981, when Karen worked almost every night at the theatre's candy counter, the situation was aggravated. After work Karen liked to unwind with the other teenagers who made the mall their headquarters. She was coming home long after midnight, to find her furious mother waiting for her.

She remembers the warm spring night Richmond Ramani and her friend Lorraine Fernandez introduced her to Ken Parks. Lorraine wanted the men to drive Karen home, but Karen felt uneasy about accepting. They were an unlikely pair, she thought, one of them a black man and the other so huge, with startlingly white skin and pale blond hair. Over Lorraine's protests, Karen wheeled away and walked home, regretting it almost immediately because she was wearing high heels that hurt her feet, regretting it even more when a strange man started to trail her. She escaped what might have been at the very least an unpleasant scene when she happened to meet a co-worker from the theatre who escorted her to her door.

Karen loved the freedom and friendships the nightly job at the theatre gave her. After work she would sit for hours over coffee or beer with others from the mall's improvised family of youth, enjoying their acceptance. One night when she went home a bit the worse for drink, her grandmother was waiting up for her. After that, Barbara and Constance were unrelenting in their efforts to control the errant teenager.

A point of mutual intolerance rapidly was reached, a terrain not unfamiliar in families with teenagers. Barbara and her wayward daughter rarely exchanged a civil word. As Barbara's frustration and exasperation escalated, Karen's stubborn defiance increased to meet it. She had been coming home at around two in the morning; she began to stay out until four.

Unlike many other parents in the same situation, Denis and Barbara had no fear that Karen was off the rails with sex or drugs or drinking. Despite the smell of beer that sometimes accompanied Karen home, her parents had complete confidence in their daughter's good sense. The sole issue for them was disobedience.

Their analysis of the situation was correct. After the mall closed, Karen was mostly to be found in the basement recreation room of the Ramani clan, where teenagers gathered to sip soft drinks while listening to music, or talking, or—the new rage—watching videos on rented equipment. The Ramanis were opposed to drugs and drank beer only moderately; if any sexual experimentation was happening in the group, it didn't occur at the home of the Ramanis. Besides, Karen wasn't much interested in any of the men in the group.

The summer was ending and Karen's frantic parents decided they would have to take serious measures before school started. If Karen continued to keep unruly hours, she certainly would fail her year. They discussed what they would do, and Denis, in his meticulous way, made a list of rules. They notified Karen that they wanted to talk to her the next day at five when Denis returned from work.

The three met tensely in her parents' bedroom on the basement floor. Denis read the items on his prepared list. Most of them concerned curfew: Karen was to be home at nine every weekday night that she wasn't working and at eleven every night that she was; on weekends she would be home by midnight.

Karen was braced for an ultimatum of some kind; the night before, she had predicted to Ken that it was coming. She was shocked, none the less, at the severity of the restrictions. Yelling and red-faced, she told her parents they were outrageous. How could she be home at eleven, *she didn't finish work until eleven.* Did they expect her to fly!

Denis and Barbara were unmoved. They said that if she wanted to continue living at home she would have to abide by the rules. Otherwise....

Karen screamed that that was fine with her, she was leaving.

She stormed out of the room, snatched some garbage bags from the kitchen, and ran upstairs to her bedroom, crying wildly. Denis stepped into the upstairs hall to be out of the way while Karen flung her clothes into the garbage bags. Karen could hear her mother pleading with him, "Den, Den, don't let her leave!" and Denis's gruff reply, "Let her go."

Barbara wept as Karen stormed around the room, recklessly jamming her possessions into the bags until three were full. She realized she would need transportation and was stymied momentarily. Then she remembered that Ken could always borrow a car from the Ramanis. She called the mall and asked to have Ken paged. "Come and get me," she said.

"Where are you going?" her mother asked.

"None of your business," Karen snapped. In truth, she didn't know.

Barbara sobbed but Denis was expressionless. As Karen picked up the garbage bags full of clothes, her brother Jonny appeared from somewhere and took one of them. He carried it down the stairs and out the front door while Karen followed with the two others, passing her weeping mother without a glance.

She waited by the road that led to the underground parking area until she saw a car with Ken and Richmond and her friend Lorraine Fernandez. The four teenagers automatically went to the mall to discuss Karen's next move and sat around a metal table in the eating area. Karen was buoyant: *her parents would be worried sick!* The only cloud on her triumph was that she had no place to stay. Then she thought of a school friend, Connie Sullivan, who had just been hired at the mall. Karen had slept at Connie's house several times when she wanted to stay out especially late.

Connie checked with her mother, who agreed that Karen could come for a few days while she looked for another arrangement. Ken was stunned by the speed and finality with which Karen had made herself a refugee. It didn't fit with his picture of her as a model of rational behaviour. In his mild way, he suggested to her that it would be better to talk matters through with her parents. She flared at him, so he gave up and drove her to Connie's.

Karen piled the garbage bags behind the bar in Connie's recreation room, and the gang of teenagers went out to celebrate. Karen was joyful and the others, with the exception of a worried Ken Parks, took vicarious delight in her audacity.

Denis and Barbara already had telephoned the police to ask for their help in finding their runaway child. The next day at the movie theatre, Karen learned that police had been asking about her. She coolly went to the police station only a block away and told them she was alive and fine.

The officer with whom she spoke said, "Your parents are worried. Why don't you give them a call?"

She replied airily, "No way."

In fact, fear was stirring in her. She's a careful and practical person, not normally impulsive, and the thought of her uncertain future made her tremble. How could she support herself and still stay in school? Where would she live?

Karen solved part of her problem when she found a job at a fish and chips store, working as cashier every night and every other Saturday for four dollars an hour. She wouldn't be seeing her friends at the theatre any more, a desolating thought, but the pay was better and she had no choice.

Housing proved more difficult, but Ken offered a temporary solution. He had left his room at the home of his Hodge grandparents because they needed the space temporarily. Their youngest child, Mavis, was about to be married, and relatives from Scotland and Saskatchewan were converging on Scarborough for the event. In the emergency, Ken had moved in with his grandmother Parks, who lived alone in a three-bedroom bungalow, down the street from Karen's parents and only a short distance from the mall. At Ken's request, Janet Parks agreed to allow Karen to stay in one of the empty bedrooms, setting a limit of two weeks.

Janet Parks liked Karen but disapproved of her flight from home. She brought gentle but steady pressure on the runaway to telephone her parents to tell them where she was. Karen politely refused. She wanted to talk to her parents, but strategy dictated that they make the first move. If she called them, they would expect her to accept their terms. Her parents seemed to take the same view and were making no attempt to contact her. Barbara tried to persuade Denis to call, but Denis, as stubborn as Karen, wouldn't hear of it.

Karen searched a bulletin board at Centennial College listing student housing and found a place offering room and board for $60 a week. It was affordable if she was careful with her earnings.

Ken remained uneasy. Finally, as a concession to him, Karen called her mother and arranged to go home for a talk. She took Ken with her for courage. Barbara served them coffee in the living-room, but the civilities were short-lived. Barbara went on the attack about Karen's late hours, her sloth with her homework, her unauthorized absences from school. Karen fired back that it was her business what she did, none of her friends had stupid curfews, and her mother had no right to interfere in her life.

Ken sat between them, his shoulders hunched in embarrassment, and sipped his coffee.

Abruptly, Karen stood up and stormed out of the house. Barbara and Ken, strangers to one another, exchanged disconcerted looks. Ken set down his cup carefully and, with all the poise he could summon, said pleasantly, "Thank you for the coffee, Mrs. Woods," and left.

School began a few days later. Ken resumed classes at Cedarbrae in Grade 11, though trailing a few subjects, and Karen returned to Albert Campbell Collegiate for a mixture of Grades 12 and 13. Her friends from the previous year were all in Grade 13 so Karen found herself in classrooms of strangers. She was appalled that her lunch periods didn't coincide with any of her gang.

She found the isolation unbearable. Two days after school began, she transferred herself to Agincourt Collegiate, a brisk fifteen-minute walk from her boarding-house. In the mood of defiant independence that had propelled her into leaving home, she somehow felt better among people who were total strangers than being able to see her friends but not be with them.

In two weeks the usually level-headed Karen Woods had discarded all the fixed points in her life: her home and family, her job, her school, her friends. Her loneliness literally threw her into Ken's arms.

And Ken Parks had been waiting all his life for a chance to be important to someone.

They made an unusual pair. Ken and Karen are oddly matched physically, the tall blond man fifteen inches taller than his tiny dark wife. Their backgrounds are dissimilar, his troubled and lonely, hers a model of closeness and stability. In the normal course of events, she and Ken Parks could have been in the same high school without speaking. Karen would be the charmer who won all the math prizes and Ken the bashful guy destined to drop out early. Academic distinctions between teenagers are rarely bridged in the ruthless caste system of high schools. The social levels are based largely on academic achievement; young people live in the solitudes of the streaming system, which sorts them out into winners and losers. The mating would not have happened except for Karen's state of rebellion. She had become dislocated from the stream of teenagers in which she belonged: the high achievers whose futures are as certain as the stars. For one startling period in her life, Karen Woods had made herself indistinguishable from any street kid.

They saw one another every day. In order to be with Karen after school, Ken gave up his beloved sports programs and was waiting for her at Agincourt Collegiate when she came out the door. She told him she loved him; he was the happiest man alive. In return, he gave her his total devotion, all he had.

"He was there for me," she explains simply. "He'd have done almost anything for me."

Ken had a girl-friend at last, the first serious relationship he had ever known, someone who counted on him. He had begun to believe that no one would ever love him. Karen's dependence on him made him feel adult; he wore an air of assurance and authority he had never known.

He loved to carry her over puddles; it became the metaphor for their relationship. The deposit money for her boarding-house came from him. Cupped in the safety of his adoration, Karen was her most bubbling, confident self. Ken was charmed by her brightness and quick responses. She was so tiny and alive next to his huge, slow self and, best of all, he filled her life entirely. He had Karen to himself, and it brought out the best in him, his tenderness and decency.

His only rival, Robert Hand, lived on the other side of the globe. Still, he hated to hear Karen speak of her former boyfriend. He was dismayed when she gave the name "Rob" to a little blue Smerf someone had given her. He insisted that she discard it in a Goodwill box and he bought her a replacement.

They became lovers one night when his grandmother Hodge was at her trailer; both were virgins. Practical Karen promptly went to a doctor in a Scarborough medical clinic and obtained birth-control pills.

He escorted her proudly to the wedding of his aunt Mavis. Karen met Ken's mother, Betty Parks, for the first time. Betty was charmed by her. Karen clearly came from a good family, so well mannered and friendly. Lil Hodge liked Karen too, but attached no importance to her presence at Ken's side. He was young; there would be other girls.

Ken moved back with his Hodge grandparents and frequently brought Karen there. Stan lurched out of the basement to greet her in a state of drunkenness that frightened the teenager. She thought the Hodge home a poor environment for Ken and wished he would move. She learned, however, that Ken would tolerate no criticism of his grandfather. When she complained about the drinking, Ken would leap loyally to Stan's defence.

Lil Hodge was an imperturbable hostess, immaculate as her house and always hospitable to Karen. Karen was an amused witness to the warm relationship Ken had with his grandmother. Lil kept up a patter of sardonic observation on her huge grandson's shortcomings, which he received, grinning, with evasions she accepted tolerantly. "School called today," she would say. "You weren't there. Where did you go?" Or, "Your room is a mess." Karen thought they had fallen into that kind of exchange as a way of expressing affection.

Occasionally Ken drove Karen to Oshawa to see his mother. Karen was disconcerted by Betty and Tyrone, and thought Ken's younger brothers were somewhat wild. Beer seemed a staple of their diet, she noted, and it alarmed her that Betty almost never spoke to her.

"I thought she hated me," Karen explains. "Then I found out that she really couldn't hear, so that's why she didn't talk."

Karen discovered that Ken wouldn't stand for criticism of his mother either. His loyalty to her and to his brothers, though both seemed to be in constant trouble with the police, was formidable. Karen learned to keep her opinions of his family to herself.

As weeks passed, Karen grew increasingly homesick. With the exception of Ken, nothing in her life was quite right. She hated Agincourt Collegiate: going there had been a mistake. Many times she signed herself out of classes; more often still she was absent because of sickness. She kept getting heavy colds, one after another, which she attributed to her irregular diet. She longed to be home but wouldn't make the first move.

Her sisters Emma and Samantha often came to visit her at the fish and chips store. They would talk about inconsequentials, but Karen suspected they were the family's scouts checking on her well-being. Her seventeenth birthday came, November 29, 1981, and she got a cordial telephone call from her mother inviting her to drop by the house and pick up presents.

Reassured by Barbara's impersonal but friendly tone, Karen accepted gratefully. The Woods family normally celebrate each birthday with a festive gathering, complete with egg-salad sandwiches and one of Barbara's delicious cakes. When Karen arrived at the time her mother had specified, she discovered that there was no party. Her father, in fact, made a point of being absent, but her mother gave her a hug when she left, and her grandmother held her tongue. The gifts were mostly of money, which Karen sorely needed.

Habits of reticence have made Ken a perceptive observer. After that visit, he noted that Karen talked about her family increasingly and with a marked absence of her old anger. He guessed that she wanted to return. Proceeding gently in case he had misread the situation, he began to talk about a reunion. He was careful not to be critical, knowing that Karen had a volatile temper on the subject of her good judgement in running away, but he privately felt that Barbara and Denis had been right to impose a curfew. He had a lot of respect for parents who cared enough to set limits.

One day when Karen was talking wistfully about her family, he grasped the opportunity. He had given it some thought, he said, and perhaps it would help if he opened the negotiations. Karen was delighted to accept; the first phone call had become an insurmountable barrier. With Ken as an intermediary, perhaps a compromise could be found. Ken telephoned Barbara and asked if he could come over.

All sides were weary of the impasse, and the preliminary meeting between Ken and Karen's parents went smoothly. When Ken said that Karen was interested in returning home, Barbara and Denis repeated their position that she couldn't return unless she followed the house rules. Ken was undismayed; in his slow, patient style, he suggested that there would have to be give and take on both sides. Karen was ready to agree to a curfew, but it would have to be reasonable.

Barbara and Denis were impressed by Ken. They liked his respectful manner and his air of calm. They agreed to discuss the curfew with Barbara on neutral ground, and fixed on dinner at a pizza restaurant called Mother's.

Karen suddenly was terrified at the prospect of facing her parents. Ken assured her that they were in a conciliatory mood, not a bit hostile or rigid, but her panic didn't ease. The meal began awkwardly. Denis Woods, controlled and pleasant, obviously had rehearsed for the occasion. Habits of preparation are strong in him: he's a man who reads consumer magazines extensively before making a purchase. Barbara Woods was tense and talkative, while Karen spoke almost not at all. Ken was the focus of the conversation, as Barbara and Denis attempted to get his measure.

The subject on all their minds—Karen's return—was not discussed until coffee was served. Predictably, Barbara raised it.

"Well," she said, drawing a breath, "let's talk about what we're here to talk about. We want you to come home, Karen, but we can't have you come home and give us the same trouble."

Karen said firmly, "Yes, but I can't live under the rules you set when I left."

"You must respect us," Denis said. "If you're going to be out late, you're going to have to call and tell us where you are so we don't worry. And there's a limit to how late you can stay out."

With that, negotiations began. Both sides made compromises until it was agreed that the weeknight curfew would be twelve o'clock and on weekends it would be one-thirty.

Karen wanted to make the transition a slow one. Her rent was paid for another ten days and she was fond of her landlady, who had been kind to her. It was decided therefore that she would move home about a week later.

She arrived in time for Christmas, 1981, after an absence of almost three months, and was thrilled to be in her own bed again.

Ken's father had abruptly entered his life. Jim Parks was living with Ken's grandmother Janet Parks at her urgent request following some crank phone calls. She was fearful of being alone in her house. For a few months around the Christmas of 1981, Ken grew accustomed to the jolt of hearing his father's voice when he telephoned his grandmother, or seeing him there when he dropped in.

The two men behaved towards each other as strangers would. They didn't touch, not even to shake hands, and their conversations were perfunctory. If Jim Parks answered the door he would say, "I'll get grandma," and disappear down the hall to shut himself in the bedroom with the television. Over time, the exchanges progressed to "How are you?" "Fine, and you?" "Fine." "Good." Then his father would wheel and leave the room.

Janet Parks consoled the shocked teenager. His father behaved that way, she said, because he was sorry he had abandoned his family. Gradually Ken overcame his own hurt feelings and was able to see his father in a sympathetic light. He sensed the older man's loneliness, so much like his own.

Because Ken is the only person in the Hodge family who keeps in touch with Janet Parks, his two brothers have never had such accidental meetings with their father. They have not seen their father since his departure when they were babies, and they show no interest in doing so.

Ken seems to be the only one of Betty's children who values family. He alone makes an effort to maintain relationships. Even when she moved a distance away, he continued to visit his grandmother Parks. He's very close as well to his mother's brother, Glen Hodge, and makes a point of staying in touch. Ken dropped by Glen's home in Scarborough so regularly that the two men, with only twelve years between them, have a relationship that is brotherly.

Ken's feelings for his mother and Tyrone were complicated when he was young by something close to embarrassment. He didn't like the casual disorder of their home or the raucous atmosphere, so unlike the decorum his grandmothers tried to maintain. His mother's deafness made her manner abrupt, so he hesitated to bring friends home. He was bothered as well by Tyrone's drinking and the instability of his brothers, who seemed always to be in some kind of trouble. It wasn't the way Ken wanted to live his life.

The Woods household, on the other hand, was Ken's ideal of domesticity. People were friendly, relaxed, dependable, polite, presentable. He watched for clues on how he could fit in, and his tact was appreciated. Denis and Barbara were disposed to like him on sight. They sensed that he was on their side in the dispute with their daughter, and they appreciated his efforts to repair the rift. They saw him as a good influence on Karen and were grateful.

They gave him the best gift: trust. When they were away, Ken was the only outsider allowed in the house. The terms of the new house rules reflected their confidence in Ken: Karen could stay out beyond her curfew as long as she was with Ken. She had only to phone to say where she was. If Ken and Karen went to a bar, Ken drank soft drinks; he has a horror of drunkenness. Under his influence, Karen almost ceased drinking, an improvement not lost on her parents, who gave Ken credit for it.

Ken became an oldest brother in the Woods family, a role that was the culmination of his dreams. Samantha, the quiet sister closest in age to Karen, brought him her confidences, and he gravely gave advice. When Karen was working, Ken would squire Samantha when she went shopping. Often he and Karen would join Samantha and her date for a night together.

When he reached his eighteenth birthday, Ken got a gift of money from his grandmother Parks, the proceeds from bonds she had purchased for her grandchildren. He used $1,700 of it to buy a used car, a big black Fury, hard-driven by its former owners, the Ontario Provincial Police.

By spring of 1982, it was clear that Ken would fail all his Grade 11 subjects. He and his friends had drifted out of the academic, college-bound stream. He saw no point in making a drudge of himself when graduation was unlikely and lacking in meaning for him.

Karen felt the same about school. The subjects, with few exceptions, seemed to her irrelevant and a waste of her time. Her marks were not impressive that year, although they were adequate enough to secure her credits.

All summer Karen and Ken talked disconsolately about the necessity of returning to school. They thought it might be more palatable if they went to the same one. That way, maybe Ken would buckle down and pass. It was decided that Karen would transfer to Cedarbrae to see that Ken didn't cut classes.

By the fall of 1982 Ken seemed almost to have moved in to the Woods household. He was there after school and usually stayed for dinner. His humour and playfulness were a huge hit with Karen's younger brothers and sisters. He wrestled with Nicky, and would walk about the house with Pru and Nicky hanging from his huge arms. Denis would disappear into his bedroom to read or play computer games, while Barbara joshed with Ken about his size. He treated her with mock condescension and liked to get a rise out of her by making outrageously chauvinistic remarks.

Privacy was hard for the young couple to come by. When Karen and Ken made love, usually it was in the back seat of a car.

Both had new jobs. Ken was working in a hardware store and Karen as a waitress in the restaurant in Zeller's in the mall.

Without saying anything to Karen about it, Ken went shopping for an engagement ring. He chose a small, brave diamond ring, paying $300. He decided on a romantic location, the spot in the mall parking lot where he had first asked Karen for a date. That night as they walked to his car, he said, "Karen, will you marry me?" She grinned and said, "Yeah."

Barbara and Denis were pleased but protested that they were too young to marry. The couple assured them that they planned to wait two or three years, until they had finished high school and their lives were in order.

That autumn Karen and Ken entered Cedarbrae high school, the only officially engaged couple in the school. Every morning they met on a corner to walk to school, and between classes they were inseparable. After school was another matter. Ken resumed playing rugby despite Karen's displeasure at the amount of time it consumed. She went to every game, a small and somewhat grumpy figure in the stands.

She saw a new side of him. Ken on a playing field was an aggressive, competitive man whose great size gave him an air of command. Ken seemed to assume that his size made him responsible for the enforcement of fairness. If anyone showed unnecessary roughness, Ken was an avenging giant.

His mantle of protector of the innocent extended off the field. Karen learned of a time after a soccer game three years earlier when Ken's attention was drawn to a frightened teenaged girl who was surrounded by about ten of the opposing team. Though she tried to get away, they pursued her, taunting her about something. Ken went roaring to her assistance, piling into all ten by himself until joined a minute later by three of his teammates. The battle turned ugly and someone called the police, who broke it up.

A few months after high school resumed that fall, Ken and Karen fell to bickering. The flash points varied, but fundamentally all the quarrels were the same. Karen was furious that Ken spent so much time on sports and that he was hanging around again with his male friends. She thought it unfair, since he was almost the only person she knew at Cedarbrae. She had transferred to be with him, she told him, and she was outraged when he deserted her.

In February 1983, just after Ken had given her a stuffed cat for a Valentine's present, they had an argument so bitter that Ken suggested they break up. Karen, shocked, promptly gave him back the ring.

Ken wasn't at school for the next few days. Karen expected to feel abandoned, but she was pleasantly surprised to find a considerable amount of sympathy on her side. Students she scarcely knew made a point of keeping her company in the cafeteria or walking with her between classes. Ken's teammates on his rugby team informed her that they were telling him he was a jerk. It helped, but Karen was in anguish; often at home she sobbed in her room.

Ken was disconcerted that his friends were flocking to Karen's support. His old insecurities came to the fore. He let it be known that no one was allowed to date Karen. To guard against a rival, he insisted on picking her up after work to drive her home. He watched her enter her house, and then, satisfied, he drove away to join his friends.

They reconciled, only to break apart again over the same cause. The engagement ring was on and off her finger; friends checked her hand to see how things were going. Her parents gave up trying to keep abreast of developments. Once Ken was so angry with her that he gave her back everything she had given him, including a car blanket.

Ken's jealousy finally brought them together. It happened one night when Karen told him not to pick her up the next night, she was going to a dance with Samantha and Samantha's boy-friend. Ken, aghast, blurted out, "How about going with me?"

She went, but she gave him a chilly time.

He was not only stung by her haughtiness; in truth Ken was missing Karen. "Hanging out with the guys," as he put it, began to lose its charm. He kept thinking about Karen and worrying that she would find someone else.

In March he went to the Bahamas with his rugby team and telephoned her twice. On his return they were reunited, this time for good.

Ken's grades improved that year and he earned five credits. Karen graduated. They considered their options and decided that

Ken should return in the fall to finish Grade 12. Meanwhile they kept their jobs. Ken worked almost full time that summer at the hardware store, while Karen continued as a part-time waitress at Zeller's.

Her mother grew annoyed. One afternoon as Karen was lolling in front of the television, Barbara presented her with two options. "Either you go to college this fall or you get a full-time job," she said. "You're not going to sit around at home."

College had no appeal for Karen; she had decided education was a complete waste of time. She found a job for $200 a week as a cashier at a Regal Photo one-hour outlet. To her disgust, her parents immediately obliged her to pay rent. Ken was cooling to the idea of going back to school. With Karen gone from Cedarbrae, the prospect was unappealing. He was too old for homework, he thought, and the byzantine politics of adolescents.

He looked for a better-paying job and found one for $200 a week in sales with an electrical company, Independent Electric. In an electrical course in high school, his marks had been excellent. He loved the field and it gave him something in common with Denis Woods, an electrical engineer.

By November 1983, they had saved enough money to buy a car together, a Chevette. Ken was nineteen and Karen was approaching her nineteenth birthday; they were a ripe age. They began to discuss marriage.

CHAPTER SEVEN

Marriage

The entire Woods family was relieved when peace was restored between Ken and Karen, and the sheepish teenager was welcomed like the prodigal son. Barbara Woods set a place for him at the dinner table every night: to all appearances, the Woodses had seven children, not six. Except that he did not sleep there, Ken was a permanent part of the household at townhouse 85, 25 Brimwood Boulevard.

Barbara and Denis saw Ken as someone with a positive influence on all their children, but especially Karen, their most headstrong child. Besides, he was easy to have around. Ken was sensitive to the family's politics and was careful not to take liberties with hospitality. He did not, for instance, help himself to something in the refrigerator uninvited or enter the house without knocking.

The Woodses provided Ken with the family of his dreams. The warm and gregarious Ramanis had given him a taste of it, but Karen introduced him to the real thing: a solid-gold traditional family. They had taken him in without a ripple, and he returned their generosity with all the consideration he could summon.

"Mom thought the sun shone from Ken," Karen says. "He could do no wrong."

A stereotype about teenagers is that they are feckless about money. In the early days of their courtship, Karen and Ken had been no exception; the money they earned trickled away like water in a hand. Their carelessness vanished, however, when Ken's car broke down for good and they urgently needed another. To the amazement of their families, they had no difficulty summoning the discipline to become thrifty. With the goal of a car and marriage in mind, both found it satisfying to be frugal. They took pleasure in seeing savings grow, and they hated spending.

Karen, who liked to joke about her father's predilection for researching cost and quality before making a purchase, discovered she was cut from the same cloth.

Ken and Karen, in fact, don't enjoy extravagance. They are not obsessed by clothes; jeans suit him fine and she's comfortable in track suits. Neither drinks much or smokes at all. The couple's biggest outlay was in restaurants where they ate a few times a week in order to have privacy to talk. Though they dined in modest places and ordered with a sharp eye on the right-hand column, the expense dismayed them. It pained them to see how slowly their savings grew.

Karen and Ken sat down to consider cost-cutting measures: The best way to save, they concluded, was to get married. The biggest economy would be on food; if they married, they'd eat at home. Also, they would save the rent money Karen was paying her parents. They pored over budget projections and decided that, if they lived cheaply for a year or two, they could save enough money to buy a modest house. Neither was going to school, so why delay?

In February 1984, just as Ken turned twenty, they announced their decision to get married. Denis Woods promptly suggested they elope and he would give them a sum equivalent to a wedding reception. Karen turned the offer down flat. She was dreaming of a formal wedding with all the trimmings: a white gown and veil, bridesmaids, a white stretch limousine—the works. Like her parents, she wanted the pleasure of having everything right. A summer wedding wouldn't give her time to organize properly, she decided; accordingly, the couple elected to be married in September.

Their families accepted the news without surprise; Karen and Ken had been engaged for almost two years. The most serious opposition came from Ken's uncle, Glen Hodge, and Glen's wife,

Diane, who thought that Ken and Karen, at twenty and nineteen, were far too young.

Grandmother Hodge was gracious about the news but showed little enthusiasm. A major concern to Lil was the loss of Ken's protection. Stan's drinking had become so severe that his employer, the Toronto Board of Education, had retired him on a medical pension. That dismissal removed the last inhibition on his drinking. Stan was growing daily more drunken, quarrelsome, perverse, and violent. Though Ken wasn't around the house much, still he slept there and was a great help to his grandmother on those nights when Stan sleepwalked, cooking his desperate meals and panting like an animal.

The wedding arrangements were marked by acrimony so bitter that the couple almost came apart. The strife centred on the tight budget that Denis had set. Looking ahead, Karen's father made a decision to provide equal amounts for the weddings of his four daughters. Karen's wedding therefore would establish the benchmark. Factoring in inflation and his annual raises over the next ten years, he fixed the cost of Karen's wedding at $2,500, which they estimated would allow for a total of forty-five guests at the reception.

The Woodses had few relatives or close friends in Canada, so restricting the size of the reception posed little hardship for them. Ten of the available spots would suffice. Ken's families, however, the Parkses and the Hodges, had numerous relatives and friends and were aghast to be notified that they could have only thirty-five guests, the wedding party included.

Ken's family protested to him and he loyally relayed their objections to Karen, who responded indignantly. She criticized his family: Why didn't they offer to chip in with the costs? Why didn't they volunteer to take over some of the myriad details of the preparations?

Neither Ken nor Karen can tolerate criticism of family. Their discussions of wedding plans often deteriorated into argument, vocal on Karen's side, mute and steaming on Ken's. Karen was prone to sarcasm and Ken would retreat into gloom. When peace finally was restored, Ken, nudged by his family, would have more complaints. Surely there would be an open bar. Shouldn't there be dancing? Karen, tired and testy, would explode again.

Another wrangle resulted when Ken discovered that the restrictions on guests meant that he couldn't have friends stand up with him; to remain within the allowable limit, he would have to choose brothers to be groomsmen. Karen retorted indignantly that the same was true for her: her attendants also would be family.

Fortune smiled on the troubled pair when they looked for a place to hold the luncheon reception. Because the Pope was visiting Toronto on the day selected, September 15, 1984, their first choice was available. It was the Guild Inn on Scarborough bluffs, an imposing and historic building surrounded by beautiful gardens with a spectacular view of Lake Ontario.

The summer flashed by, a hectic time of showers and fittings. Over the months that Karen and her mother worked on preparations, their relationship underwent a marked transformation. The mother-daughter power struggle quietly ended and they became allies. Both were outraged by the complaints from Ken's family and both were determined to produce a lean masterpiece of a wedding. As the two women bent their heads over lists of errands and catalogues of announcements, they discovered, tentatively and with delight, that they were very similar. In fact, they liked one another very much.

Ken and Karen priced city hall weddings with a justice of the peace, but the cost was not much less than a church wedding. Though neither was attached to any religious denomination, the thought of a solemn ecclesiastical service appealed to both. They sought the United church where Ken's mother had married, and an obliging minister there agreed to perform the ceremony.

With increasing alarm, Ken and Karen hunted for an inexpensive place to live. Confronted with Toronto's notoriously low occupancy rates and high rents, they began to despair. At a point only weeks from the ceremony when they were close to panic, Barbara saved the situation. One day when she and Karen were cruising the Victoria Park and Lawrence Avenue area looking for vacancy signs, Barbara suggested that they buzz the supervisor of an apartment house that didn't have a sign. The supervisor said a two-bedroom apartment had just come available, renting for $424 a month, and could be occupied on October 1.

Ken and Karen were thrilled. The apartment wasn't impressive, but it cost only slightly more than they had decided they could afford and the building was clean. They took it, and Lil Hodge said they could stay with her in Ken's former room until it was ready.

The morning Karen Woods and Ken Parks were married dawned cloudy with rain, but the sun emerged in time for the eleven o'clock ceremony. Denis Woods, who had refused to rent a tuxedo, was gallant in a business suit as he helped Karen into the white stretch limousine of her dreams. She sank into the deep seats, looked down with satisfaction at her bouquet, smiled blissfully at her excited sisters clambering into the folding seats of the limousine's vast interior, and suddenly felt a cold wash of terror. *What am I doing?* she thought. She began to shake. *Oh my God. This is for ever! How can I be doing this?*

Ken was in an even greater state of fright. His mind was on the ordeal of the speech he would have to make at the luncheon reception, the groom's obligatory response to the toast to the bride.

The double-ring ceremony was simple and moving. A touch suggested by the minister made an arresting tableau. Betty Parks and Barbara Woods, standing on either side of the bridal couple, held lighted candles, which each mother gave to her child. After the vows, Karen and Ken exchanged the candles their mothers had given them and joined them to light a single symbolic candle.

Ken spotted his father sitting at the back of the church, a solitary, drooping figure trying not to be noticed. When the wedding party moved outside for pictures, Jim Parks drew his son aside and pressed an envelope containing money into his son's hand. He said, "Don't make the same mistake I made." With that, he mumbled an apology and left.

Karen's memories of the service are full of sweetness. She loved the feeling the church gave her; it was the magical moment in her life that she had hoped it would be. She was vastly amused that Ken, earnest and red-faced, was dripping with sweat. He

126

later confessed that the ceremony was a blur; he couldn't get his mind off the horror of his impending speech.

As his moment approached at the luncheon reception, Ken's terror mounted. Champagne was served for the toasts, and Ken bolted his down. That did nothing for the butterflies in his stomach, so he drank Karen's too, and then a moment later begged someone else's champagne. "What'll I say?" he whispered to Karen. "What'll I *say?*" She made some hasty suggestions as he rose to his feet. The three fast champagnes gave him such a glow that when he finished the speech he thought he might just make another, but Karen held him down

They spent their honeymoon in Florida, having fun at Disney World in Orlando. They returned to stay with Lil and Stan Hodge, an uncomfortable period for Karen, who dreaded encountering Ken's grandfather, but the time passed quickly. The move into their apartment was delayed a week to allow time for cleaning and painting. Barbara Woods came to help, providing invaluable assistance to the inexperienced young couple, and Denis pitched in to lay a paint-stained but otherwise presentable carpet a neighbour had discarded. On October 8, 1984, Ken and Karen proudly moved into their new home.

The furnishings, acquired with the help of wedding gifts of cash (Grandmother Parks gave the couple $1,000), were spartan and cheap. They did without a bed, sleeping on two queen-sized mattresses stacked on the floor. Their television set was an old one that had belonged to Lil Hodge.

Karen's family was invited for Thanksgiving dinner, a brave undertaking since Ken and Karen had discovered, to their mutual astonishment, that Karen couldn't cook. "Thanksgiving dinner went all right," Karen recalls, her eyes dancing. "Once I figured out how to turn on the stove."

Barbara had never allowed her children to help her with meal preparation, an arrangement that had always suited Karen just fine, but she came to regret her lost opportunities. Ken's dismay over the mess Karen made of even simple dishes like scrambled eggs was unnerving. His efforts to help, prefaced with "This is the way my grandmother does it...," drove her wild.

As Karen floundered in the kitchen, Barbara came to the rescue. Mindful of how she had felt when her own mother interfered, Barbara never criticized or belittled Karen. Karen could ask her mother how to roast a chicken without fear of ridicule. As a result, Karen consulted her mother every day, and often several times a day. What kind of cleaner is best for windows? And how do you clean windows? Barbara always went with her on Tuesdays, when Karen did her weekly grocery shopping, and taught her daughter the intricacies of finding value in a supermarket. The first time Karen used a laundromat, Barbara was with her to explain that coloured garments had to be separated from white, and how to use bleach.

Though only twenty years old, Karen and Ken were an earnest, hard-working pair. They were bringing home about $160 a week each, out of which they made regular deposits in a savings account. By natural selection, and without even a discussion, responsibility for money management fell to Karen. Always a methodical person, she showed a shrewd head for figures and a will of iron against the temptations of impulse buying. It was her idea, for instance, to purchase their appliances and furniture on time, even though they had the cash available. She argued that their money could be earning interest in a savings account; meanwhile, by making payments promptly, they would build up a credit rating against the day when they would apply for a house mortgage.

Ken was transferred to Markham, a half-hour drive from their apartment, and he worked Thursday nights in addition to five days a week. Though no salary increase went with it, the move was something of a promotion. Instead of domestic fixtures, Ken was selling industrial wiring. Karen worked two nights a week and all day Saturdays, with Tuesdays off. Their ill-matched shifts meant they had long stretches of time alone. Karen usually spent her days off with her mother; on Saturdays, when Karen was working, Ken resumed playing rugby for Balmy Beach.

Ken's place in the Woods family was already secure, but the marriage increased the cosiness of his position. That Christmas of 1984 there were gifts under the tree for him from everyone.

Barbara's present was his favourite cookies—chocolate chip— and his favourite carrot cake, which she baked for him and wrapped with a big bow. She knew he would be touched, and he was; his pleasure made him inarticulate. Several Woods children protested that she didn't make cookies for them, but Barbara replied serenely that Ken was different. "He's my favourite son-in-law," she told them, adding dryly, "Also, he's my only son-in-law."

His role with the children in the family was often that of fatherly arbitrator in their quarrels. One or two of Karen's half-grown siblings were in a brash period of annoying self-centredness, but they accepted Ken's gentle chiding in good grace.

To Karen's surprise, Ken even got along well with Constance Lancaster, Barbara's tart mother. Ken had an easy way with her, and Constance thought he was wonderful. He was perhaps the family member who was most sorry when Constance went to England for a visit in the spring of 1985 and wrote to say that she had decided to stay there.

Ken remained in close touch with his grandmothers and his uncle, Glen Hodge. He almost never saw his brothers or half-sister, and rarely saw his mother and Tyrone. Once his mother and Tyrone popped in to see the apartment, but otherwise there was no contact. He explains, his manner reflective, "I was more interested in pleasing Karen's parents than mine. I liked the stability of their home, the good family atmosphere."

As 1985 began, the couple had a serious talk about becoming parents. Their savings account was growing, so a baby was something they could afford. Karen was the one who was eager to begin a family and Ken, who likes children—"Especially my own"—had no objection. "Let's have ten," he suggested.

Karen stopped taking the birth-control pill and became pregnant immediately.

The pregnancy did not go well. In March, when she was three months' pregnant, some spotting of blood signalled trouble. Karen's family physician recommended bed rest for two weeks, but Barbara was worried.

She took Karen to a specialist, who was concerned that Karen's abdomen was more distended than could be expected. He told her she might be carrying twins and arranged for an ultrasound examination. A few hours afterwards he telephoned to tell Karen that she didn't have a baby. Instead she had a rare form of reproductive malfunction, a molar pregnancy. There was no foetus in her womb, only a rapidly expanding placenta, which he would have to remove at once.

Karen was shocked and devastated. Her first thought, and one she couldn't shake, was that she was defective. She underwent surgery to scrape her uterus. Ken and Barbara waited in her room for hours, playing cards and drinking too much coffee, and were there when she returned from the recovery room. When Karen saw them sitting exactly where she had left them three hours before, she burst into tears of gratitude for their patience.

Because Karen's hormonal level was dangerously high, it required careful monitoring by means of regular blood tests. The weekly routine intensified her morbid view of herself as abnormal. Her conviction that she was a freak was strengthened when her doctor warned that she should not attempt another pregnancy for a year.

Her story for everyone outside the family was that she had suffered a routine miscarriage. When she was alone with Ken, she often retreated into inconsolable despair. Ken longed to give comfort, but her sorrow was so deep that he decided it was more helpful to try to keep her distracted. For months she was deeply depressed. In order to avoid questions that could bring on tears, she notified her employer at Regal Photo that she was taking some time off her job.

The manager called a few times, pressing her to hurry up and return. Her sisters reported that other employees were sneering that Karen was having a "vacation". Karen has a low tolerance for being pushed. She quit and applied for unemployment insurance. In May she was feeling better and got a job on a part-time basis as a cashier at a new Safeway supermarket in Scarborough. Within a few days her bright efficiency was recognized and she was trained to make price changes in the computer.

Starting pay was $4.88 an hour, but employees who stay are rewarded with raises. Four years later, Karen's wage had risen to $10 an hour.

Ken bought her a thoughtful gift, a black-and-white kitten she named Muffin.

Apart from the periodic bouts of mourning that Karen suffered, their life went smoothly that year. Sometimes she and Ken marvelled at how easy it was to be married. Their bad times at Cedarbrae high school seemed to have washed away all doubts about the permanency of their relationship. They had been almost inseparable for four years, since they were sixteen, so they saw themselves as having travelled comfortably beyond surprise.

In many ways they were alike. Both had a casual attitude towards housekeeping, both enjoyed being careful with money, and both slept deeply. Both were so sleepy in the morning that they set the alarm for half an hour or an hour earlier than necessary. Ken was especially hard to rouse; Karen had to struggle to get him going.

Their tiffs were rare but always on the same theme—his family. Betty and Tyrone frequently called Ken to obtain something for them on his company discount or to come to Oshawa to help with a repair, and he always rushed to oblige. Karen would fume. She thought that Ken's family took advantage of his good nature and pointed out to him that *her* parents never asked for anything.

Ken's style when Karen was angry was to button up and wait for her to cool. He was humiliated when she compared his family to hers, but he never put that into words. On the other hand, Karen didn't convey to him how his readiness to be available to others made her feel unwanted. Instead she attacked his family, and Ken, hurt that something integral about himself was being rejected, defended them with his silent pain.

They rarely saw their old friends. Marriage changed their social habits and they spent their evenings together in front of their VCR watching rented movies. Mostly, however, they worked to build their savings in order to buy a house. In the fall of 1985, Karen took a full-time job at a Shopper's Drug Mart outlet while continuing to work part-time at the supermarket. Ken had changed jobs and was working for a thriving electrical outlet in Scarborough, Revere Electric Incorporated, where he was making about $315 a week. With Karen's two jobs bringing in about $300 a week, they managed to save enough to start house-hunting.

They found a condominium, a seven-year-old, three-bedroom, steeply stacked townhouse in Pickering for $61,500. The financing obliged them to put up 10 per cent of the cost in cash by the end of December 1985. To meet the deadline they resorted to heroic measures. For a while, Karen kept the grocery budget to twenty dollars a week and Ken took a second job working nights as an electrician's assistant.

They made the final payment of $4,000 cash just under the wire. During the suspenseful period when their ability to handle the mortgage was being investigated, Denis Woods lent them a thousand dollars to make their bank account more impressive.

On December 31, 1985, they moved into 1655 Geta Circle, unit 13, their own home. The two twenty-one-year-olds were as proud a pair as could be found anywhere on the planet.

The first mortgage carried for $460 a month, the second for $90 a month, and the condominium fees were $97.50 a month. For a couple holding four jobs, the overhead could be managed with savings to spare.

Barbara and Denis made them a house-warming gift of bunk beds. Ken and Karen owned an impressive array of appliances, a VCR, a microwave oven, a freezer. They could afford a new sofa and love seat, they decided.

In March 1986, her doctor advised Karen that it was safe for her to become pregnant again. "Don't worry," the doctor said. "It might take you a while. Just relax." Their fertility, however, was impressive. Once again, Karen became pregnant immediately. At eight weeks an ultra-sound examination was done.

"Is there a baby there?" Karen asked anxiously.

"Yes," said the technician. "I've even got a heartbeat."

At twelve weeks, Karen felt confident that everything was fine. She began to delight in her pregnancy.

Ken was enjoying success as well. In the spring of 1986 Revere promoted him, assigning him to deal with Begg and Daigle, store and office outfitters, the company's biggest customer. It was his job to ensure that electrical material arrived at the job sites when it was required, in addition to which he had to read blueprints and quote estimates. The stress of it was unnerving and he often put in ten-hour days, but he was exhilarated to be rising so fast in the company.

He joined a rugby team, the Ajax Wanderers, and relished the exhilaration of hard-fought weekly games.

In June 1986, Karen and Ken joined some friends for an unusual outing, Queen's Plate day at Woodbine race track north-west of Toronto. They decided in advance to limit themselves to one two-dollar bet a race. Ken, always good in matters involving mathematics, was intrigued by the Racing Form. Ken's friend showed him how to read it, and Ken compared the past performances, weighing each against track conditions and the quality of the competition.

His selections in the early races mostly lost, but there were some modest wins that allowed the couple almost to break even. When the exciting Queen's Plate race came late in the afternoon, Ken was feeling confident. He pondered long over the chart, selected a horse at acceptable odds, neither a favourite nor a long shot, lined up at a wicket, and bet five dollars to win. The horse won in the stretch, and Ken jubilantly collected forty-five dollars. His friends pounded his back, chortling that Ken was a natural, a born winner.

Ken was amazed that money could be so easy to make. He reasoned that if he studied the Racing Form carefully, he could astonish and impress everyone. He would surprise Karen with the price of a trip to Australia. She often talked wistfully of going back for a visit and it would be wonderful to make it possible.

Ken had never been a gambler. In high school when friends bet on baseball or football games, he was never interested. The risk-taking behaviour of his youth when he stole from stores and tried drugs was behind him. Others in his family loved the races. His grandmother Parks went to the track every day and his brother Rob also followed the horses; it didn't seem to do them any harm. He had been missing a sense of adventure, and gambling filled that void.

The next Saturday afternoon while Karen was working, Ken went to the track and came home a winner. After that he was hooked. He slipped away whenever he could, and the size of his bets increased. Most of the time he lost, but sometimes he won and felt like a king. He loved the atmosphere of the race track— the festive mood of the good-natured crowds, the suspense as the horses lined up for the start, the undercurrent of raw emotion. Even rugby wasn't as exciting as holding a ticket on a horse pounding down the stretch to the finish line.

His losses, however, were a worry. He was dismayed but put it down to temporary bad luck. He would make it up in the next race, or the next week; meanwhile, he couldn't tell Karen. She would be appalled at his foolishness. As soon as he won back the money he'd taken from their savings, he'd quit.

By the end of the summer his losses were substantial. Desperate to replace the money, he went most nights to the harness races at Greenwood race track in Toronto's east end, telling Karen that he was moonlighting as an electrician's assistant. He needed a big win. He started betting the triactor; nothing at the track pays off better than the triactor. It requires that the bettor pick the win, place, and show in the order they finish. The odds against picking even one horse to finish in the money are poor; the odds against picking all three are astronomical. A winning triactor ticket, therefore, can be worth many thousands of dollars.

One good triactor ticket, he reasoned, and the mess he'd made would be behind him.

By the end of the first month the triactor bonanza still eluded him. Karen soon would see the bank statement and spot the withdrawals; he had to replace the money right away. He started to steal from his employer. He thought of it as borrowing; Revere was merely loaning him the money until one of his triactor bets paid off.

The scam was ingenious. He based it on the normal purchasing and supplying practices of his firm. He would enter a phoney order for supplies into the computer, using the name of a regular customer to avoid arousing suspicion, and then make out a purchase order on a bogus wholesaler for the required goods. A cheque made out to the fictitious wholesaler would be presented for signature to his employer, Revere vice-president Neil Wagman, who signed such cheques without hesitation. The "wholesaler" actually was Ken, using an invented company name, Minaz; one of the Ramani brothers had a name something like that. Ken cashed the cheques at his own bank, explaining that Minaz was his company.

Towards the end of the month, before the bills were sent, Ken erased the computer record of the fake sale.

Revere, a small company with twenty-five employees, did a million and a half dollars in business every month. In such a blizzard of activity, discreet stealing can go undetected for a long time.

The first cheque Ken created was for three thousand dollars, most of which he needed to cover withdrawals from the joint savings account. His boss signed it without looking up. Ken had an explanation ready for Karen when she saw the withdrawals and deposit on the bank statement. He explained that he was making purchases of supplies as a favour for the electrician he assisted at night. Since the amounts always were replaced, Karen accepted his story.

In September Barbara came to Karen with the wonderful idea that they should go to England together. The trip wouldn't cost much except for the air fare, she pointed out, because they would stay with relatives. And it would be Karen's last chance to travel for a long time, because she would soon have her baby.

Karen jumped at the chance. There was money enough in their savings and she could think of nothing better than three weeks in England with her mother.

The day Ken dropped an excited Karen off at the airport, he drove straight to the race track.

Barbara, Karen, and Nicky, the youngest Woods child, had a great time in England. They visited Denis's formidable parents and got along merrily with them. Barbara's mother, Constance Lancaster, was failing in health, so the time with her was gentle and healing. Karen shopped for rugby shoes for Ken and bought toys for her baby. Photographs they brought home show Karen and Barbara grinning with delight, arms around one another, and they returned better friends than ever.

As Karen entered her eighth month of the pregnancy in November, she suddenly developed toxemia. Her doctor was worried about her soaring blood pressure and, fearing a stroke, he ordered her into Centenary Hospital in Scarborough on November 28, the day before her twenty-second birthday. The enforced idleness made Karen restless and depressed. On December 13, she persuaded her doctor to allow her to leave on a day pass. Ken drove her home, and Denis and Barbara arrived with a gift, a crib for the baby. Then Karen and Ken went to a movie, *Crocodile Dundee*, and afterwards to a restaurant for a bite to eat.

As Ken was parking the car outside the restaurant, Karen had "a really weird feeling". Amniotic fluid was seeping from her vagina, but she was in no hurry to go back to the hospital. Her contractions started, five minutes apart. Unperturbed, she announced she'd like a sandwich or a milk shake, but Ken wouldn't allow either. He ordered a sandwich for himself but was too nervous to finish it. He was becoming thoroughly frightened, but Karen remained relaxed. To allay his concern, Karen consented to stop for an examination at a nearby hospital, Ajax-Pickering. The nurse who saw her told them she was dilated. The baby was on the way.

Karen was unimpressed and insisted that there was time for her to travel to Centenary Hospital for the delivery. Ken drove in a panic, swearing at every delay while Karen laughed helplessly at his agitation. Around five she was wheeled into a labour room and the work of labour began, but there were intermittent stops. Ken stayed with her until one in the morning, when a doctor advised him to get some sleep. "Nothing's going to happen for a while," he was told.

His grandmother Hodge lived around the corner from the hospital so he went there. About an hour later, he was roused by a call. The baby was about to be born.

Ken hadn't been able to reach Barbara and Denis, who were out that evening. When they returned later on and heard the news that the baby was coming, Barbara was too excited to go to bed. To calm herself she started to clean the house, and she was still scrubbing at three in the morning when Ken called to say that the baby's birth was imminent. She reached the hospital with only minutes to spare. The infant was a girl, six pounds and half an ounce, and mother and baby were fine.

Ken was appalled at the sight of his daughter covered in bloody muck. In the films of childbirth he had seen, new-borns always were pink and clean. Though his heart sank, he said to Karen, "The baby's fine. She's just fine."

While Karen dozed, Barbara and Ken went for a coffee to celebrate. They came back by way of the nursery and pressed their faces against the window in rapture at the sight of tiny Melissa Anne Parks curled up in a pink blanket.

The name had been chosen well in advance. If the baby had been a boy, they had decided on Geoffrey (Karen's choice of spelling) or Jeffrey (Ken's choice).

In their practical way, Ken and Karen already had discussed their finances and worked out a way of keeping up their mortgage payments. As soon as Karen was able, she would go back to her part-time job at the supermarket. Barbara volunteered, and insisted, on caring for the baby when Karen returned to work. With commissions, Ken was earning as much as $500 a week at Revere, a real achievement for a twenty-two-year-old high-school drop-out, but he was working long hours. Often, the responsibility he was asked to assume for making estimates frightened him.

His employer saw Ken as an easy, friendly person, a favourite with customers, who showed good judgement and accepted over-time assignments cheerfully. He was marked as an industrious young man on the rise.

Ken's losses at the race track continued. He was betting hundreds of dollars on a single race, caught in the gambler's downward vortex. He couldn't stop gambling until he won enough to repay Revere Electric what he had stolen, and he couldn't continue to bet without stealing more from his employer. He estimated that he already owed Revere close to twenty thousand dollars. He had figured a way to pay it back as soon as his horses came in. He would issue cheques for the stolen amount and call them refunds.

When the Revere money was exhausted, he took betting money from their savings account, to be replaced with his next falsified cheque at Revere. Karen noticed the money coming and going from the account, but Ken's plausible explanation that he was buying supplies continued to satisfy her.

Ken's behaviour was changing. His light-hearted approach to life was disappearing. He seemed a deeply worried, exhausted man. Karen assumed that his new responsibilities at work and with the baby were weighing on him. Sometimes when she spoke to him, he was so distracted by whatever was on his mind that he didn't hear her. Ken seemed addicted to television, snapping it on every evening. At bedtime he was hyper, too tense to sleep, so he sat looking at television long after Karen had fallen into bed. When she woke to attend to Melissa, she would find Ken asleep in the living-room in front of the television set. She had to shake him awake to get him to go to bed.

Melissa slept poorly. At the age of one month, she developed colic and cried through the night. Ken's original enchantment with his daughter evaporated. By the time she was a few weeks old, he took little interest in the infant, refusing to change her diaper or bath her, protesting when asked to hold her, refusing to get up in the night when she cried.

Karen put all that down to the rough time he was having with the responsibilities thrust upon him at Revere Electric.

"He wasn't what I expected from him as a father," she says. "I thought it was because he was working too hard."

His excuse was that the baby was her job, her only job. "When you go back to work," he told her, "I'll help more."

She protested, "But this *is* work."

To Karen's exasperation, Ken was indifferent as well to household tasks she thought were his responsibility. She asked him to fix a light that was out of her reach, but he never seemed to get around to it. Glued to the television, he didn't even seem to hear her when she complained. She saw herself turning into a nag.

Because Karen resented his absences, Ken was finding it more difficult to get away in the evening to bet at Greenwood race track. He was becoming frantic. He was convinced that the race he missed was the one he would have won, solving all his problems. Time was running out. In the spring there would be an inventory and an audit at Revere, either of which could reveal his fraud. The need for a big win was urgent; he could see disgrace and prison ahead. He thought about winning, dreamed about it, saw himself cashing a ticket for $100,000 on the triactor. One big win would be more than enough to put his troubles behind him. If he could get out of the mess he was in, he promised himself he'd never steal again.

He started to "box" the triactor, meaning that he was purchasing triactor tickets on six horses that would pay off if any three of his selections finished in the money. The track takes a bigger risk with such tickets, and therefore the bets are expensive. A one-dollar box costs $120, a two-dollar box $240, a three-dollar box $360, and so on. He liked the three-dollar box. Winning the triactor was his only hope of saving his job, his marriage, his reputation, his future.

He won rarely. When he did cash a ticket, it was for small amounts such as $150, less than the cost of his bet.

He was consumed with guilt and terror, but there was no one to confide in. Barbara and Denis thought he was wonderful; they were the last people on earth he wanted to know of his shame. His grandmothers doted on him; he couldn't tell them. And Karen would be furious. Maybe she would leave him.

Karen, fully occupied with the baby, seemed completely unaware of the distress that was devouring him. She talked of getting a better house and they went looking. They had always regarded their Pickering townhouse as a "starter" house, the first step in moving up in a real estate market that saw housing increase steeply in value every year. By paying down the mortgage with their hard-earning savings, they had succeeded in reducing it to $45,000, giving them enough equity to move into something grander.

They found a detached house in Ajax that they loved, asking price $138,000. It wasn't out of their reach: they expected to be able to sell their Pickering townhouse for about $105,000, a stunning profit for a property purchased only two years earlier for $61,500.

The new house required a deposit of $3,500, the sale to be conditional on approval of their financing. Ken sweated. The money to cover the cheque was gone from their account, drained by him to bet the horses. The fastest way to replace it, he decided, was a finance company. He obtained a loan of $3,500 to cover the deposit cheque, putting up their appliances as collateral.

Ken fell in with other regulars at the track, and they groused together about sure winners that inexplicably trailed the field. If the others were desperate and over their heads, as he was, no one spoke of that. In the gamblers' code, no one ever mentions losses; it's always the next race that consumes their attention.

In February 1987, Karen and Ken went to the Bahamas. They had reached the point where they both thought they would crack if they didn't get some respite. Ken was owed some time off, and they found a package deal at a resort near Freeport at an affordable $800 each, with air fare, hotel, and meals included. To make the trip possible, Barbara offered to care for three-month-old Melissa while they were gone. Karen was spending so much time at her mother's that it was already home to the infant. Barbara had equipped the house for her grandchild's comfort, purchasing a small play-pen that could be used as a crib, together with such amenities as sheets, blankets, and a baby bath.

The young couple had some good times in Freeport, where Ken celebrated his twenty-third birthday, but the rift that had opened between them was still there. Once when Karen wanted Ken to take her into Freeport to shop, he went fishing by himself instead. The truth was that he wanted to avoid Freeport and its gambling casinos. On the first night of their vacation they had gone to Freeport to enjoy the casinos. Ken had a thousand dollars with him, money stolen from Revere, and he slipped away from Karen in the crowd. While she played the slot machines, limiting herself to quit when she lost $20, he hit the roulette wheel and the blackjack tables. In less than an hour most of the $1,000 was gone.

They returned home more relaxed and rested, but the strain between them was still there. Karen was preoccupied with Melissa and irate that Ken continued to ignore the baby, and Ken was too choked with panic to care.

"We didn't think about divorce, or anything like that," Karen says sadly, "but we weren't communicating very much. It was partly my fault. I was concentrating on Melissa and I didn't have much time for him."

Karen returned to work on a part-time basis with Food City, dropping Melissa off at her mother's. The entire Woods household was pleased with the arrangement, and Barbara was ecstatic. Melissa settled down comfortably with her grandmother three days a week. Karen tried to press money on her mother, but Barbara indignantly refused it.

Ken was out most evenings, telling Karen that he was helping an electrician. Usually she was asleep when he returned. Depressed by his fresh losses at the track, he didn't feel sleepy. He would turn on the television set, get a soft drink from the refrigerator, and settle on the couch to escape into late-night movies. On television people were always having fascinating adventures, and most of the time the endings were happy.

CHAPTER EIGHT

The Gambler

In retrospect it seems that Ken Parks wanted to be caught. In February 1987, just before he and Karen went to the Bahamas, he falsified the most audacious of his frauds, a $9,984 invoice made out to his invented supplier, Minaz. He had an idea that all purchases of more than $10,000 required a stringent authorization, so he had reached the ceiling. As usual, he justified the fake purchase by entering a matching order from one of Revere's regular customers. This time he chose Concept Electrical Contractors and entered that billing into the computer.

Ken planned to delete the Concept Electrical order from the computer before going on vacation because he knew that bills would be sent out while he was away. Inexplicably, he forgot.

Ken and Karen returned on February 28, 1987, and a few days later a woman who worked in accounts receivable said to Ken, "Something funny, Ken. Do you know anything about this? Concept Electrical is complaining that they got a bill for something they didn't order."

Ken felt an icy chill. "I'll deal with it," he told her in an offhand way.

She nodded. These mix-ups happen, her attitude said.

He called Concept. "There's been a mistake," he said apologetically. "I'll straighten it out. Don't worry about it."

That day went by, and the next. Ken's lassitude was profound. He couldn't seem to concentrate long enough to erase the damning evidence from the computer, though he used the computer

142

every day. It would have taken him only a few minutes to make the alterations, print out, and destroy the copy. Often he was alone in the office, working overtime at night or coming in early, but he somehow didn't do it. Two weeks passed, and he couldn't summon the will to hide his theft.

He had been keeping count of how much money he had taken. He needed to have the accurate amount because he intended to replace every penny as soon as his horses won. By his estimates, in mid-March he owed Revere $32,000. The only possible way for him to get that much money was to win a big triactor. He thought it could happen any day now; certainly, he was due.

When the rest of the $9,984 was lost at the track, he hesitated to take more money from Revere. To postpone that shameful moment, he dipped into their joint savings again. Meanwhile he knew he should wipe the Concept Electrical bill from the computer. Part of him was screaming at him to do it but something else prevailed. He really didn't care what happened to him. He couldn't go on like this much longer.

As it happened, it wasn't the Concept account that tripped him up. On a sunny cold Friday morning, March 24, 1987, Ken's crime was discovered when the $9,984 cheque for Minaz came back from the bank. Someone turned it over and thought it odd that it was endorsed by Ken Parks.

A major flaw in Ken's plan always had been that the bank returned Revere cheques to the office. The annual audit certainly would have caught him, but his signature had escaped earlier notice. It was the bookkeeper's habit to put the monthly bundle of cancelled cheques in a file without examining them closely.

Perhaps it was the substantial amount that drew attention; it was more than double any previous cheque that Ken had falsified. In any case, the bookkeeper spotted it and showed the cheque to the company accountant, Irving Pinsky, who immediately suspected fraud. Irving Pinsky took the cancelled cheque to Ken's boss, Neil Wagman, vice-president of Revere.

Ken wasn't at work that fateful day. When he awoke he had a strong premonition that everything was about to come unravelled, so he called in sick and went back to bed. Karen thought nothing of it. Ken worked irregular hours and not infrequently went to work late, making up the time in the evenings. At Revere, Ken Parks, a favourite employee, could almost do as he pleased.

That morning someone knocked at the door of the townhouse. Karen started down the stairs to answer it, but Ken stopped her. "Don't go," he whispered.

He peeked out the upstairs window, keeping himself concealed behind the drape, and recognized the car of his friend Sean Trainer, a salesman who worked at Revere. From another angle he noted that Neil Wagman was with Sean. The knocking continued. Karen made a face at Ken signifying, "What's going on?" but got an impatient *sssh* in reply.

When the knocking stopped and Sean's car left, Ken said lamely, "That was a salesman. I just didn't want us to be bothered."

Karen didn't believe it.

At noon Sean returned alone. Ken stepped out the front door and closed it behind him so that Karen wouldn't hear while they talked. Sean told him that a cheque had been found with Ken's signature on the back. Sean's suggestion on the doorstep was that Ken raise the ten thousand dollars and return it to Revere with the explanation that it had been a joke.

"They'll never believe it was a joke," Ken protested.

Sean shrugged. "Well, what are you going to do?"

Ken didn't know. "Tell Neil Wagman that I'll meet him here at seven tonight," he said. "We'll talk it over then."

When he stepped back into the house, he faced Karen, who insisted on an explanation.

"I made a mistake at work," he said.

"How bad a mistake?"

"Really bad."

"Is it money?" He nodded.

"How much?"

He couldn't look at her. "Thirty thousand."

She was stunned. *"Thirty thousand!"*

Karen wondered about the repercussions of a blooper of that extent. She asked, her voice rising as it does when she's anxious, "Are you going to get fired?"

Not looking at her, Ken paced the room with the urgency of a man who would rather be running. "Yeah, I guess so."

Her loyalty flashed. "They put too much pressure on you," she said heatedly. "You've been working too hard. It's partly their fault. Sooner or later when you're tired and overworked you're bound to make an error."

Ken realized that she had drawn a wrong conclusion. She thought he had been talking about an accounting slip or a mistake in an estimate. For a wild moment he considered fabricating a story to fit her image of him as an exhausted employee pushed too hard, but she was pelting him with questions faster than his mind could work. Besides, there was a certain peace to be found in telling Karen the truth at last.

He told her flatly that he had stolen the money.

"You stole thirty thousand dollars?" she gasped.

He nodded.

"I haven't seen any of it. Where's the money?"

"Gone. I've been gambling."

She couldn't take it all in. "Gambling! You don't gamble! What kind of gambling?"

"Horses. I've been going to Greenwood race track."

"Those nights when I thought you were working?"

"Yeah."

She stared at him, the pieces coming together: his absences every night, his lack of interest in the baby, his depression and abstraction. Her first reaction was almost relief. After months of fearing that he didn't love her and didn't care for the baby, she had an explanation that gave her back her dignity. She studied the abject misery on his face and felt sympathy. She said slowly, "I'll support you through this. We'll have to sell the house to pay the money back, but there's enough equity in it. We'll give back the money and we'll start over. We can get through."

She found she had almost no anger in her. She had never seen him so humble and ashamed, so there seemed no point in blowing up at him. She was still amazed and uncomprehending that the honest, mild man she thought she knew could have carried off such duplicity, but adversity brings out Karen's stubborn streak.

She was already considering what they must do to survive the crisis.

The most urgent matter was that they were on the brink, that very day, of entering into final negotiations to buy the new house in Ajax. By an ironic twist of fate, approval of their financing had come early that morning. Karen and Ken promptly had signed a waiver and it was waiting at that moment in their mail-box for the real-estate agent to collect.

Karen plucked the waiver out of the mail-box. Obviously, she said, they weren't in a position to be buying a new house. In perfect control, she called the real-estate agent to say that the arrangement was off. "We can't fit under the terms of the financial arrangement any more," she said crisply. "My husband has lost his job."

"That's too bad," the agent said. "What happened?"

Karen is acutely uncomfortable with deception. "Something about cutting back staff," she said lamely.

When she hung up, they could think of nothing to say. Ken contemplated with a sinking heart the coming scene with his employer and decided he couldn't bear to have Karen witness his disgrace. He sat cracking his knuckles, head down, and said, "Neil is coming here this evening to talk about it. You'd better take Melissa to your mother's while we sort it out."

It was decided that she would stay overnight with her parents. Karen packed a small bag for herself and the baby and Ken drove her to the Woodses' Scarborough townhouse. On the way she asked, "What will I tell my mum? She's going to wonder why I'm suddenly on her doorstep with my overnight bag."

He said, the full wretchedness of his predicament hitting him afresh, "Make up something. Please don't tell her what I did until I get this straightened out."

She agreed, but when she saw her mother she threw herself sobbing into Barbara's arms and told her everything. Her mother was incredulous. "That's impossible. That's not like Ken. Are you sure?"

On his way back to Pickering, driving very fast along Highway 401, Ken suddenly was seized with the idea of simply running away. He didn't have to face this mess. He could hide somewhere for a while until he felt more in command of himself. He started to feel better.

He remembered that he had no money with him, so he drove to his mother's house in Oshawa. His brother Darrin was there. "I'm in trouble with the police," Ken explained. "Can you lend me some money?"

Darrin was shocked. This was Kenneth, the good Parks boy who didn't drink and didn't get arrested and didn't make girlfriends pregnant: the family's big success. Darrin had about forty dollars in his wallet and handed it over without hesitation. Ken suffered Darrin's grin and stuffed the money in his pocket. He got back in the car and drove east on the rolling Highway 401, which parallels the Lake Ontario shore, his thoughts churning in a black void. He considered suicide. If he drove into an abutment and made it look like an accident, Karen could pay back Revere and have money left over.

The notion passed. He didn't seem to have the energy for it. He'd go to the States, he thought, take a new name.

He was too tired to drive any farther. He pulled off the highway near Kingston and checked into a cheap motel. For an hour or two he lay on his back studying the ceiling. Sometimes his mind was completely blank.

At seven that evening Neil Wagman and Sean Trainer knocked on the door of the darkened Pickering townhouse and got no answer. Concluding that Ken had fled, they returned to Revere and looked up Ken's employment record. It contained an emergency number: his parents-in-law, Barbara and Denis Woods in Scarborough. Sean made the call, asking for Ken. Karen came breathlessly on the line.

"If Ken doesn't turn up right away, Revere is going to the police," Sean told her.

Karen begged him to ask Revere not to do that. "We're going to pay the money back," she said. "There's no need to call the police."

She was fearful for Ken. Where was he? Karen called Betty Parks' number in Oshawa and got Darrin. "Have you seen Ken?" she asked.

"He's taken off," Darrin told her. "Up north somewhere I think."

Sean called Karen a short time later. "He still isn't here. Neil Wagman is furious. What's going on anyway?"

"I don't know," she told him honestly. "But please don't go to the police. We're going to sell our house and make it good."

Sean said he'd do what he could.

Karen's alarm was turning into panic. She had a terrible fear that Ken was dead against an abutment somewhere.

Barbara decided matters were getting out of hand. It was time to tell Denis what Ken had done and get his advice. Denis was astounded by the story of Ken's theft and gambling, but he was also outraged, a reaction far stronger than that of forgiving Karen or bewildered Barbara. He had a practical concern: did Ken have credit cards with him? Karen considered. Yes, he did, her Visa on the Canadian Imperial Bank of Commerce and his own on the Bank of Nova Scotia.

"He could be running up quite a tab on plane tickets or something like that," Denis warned her. "It's hard to tell what frame of mind he's in right now."

Denis called emergency numbers for Visa and was relieved to find that vendors likely wouldn't accept Ken's signature on Karen's Visa and she wouldn't be responsible for debts he incurred on his own.

In the motel in Kingston, Ken was gaining fatalistic resolve. *Can't run away*, he thought. He could see no workable alternative but to go back and face whatever consequences awaited him. Karen seemed to have forgiven him the stealing, but she would never go into hiding with him. He got wearily to his feet and drove back down the highway to Scarborough, stopping only to use his credit card to get some food. He parked in the lot of 41 Division of the Metropolitan Toronto Police, the police station closest to Revere Electric.

"There's a warrant for fraud out for me," he politely informed the person behind the desk. "I believe my employer at Revere Electric has sworn out a warrant."

The officer looked through the files, then checked them again.

"Wait a minute," he said brusquely, and went to consult his colleagues.

Half an hour later the officer returned. "There's no warrant," he told Ken.

It was night, around ten o'clock. Ken called Karen.

"I'm at the police station," he said. "There isn't a warrant so I think I'll just go home."

His voice sounded listless and strange. Karen had been about to tear into him for taking so long to contact her, but she held back. "You'd better come and get me," she told him, her anxiety showing. "I should be with you."

"No, no," he said. "You stay where you are."

She remembered the calls. "Revere has been looking for you," she told him. "Neil's upset because you didn't show."

He felt tired. "Yeah, I figured that. It's too late now to do anything about it," he said. "In the morning I'd better talk to a lawyer."

Karen called him minutes after he got through the door, needing assurance that he hadn't killed himself on the way.

"I'm fine," he said, his voice full of sadness. "I'll talk to you in the morning."

"Come and get me before you see the lawyer," she told him, and he promised. They said a strained good night.

Though he was exhausted, his mind was churning so that he couldn't sleep. He sat watching television in the living-room until, close to dawn, he fell asleep in his clothes. He woke feeling grubby and gritty-eyed, his thoughts sluggish. The yellow pages of the telephone directory listed lawyers with Saturday office hours, and he picked one, Gary McNeely in Oshawa. He made an appointment for later that morning.

He collected Karen and Melissa at her mother's, spending as little time in the house as he could decently manage. Denis wasn't around, but Barbara seemed her usual self. Ken believed she didn't yet know of his shame, but still he couldn't look her in the eye.

Karen called Food City to say she couldn't work that day and, at his insistence, Ken went alone to see the lawyer. He was disconcerted by the lawyer's appearance and manner. Gary

McNeely turned out to be a casual man, wearing cowboy boots and blue jeans. Ken wondered if all lawyers dressed that way for work. The lawyer listened to his story and flatly informed Ken that he'd be arrested soon, he'd be convicted, and he'd go to jail.

Ken signed something, a sort of contract; he was too devastated by his prospects to pay attention to the lawyer's explanation of the agreement. McNeely then telephoned Neil Wagman to ask what Revere planned to do. Wagman said he didn't intend to press charges so long as the money was returned. McNeely said he would handle the arrangement.

"How are you going to get the money?" McNeely asked Ken when he hung up the phone.

"We're putting our house on the market," he said.

"You own a house?" said the lawyer, looking with new respect at the big twenty-three-year-old in front of him.

Ken returned to the townhouse with the good news that he wasn't going to be arrested. He and Karen discussed what would happen next. She was in a quiet, determined state of mind, and his mood was contrite and resigned. The Pickering townhouse should go on the market right away, they agreed, and Ken would have to start immediately to find another job. From time to time, Ken was so overcome by remorse that he wept, his face in his hands, and said, "I need help."

Ken's brother Rob Parks turned up. His own recent problems with the law consisted mostly of bar fights, so he was curious to learn what kind of trouble his big brother was in. Ken was evasive. Just a minor matter, he said; it had been straightened out.

Ken was beginning to feel almost light-headed with relief that the worst was over. The months of lies and deceptions to Karen were over, and he was a lucky man: Karen was taking his disgrace in stride. Indeed, she had settled into a managerial mood and was organizing them both. To tide them over until he found work, she would ask for more hours at Food City. As soon as McNeely, the lawyer, worked out the payment schedule with Revere, they would sell the house. By that time, Ken should have another job. With his experience at Revere, it shouldn't be too difficult for him to find something in the same range of salary, around $23,000 a year.

Ken couldn't let a prospective employer call Revere for a reference. He had to concoct a plausible story to prevent people from finding out he had stolen money. He decided that when he applied for a job he would say he was still working at Revere. He would ask the personnel manager not to call his employer because he didn't want it known that he was job-hunting.

Karen nodded. "I guess that's what you've got to do," she agreed reluctantly. They could get through this, she concluded sternly, but some changes had to be made. For a starter, Ken must promise her that he would never gamble again.

"I know I can't gamble ever again. I know that, but I'll need help," Ken agreed humbly. Karen asked, "Isn't there something like Alcoholics Anonymous for gamblers?" Ken didn't think so, he'd never heard of it. He promised to find out.

Melissa, four months old, sensed the tension in the house and wailed for attention.

Neither can remember much about that weekend. Karen recalls that, after the flood of adrenalin with which she met the crisis of the first two days, she was overcome by a deep fatigue. She went to bed early leaving Ken watching television. That night he slept on the couch. Their sex life hadn't resumed following Melissa's birth, and he thought it best to give Karen privacy to adjust to the calamity he had brought on them.

On Monday morning Ken bought newspapers and looked in the classifieds for jobs. He saw one for electrical estimating and applied. He was told he wasn't qualified enough, which came as a blow. He tried five more places, but was turned down at each.

"Did you check the jobs posted in the unemployment insurance office?" Karen asked.

"Of course," he assured her.

He had no intention of doing that. In order to apply for positions listed there, he would have to fill out a form that asked the reason for his leaving his previous employment. He didn't want to lie—that would be useless, in any case, because references would be checked—and he couldn't write "embezzlement". Who would hire him if he did?

Ken and Karen waited tensely but no call came from the lawyer. It worried them that negotiations with Revere seemed to be taking so long. Meanwhile Karen worked almost full-time at the supermarket, where the manager was delighted to have her. Barbara insisted that it was no trouble to look after Melissa every day, and she continued to refuse Karen's offer to pay her.

Ken, miserable and ashamed, sat in the car while Karen went inside with the baby. He couldn't bring himself to face Barbara; he didn't think he could carry off the pretence of being light-hearted with her, in the way they had always been together.

Denis got reports from Barbara. He wasn't impressed by stories that Ken was looking everywhere for work. He wanted to hear about rehabilitation. Was Ken going to Gamblers Anonymous? Barbara relayed Karen's information that Ken didn't think such an organization existed. The next time she dropped Melissa off, Barbara told her that Denis had found a listing for Gamblers Anonymous in the telephone book.

Karen gave the number to Ken, telling him she had happened to pick up the information at work. Ken said he would call right away.

He never did. He doesn't know why.

Around ten o'clock on Tuesday night, March 31, 1987, just as Ken and Karen were preparing for bed, there was a knock at the door. Karen watched from the living-room while Ken went down the stairs to the entrance and opened it. Two big bearded men in jeans and sweat-shirts stepped in; they looked to Karen like bikers. They said they were police and produced badges to prove it. They had come to arrest Kenneth James Parks for fraud.

Karen burst into tears. One of the officers went up the steps to her and offered gruff comfort. "Don't worry," he said. "He'll be back tonight. This won't take long."

The other officer kept an eye on Ken, who was zipping up his jacket. "Call the lawyer," Ken told Karen, and she nodded, still crying.

Ken paused and studied her. "Please don't tell your mother," he said. Karen nodded again, embarrassed.

Outside, where Karen couldn't see, the police searched Ken and put handcuffs on his wrists.

One of them seemed sympathetic. "It's too bad," he said to Ken. "Gambling is an awful addiction."

Karen was on the telephone, talking to the lawyer's answering machine.

Gary McNeely returned Karen's call a few minutes later. He told her not to worry and telephoned the police station, 41 Division, asking to speak to his client.

"Just answer the questions they ask," he advised Ken.

Ken agreed and listened numbly as a police officer read him his right to remain silent and some other stuff he didn't catch. Then he was asked to make a statement. He freely admitted the fraud and provided details. A police officer was summoned and Ken dictated a confession to him, which the officer then typed. Ken read it through and signed it.

Karen heard again from McNeely, the lawyer. "He'll be home soon," the lawyer informed her. "They aren't going to hold him."

An hour later he called again. "They've changed their minds," McNeely said. "They're keeping him overnight, and you can go down in the morning and post bail."

Karen called her mother. She'd kept her promise to Ken long enough; she needed Barbara's shoulder to cry on.

An officer came to the holding cell where Ken was awaiting release and advised him that he was going to be held overnight. "In the morning you'll go for a bail hearing," he was told.

Around one in the morning Ken was stripped of his shoes, his jacket, his belt, and everything in his pockets. Police put him in a cell so stark he was shocked. A metal shelf served as a bed but there was no mattress, pillow, or blanket. The only thing in the space other than the shelf was a toilet with no seat or cover. He stretched out, but the metal was icy to the touch and the room so cold he shivered.

He heard people screaming, a woman and a man. From what he could gather they were part of a family that had been arrested on a drug charge. The woman was being strip-searched, a procedure that obliges the person to undress completely and submit to examination of the rectum and vagina.

In a cell not far from his, a drunken prisoner spat at a passing police officer. As Ken watched in horror, the prisoner was taken out and beaten severely by two officers and then thrown back into the cell.

Ken slept fitfully. In the morning he was given toast and coffee and his clothes were returned. He was handcuffed again, his wrists behind his back, and loaded into a paddy wagon.

Karen was on the phone to Barbara several times that night and the next morning, pouring out her grief and receiving comfort in return. Barbara offered to take Melissa while Karen arranged bail.

Karen paused in thought. "No," she said slowly. "I guess I can't do it that way. If I don't have Melissa with me, Ken will know I've talked to you. He's feeling terrible and doesn't want you to know."

Barbara sighed and agreed that Karen was right.

In the morning Karen dressed Melissa warmly against the cold and packed a bag of diapers and formula bottles. Gary McNeely had instructed her where to go, the Scarborough court-house at Warden and Eglinton. She tried to enter the courtroom but she was barred because of the baby. Instead she waited on a bench in the corridor, watching the human misery around her: lawyers with briefcases and the air of busy people, and an assortment of young people, dressed in their best and looking frightened.

The court proceedings started at ten; Gary McNeely appeared at eleven just as the judge recessed the court for morning coffee. McNeely told her regretfully that the morning roll-call of bail applications was over. Ken's case could come up again at one o'clock.

"Could I see Ken?" she asked.

"No."

The Crown attorney on duty that day set bail for Kenneth James Parks at $10,000. Ken's lawyer offered no argument. In fact, he hadn't consulted with Ken in the holding cells where he was waiting his turn. His only communication with his client was a curt nod of recognition when Ken was led into the courtroom.

McNeely stepped into the corridor and informed Karen she would have to post $10,000 bail. When she burst into tears, he lost patience. "Stop being so stupid," he told her roughly.

Karen has a low tolerance for bullies. She yelled at him, tears still running down her cheeks, and said she wouldn't take that kind of abuse. McNeely sat beside her and went through the steps she would have to take to get Ken released.

"It's late," he warned her. "You probably won't be able to get him out today."

Karen called the lawyer who had handled their real-estate transactions and asked if he had a copy of the deed for the house. He didn't, but he gave her directions to the registry office in Whitby. Karen drove as fast as she dared and after a long wait in the registry office got a copy of the deed. As she left Whitby she noticed that the needle on the gas gauge in her car was resting on E, for empty, but she didn't want to take the time to stop to refuel. The court office would close at five and she couldn't bear the thought of Ken's spending another night in jail.

She arrived back at the court-house just after five to find it almost deserted. She asked to see the Crown attorney, as McNeely had instructed her, in order to get his approval on her surety. She was informed that it was too late, the office was closed and she should come back in the morning. She said, her voice rising, that she wasn't going to do that. "You don't know what I've been through today," she cried. "Please, please, please."

She was irresistible: a small woman, very young, clutching a baby, and weeping. To her relief, the Crown attorney saw her, checked the papers, and signed them.

Ken was in the Metro East Detention Centre. Karen found it around six that evening and discovered that visitors don't just walk into prisons. Printed instructions on the solid metal door told her to press a button. An electronic voice crackled out of a speaker in the wall, asking whom she wanted to see.

"My husband," she told the wall.

"What's his name?" asked the wall.

"Ken Parks."

"Just a minute."

After a while a buzzer sounded and the wall told her to enter. Inside was what seemed a mirror but proved to be one-way glass. Someone behind it told her she would have to wait. The justice of the peace who issued bail bonds would not arrive before nine o'clock. Baby and mother were exhausted, but there was no choice but to sit with the baby in the prison waiting-room for three hours. She had been rationing her supply of diapers, but they were almost gone. To soothe the fretful baby, Karen walked the length of the waiting-room and back until she was almost dizzy.

Ken waited on range 5B; he had not yet been assigned to a cell. On his arrival he had been photographed—"the mug shot", he thought, something learned from television. His fingerprints were taken, the technician rolling his fingers expertly on a card. Then Ken was given a number and prison clothes.

His state of mind was peculiar. He saw himself being pleasant to everyone, an affable, polite person who was getting along swimmingly with police and guards and other prisoners, most of whom were burglars and drug offenders. He could admire the good-natured person he was being, since it seemed to be someone else. The real Ken Parks had gone to a place so deep within him that he couldn't be found.

A guard summoned him. "Your wife is here," he said. "She's bailing you out."

Karen drove them home, surprised that Ken seemed so normal and relaxed. He was non-committal about what had happened to him in the cells, content to listen to her account of her adventures. People weren't very considerate, she complained. He said gravely that he had noticed the same thing.

"One thing sure," she said, getting angry. "We're not going to rush to pay Revere back. They promised not to charge you, and then they go ahead and do it."

That was the night Melissa's bottle exploded in the microwave oven. Karen was so distracted that she hit the wrong settings. The resultant mess took a long time to clean up.

On Thursday Ken was too disheartened to leave the house. He searched the papers and made phone calls, setting up appointments for job interviews. Karen stayed with him, telling her employer at Food City that she had some personal problems she was sorting out. The man was understanding; Karen was such a dependable person that he accepted that something serious must have happened.

Ken's court date was set for the second week of April. Revere had not given Ken his last pay-cheque so their financial needs were acute. They hesitated to touch their savings, so Karen worked every day at Food City. Day after discouraging day, Ken could find nothing.

The mood between them was tranquil. "I was angry at him," Karen admits, "but he was my husband. People make mistakes. I wondered why he'd done such a thing; but he'd done it, so we just had to make the best of it. That's what it's all about. He'd made a mistake and we had to work together to get through it."

Their relationship, in fact, was markedly better. Ken was relieved of the burden of juggling lies, and Karen was grateful for an explanation for the strange way he had been acting. Now she could understand his bad moods, his absences, the indifference to Melissa.

"It wouldn't have done any good to yell at him," she reflects today. "Why make him feel any worse than he already did? He was obviously upset at what he'd done to himself and what he'd done to me, so there was no point making a big deal about it."

A week went by, two weeks, without a job. Karen asked if he was checking every day at the employment office to see what jobs were posted there. He always assured her that he did, without fail. Had he called Gamblers Anonymous? He'd do that right away.

He went to court on the day set for his hearing, but his lawyer, Gary McNeely, wasn't there. The judge adjourned the matter for two weeks. On the next appointed day, his lawyer was absent once more, so the case again was adjourned. McNeely sent Ken a letter stating which days he would be available. Ken went to court with the list and another date, December 14, was fixed. Easy to remember, Ken reflected; it was Melissa's first birthday.

Ken and Karen thought that Gary McNeely's behaviour was peculiar, but they assumed all lawyers were the same. A bill arrived: $1,200.

Ken's confidence, never robust, vanished entirely as his efforts to find a job proved fruitless. He was humiliated that they were living on Karen's income, less than half the money they were accustomed to receive. He dreamed of a magical solution, a pot of money that would end their problems. He had been avoiding the race results in the newspapers, but he began to take a quick peek every now and then. He recognized horses that he had bet in the past. They were winners now, confirming his judgement. People were cashing tickets for huge amounts of money.

It couldn't hurt, he thought, to try a bet or two. Often he had been so close on the triactor. One more try, he thought; all it would take was one big win. His luck was due to change.

He wrote a cheque for $1,000 on Karen's savings account, forging her signature, went to the track, and lost it.

"When I was gambling," he explains with a distance in his manner as if he was discussing an eccentric stranger, "it didn't seem that I had any problems. Gambling's a great escape."

He told Karen he was looking for work, but instead he went almost every day to the track, using money he was draining from her account. He still liked the triactor: such a big pay-off. He bought one-dollar tickets because they cost the least, $120 a race. Still he lost, and lost.

Occasionally, not expecting much, he called people about jobs advertised in the classified ads. One day in mid-April he was hired. He went home jubilantly to tell Karen that he would be starting work right away at Guild Electric and that a company vehicle went with the job.

However the manager at Guild Electric called Revere to check Ken's story that he was working there. When Ken reported to work the next day, he was told that the offer was withdrawn. Ken was devastated. The worst part of the disappointment was facing Karen, who had been excited and proud that he was on his feet again. He made a desperate, crazy decision not to tell her that the job had fallen through. He'd get another job soon to replace it, but meanwhile he didn't have to give her bad news just when she was feeling happy for the first time since the nightmare had begun.

The hitch in the deception was that he had mentioned a company vehicle. He stopped at a car-rental place. Using his credit card, he rented a car.

"I thought you said it was a company car," Karen said when she saw it.

"The company car is in the shop for repairs," Ken explained. "They gave me this one until it's fixed."

His fiction that he had a job obliged him to be out of the house all day. He looked for work, still without success. To forget his troubles, he liked to go to the track. He continued to forge Karen's name to draw on her savings account. It was a loan, he told himself. One win, one *big* win, and everything would be fine again.

Ken's absences from the Woods family's townhouse did not go unnoticed by Karen's brothers and sisters, who were puzzled that suddenly they didn't see him. Barbara issued invitations but Karen declined them on Ken's behalf. "Wait until we get this mess behind us," she explained. "He's feeling too ashamed to be comfortable with you."

Karen was clinging to Barbara, the family's bulwark in a time of trouble. Barbara had a clear-headed solution to everything. In Karen's case, however, she paid her daughter the compliment of offering no advice, while making it plain that her affection for Ken hadn't changed. Her line was, "You'll get through this, I know. Whatever you decide to do, your father and I are with you."

Once when Karen was berating him for something, Ken looked at her bleakly. "I've got life insurance," he said quietly. "You'd be better off without me. Maybe I'll just drive off the road and kill myself."

She stiffened in shock. It was a moment before she could speak. Then she burst out, "You can't. We don't have insurance any more. We're behind with the premiums."

Ken had to invent a story for his family to explain why he wasn't at Revere. An argument with his boss, he said. They wondered why it was taking him so long to find another job. He told them he was being particular—he wanted something with good prospects in the electrical field. He asked Karen to back up his stories when she talked with his mother and grandmothers. She did, but it galled her. She hated lying for him, she told him.

Ken pleaded with her not to embarrass him. He'd make a clean breast of it when he had a new job and the trial was over.

When Karen's brothers and sisters asked why they didn't see Ken, Barbara made excuses that Ken and Karen were busy with the new baby. As Easter approached the story was wearing thin. Barbara's invitation to a family gathering on Easter Sunday couldn't be refused.

Ken was profoundly uneasy on the drive to Scarborough that day but Barbara greeted him with great warmth, and he soon relaxed. Denis seemed reserved, but that was Denis's way. Samantha, Emma, Pru, Nicky, and Jonny teased him fondly in the way they always had, and he almost recaptured his old sense of being at peace in the Woods family.

April was turning into May when Karen began to have suspicions. Some odd things were happening. For one, Ken always found some excuse to stall her when she talked of going to the bank to examine her statement. She was working out a new budget for them and wasn't sure where their savings stood, but he kept finding a reason for putting it off. A utilities bill she was certain she had paid came a second time marked "unpaid", with a penalty added. Ken's pay-cheque from Guild Electric was strangely delayed. First he said that the company always held back the first two weeks' pay. When two weeks had passed, he then said the process to put new employees on the payroll was slow. He'd been promised it soon.

He brought home a puppy he found. Karen told him they couldn't keep it. They were away from the house too much, she reminded him, and since they would have to move soon it might not be possible to find a place that would accept a dog.

Ken tried to coax her to change her mind, but she was adamant. He left with the puppy and on his return said he had found a friend to care for it.

In addition to the puzzling matters concerning money, Ken was acting strangely again. When she tried to talk to him about his long silences and his obsession with television, he was remote and out of reach. She could understand that he was preoccupied with his dread of a prison sentence and the humiliation of the embezzlement trial, but there seemed to be darker forces at work. Not infrequently, he cried.

Anxious for him, she pelted him with sharp questions. Had he made an appointment with Gamblers Anonymous? Well, why not? Ken's response was to put his face in his hands and weep. "I need help," he said brokenly.

Karen talked to her mother about it the next day. "I can't stand it that Ken thinks you don't know about this," she complained. "I hate lying to him. I'd like us to come over there and have a talk about it, all of us. It's time the family got together on this. Could we maybe come on Sunday?"

"Sure," Barbara said promptly. "We're having a barbecue. That would be a good time."

The following day, May 20, 1987, Karen was exasperated that Ken still had not called Gamblers Anonymous. She made the call herself and was directed to the office of the Canadian Federation for Compulsive Gamblers, an organization that places people in Gamblers Anonymous self-help groups. That afternoon she and Ken and Melissa sat in the office of the president, Tibor Barsony, a quiet man, who talked reassuringly to them. He explained that the compulsion to gamble is an addiction like alcoholism. "It's a sickness," he emphasized. "I'm a compulsive gambler myself."

He told his story and Ken was astounded at the resemblance to his own: the absolute belief that the next bet will be the big one, the stealing to get betting money, the lies.

Barsony administered a written test. "If you answer more than seven of these twenty questions," he told Ken genially, "then you're a compulsive gambler."

To his discomfiture, Ken answered yes to fourteen.

Barsony gave them a schedule of meetings of Gamblers Anonymous and advised Ken sternly that he should make a clean breast of his activities with his family and Karen's family. He agreed unhappily.

The next day, Thursday, May 21, 1987, Karen was at work when her employer in some embarrassment came to her with a cheque she had written for groceries. It had been returned by her bank, Canada Trust, with the notation "NSF". She protested it was impossible, there was money in that account. At the back of her mind, fear was gathering. Surely Ken wasn't stealing their savings. Dear God, surely not.

Only hours later, someone called from a Scarborough branch of the Royal Bank where Karen had an old account. The teller said there was a cheque signed by her for $1,500, payable to Ken Parks, but there wasn't sufficient money in the account to cover it. Karen walked to the Canada Trust bank that had bounced her food cheque and was given a sheaf of cancelled cheques, several of them drawn to Ken Parks. The account had been wiped out.

She walked home weeping all the way, oblivious of the stares of passers-by, and called her mother in a state close to hysteria. While waiting for her, Karen tried to reach Ken at a number he had given her for Guild Electric. The man who answered said Ken had stepped out of the office. Karen was certain she recognized the voice of a friend of Ken's. He said he would have Ken return the call.

Ken called a few minutes later and Karen asked him about the missing money. "I took it," he said. "We'll talk about it when I get home."

When Barbara arrived the two women paced the living-room, a habit they shared when agitated. Obviously Ken was gambling again. There could be no other explanation.

Barbara consoled her daughter. "This is a bad time, all right," she said. "I can't understand it at all. This really isn't like Ken. It doesn't make any sense that he would go back to gambling."

Karen described the visit to the compulsive gamblers association. "It's a sickness, like being an alcoholic," she said wearily. "He can't help it."

Barbara said, "I'm sure Gamblers Anonymous can help. They say Alcoholics Anonymous does wonders."

"I'll be glad when Ken talks to you on Sunday about it," Karen said resentfully. "I hate being in this position. It will be better when it's all out in the open."

Barbara said warmly, "It's time for a family reunion anyway. The kids have been missing Ken."

Karen nodded sadly. "We haven't been over there together since Easter."

"Two o'clock," Barbara said, giving her daughter a hug. "We'll see you at two."

Barbara was gone before Ken returned. The scene between Ken and Karen was the worst they had ever experienced. Her temper wildly out of control, she called him every name that came into her head, some of them words she had never used before. She accused him of taking her money and he admitted it without hesitation. His expression was wretched, but this time her heart wasn't touched. She told him what was going to happen: the house would be put on the market at once and when it was sold she would leave him and take Melissa with her.

Was he gambling again? Only a bit. Had he lined up a meeting with Gamblers Anonymous yet, as Barsony had suggested? No. There was a meeting on Friday at an address on Dundas Street and he would go to that.

She was screaming. "I can't go on this way," she yelled. "You're hopeless."

She needed to unburden herself of her own secret. "I'd better tell you my parents know everything," she said. "I've been talking to my mother about it all along."

She saw his shock. The one shred of comfort Ken held through the débâcle was that no one knew except Karen. He plunged into fresh despair, thinking of how Barbara and Denis must despise him.

"What am I supposed to tell them?" he said, weeping.

"They aren't mad at you," she said. "They're just concerned for me and Melissa, and they need to hear from you how you're going to sort this out. It will ease their minds for you to tell them that you're going to Gamblers Anonymous and that you've got things under control."

"I've really let them down," he groaned. Karen had nothing to say; it was true.

He could sleep on the couch, she said coldly, and she went to bed.

Ken couldn't sleep. He had never known such pain. He thought maybe he was losing his mind; he wished he was dead. Full of self-loathing, he watched movies on television, sipping Kool-Aid. He tried to concentrate on the sunny world occupied by such mythic beings as the charming Harts, wealthy, handsome, assured, carefree, and so in love. He was still awake at dawn.

The next morning after Ken left, ostensibly for work, Karen looked up Guild Electric in the telephone book and called. She was informed that there was no employee there named Ken Parks, and never had been. She slammed down the receiver.

Her Visa bill arrived. On it was an item for a Budget car rental.

When Ken strolled in around dinner time that Friday, Karen was wild with anger. In rough language she told him of her contempt. She repeated that they would be selling the house at once, but he caught a significant change. The night before she had been definite that she and Melissa would leave him. This time she was saying that they would go *if he didn't straighten up*.

He took hope.

Head down, too ashamed to look at her, he said, "I need help. I know that. I can't control myself. Gambling is such a great feeling."

She was shouting at him and crying at the same time, but she too had noticed the shift. Her message was, "Tell me you'll stop gambling and lying, so I can stay."

She said flatly, "Give me the straight story about Guild."

He didn't spare himself. He told her it was true he didn't have a job. He had rented the car because he didn't want to admit his failure to get a job.

Minutes later they were on their way to return the car. After that she demanded a full accounting of his gambling losses and pushed him without mercy to tell what he had done with the money. He was open with her about everything, including the finance company. He had borrowed to cover the cheque for $3,500, the deposit on the house they intended to buy in Ajax.

"Why did you do that?"

"Because I took the money out of savings to gamble. I had to cover it with money from the finance company or else the cheque would have bounced."

Her head was reeling. "What interest did the finance company get?" she asked.

He cringed from her blazing eyes. "Thirty per cent."

"What collateral did you use?"

"It gets worse," he told her. "The house and the appliances."

"How could you do this to me!" she exploded.

"I couldn't seem to help myself," he told her lamely.

Then she remembered. "Weren't you supposed to go to Gamblers Anonymous today?" she snapped.

"It's not in Toronto," he said. At her look of disbelief, he pulled out the pamphlet. "See, the address is Dundas Street, but it's in London. The next meeting in Toronto is Sunday night at six. It's something for wives too. We can go together if your mother will take care of Melissa."

She cooked him a steak and they ate a desultory dinner. Sometimes she returned to the attack and sometimes she wept uncontrollably. He said little and picked at his food.

"You've got to start right away with Gamblers Anonymous," she told him bitterly.

"Yeah, I will."

"You've said that before."

"This time I mean it, I really do. I know I need help."

Cleaning up the kitchen from the meal, she hit on another point of resentment. "I'm sick of covering up for you," she told him. "Tomorrow you're going to go to my parents and your grandmothers and your mother and tell them everything."

He couldn't object though every fibre of him, a man who hates a scene, was protesting. His mother wouldn't care, he thought, but he cringed at the idea of telling his grandmothers, who doted on him. They would be shocked and disappointed. Would they turn against him? Probably not. The worst would be facing Karen's family.

"I don't want to lose you and Melissa," he said in a broken voice.

"So smarten up," she told him.

Karen went to bed and Ken switched on the television to keep himself from complete disintegration. His mind was in a turmoil. Though this was his second night without sleep, he couldn't escape his frantic thoughts. He watched television and waited for morning.

The next morning he heard Melissa stirring. Remembering that Karen would be working late that Saturday night, he decided she needed the rest. He hurried to the baby's room and picked her up, changed her, and fed her a bottle. When Karen awoke he announced a change in plans. He might as well wait until the barbecue on Sunday to tell Denis and Barbara, he said. Then, after the six o'clock meetings—Gamblers Anonymous for him and Gam-Anon for her—he would make a circuit and see his grandmothers and maybe his mother. It would be easier for him to confess if he could say he already had started to do something about it. Maybe when the people he loved saw that he was trying to deal with the mess they would accept it better.

Karen could see his point, but she was still snappish. To escape her tart tongue he announced that he had a rugby game with his team, the Ajax Wanderers. The season had started a few weeks earlier and he was looking forward to the outing. "I need to let off some steam," he said. "Why don't you come?" She gave him a frosty refusal. He picked up his gear and went out, leaving her in a baleful state. She was outraged that he could go carefree to play rugby and leave her alone with the shambles he had created.

When he returned, she said with sarcastic fury, "So, do you feel better!"

He read her mood and bowed his head. He didn't really feel well at all, he said. He hadn't been sleeping, and besides he was so out of shape that he had played badly. With junk food consumed in front of the television every night and lack of exercise, his weight had ballooned to three hundred pounds or more, at least fifty pounds over his normal playing weight. To avoid meeting Karen's furious glare, he gazed mournfully at his bulging belly. "I'm exhausted," he told her. "I didn't sleep last night."

She was unmoved. In a white anger, she descended on him again for gambling. He sat with his head down and listened. "Your whole family is a mess," she told him. "Your brothers are always in jail, your sister gets into trouble. I thought you were different, but you're just the same."

That hurt. He winced visibly.

"I'll never gamble again," he promised her. "I know I can't. I have to stop."

"If you go back to gambling," she told him, bursting into tears, "it's game over. Melissa and I are gone."

He looked at her levelly and said quietly, "I know that."

Her anger evaporated. Two days of tirade had spent it all. She couldn't change the way she felt about him. She loved him. Ken had messed up, but everything could be explained as an illness that had swept him away.

Peace was restored when Karen left for work around four that afternoon. She was chief cashier that night, responsible for all the cashiers, but found it difficult to concentrate. From time to time she called home to ask about Melissa. Ken admitted he was having trouble getting her to settle down. The baby's usual bedtime was six, but she wasn't as comfortable with her father as with Karen. It was nearly nine before she fell into an exhausted sleep in her crib.

Ken realized he hadn't eaten all day. He warmed up some ravioli, made himself a salmon and cheese sandwich, and opened a bag of potato chips. He mixed a pitcher of Kool-Aid and drank that. He could hardly keep his eyes open. He was certain he'd be able to sleep at last. He prepared himself by taking off his underwear and socks, putting his track pants and jersey back on. He sweats so much in his sleep that Karen insists he wear something to sop it up so as not to stain the sheets. It was about a quarter to eleven, and he was trying in vain to relax enough to sleep when he heard the car in the driveway.

When Karen came in, he stood up and went to the door to hug her as she was kicking off her shoes.

"Hi, there," he said, bending to kiss her. They hadn't been physically close for a long time, and the embrace felt good. Then they went to the kitchen and talked idly for a while as she drank a cup of tea. The mood between them was the best it had been for months. Karen suggested Ken come to bed with her, but he said that he would wait until she could trust him again. Besides, he was feeling very awake, his mind churning again.

"Okay then," she said. "I'm going up to bed. I love you."

He said, "I love you too."

167

As she left he called after her, "I'll get up with Melissa tomorrow. You sleep in."

After she was gone, he found he couldn't sleep. He hated the prospect of telling his grandmothers he had stolen money from his employer and his wife and gambled it away like a fool. The thought of facing Denis and Barbara was even worse. His grandmothers would be distressed but they would forgive. He wasn't so sure about Denis.

He buried himself in the television. *Saturday Night Live* was almost over and it was pretty funny.

His next memory was of Barbara's face, pleading with him....

CHAPTER NINE

What Is It?

Marlys Edwardh began to construct the case for the defence. A medical and psychiatric investigation was indicated, but her instincts suggested strongly that she was dealing with a very peculiar situation. Ken Parks was not a wilful killer. He seemed to her a sane, perfectly normal, lucid person. The psychiatrist at Sunnybrook, Ron Billings, had that same opinion after seeing Ken for only a few minutes.

The lawyer has seen many people with a glint of craziness in their eyes, and many sly and charming ones who are skilled in deception, but Ken Parks fell into neither camp. To her he was a pleasant, intellectually average, thoroughly conventional young man with a strong commitment to family values.

That left her to grapple with the mystery of a completely sane person who suddenly behaved insanely without the ability to remember what he did. She knew of nothing like this situation, and every specialist she consulted was just as baffled. Her client had committed a brutal killing with no apparent motive and couldn't remember doing it.

Marlys is a logical person. A strong adherent of rational thought, she believes that there are always explanations: whatever *is* is knowable. She was certain from the beginning that a perfectly reasonable explanation existed for this strange case; all she had to do was find it.

She never saw Ken Parks as a fabricated person, pleasant on the exterior but with depths inhabited by homicidal demons.

When she learned about his gambling and the fraud charges, she was startled but unshaken.

"The Ken Parks who went to the race track was not the Ken Parks I saw in jail," she comments. "Never saw that. Never saw a part of Ken that related at all to a man flashing money around at the track."

She analyses his disastrous gambling spree as evidence of two elements in Ken's personality. One of these is his naïvety; there is much in Ken's nature that is gullible; he is credulous rather than cynical, and easily impressed. The other aspect of his nature is his strong need to demonstrate to himself, to Karen's family, and most of all to Karen that he is capable of tremendous accomplishment. Like many people living unremarkable lives, he had strong longings to accomplish something that would set him apart from the crowd.

The lawyer isn't convinced that Ken really is a compulsive gambler, a view shared by psychiatrists who testified at his trial. He descended rapidly into fraud and forgery because he's an innocent who came to believe sincerely, as many older and wiser people have, that he was uniquely gifted at picking horses. The temptation for a man anxious to shine was irresistible. When his horse won the Queen's Plate on that festive and fateful day at the track, Ken felt a rush of omnipotence. As his losses mounted, he could see no way to rescue himself from debt except to continue betting until he won enough to pay everything back.

"Ken had taken on many responsibilities at an early age," Marlys comments. "You have to remember that. He was only twenty-two, twenty-three, with a wife, child, and mortgages. And he is a man with an incredible need to please others, especially to please Karen. When he got into trouble, he found it hard to confront the reality. He went on hoping to make it right."

The lawyer's most pressing concern when she accepted the case was that Ken would kill himself. This was a realistic fear. Very often people who have killed go through a period immediately afterwards when they wish to end their own lives. A good many succeed in doing so: murder commonly is followed by suicide. Marlys turned to the help nearest at hand, the psychologist

170

to whom she is married, Dr. Graham Turrall. At her urgent request he went immediately to the Don Jail to determine if Ken was a suicide risk.

Graham Turrall spent two hours with Ken and came away as confident as one can be in the troubled waters of human predictability that the young man was not likely to commit suicide. He added that he agreed with the opinion of the psychiatrist, Ron Billings, that Ken Parks was absolutely sane.

"I found him a co-operative and gentle man," he advised Marlys. "It's hard to understand what happened. I think you'll need to do a complete neurological work-up on the condition of his brain."

Marlys nodded. "That's next," she said.

"When you start a homicide case," she explains wryly, "you always have a whole range of fanciful possibilities you can work with."

The first to investigate was that of damage to the brain, possibly from a fast-growing tumour. If that wasn't the explanation, she could start looking at insanity, which was where the Crown and police were expecting the defence to make its case. On the other hand, perhaps Ken had been fully conscious when he killed but had repressed all memory. Extreme horror can produce a kind of selective amnesia. She also speculated that Ken might have suffered a blow to the head in the rugby game on the morning before the killing.

Ken assured her that he hadn't been injured in the game, but she wanted to be certain. She tracked down several players and interviewed them separately. All confirmed that Ken hadn't suffered a blow to his head or a hard fall that might have caused a concussion.

"Was there any moment when he seemed out of touch, when he might even have lost consciousness briefly?" she asked.

Most positively, they stated that Ken had been fully conscious and alert, but that at the end of playing the full sixty minutes he had seemed wiped out.

She next needed the results of the electroencephalogram (EEG) and brain scans that Ron Billings had ordered in Sunnybrook. If Ken had a neurological disorder, her case was a simple one: not guilty by reason of a brain tumour, or whatever. The medical order for those tests had been signed by Billings in Sunnybrook and went with Ken to the Don Jail. The difficult feat the lawyer set for herself was to have those tests done at Sunnybrook, rather than within the prison system. Unless she moved quickly, the Crown would insist that the neurological and psychiatric testing be done at Oak Ridge at Penetanguishene, the institution where the criminally insane are confined. Marlys viewed that eventuality as a disaster.

"If Ken had been taken to Penetang for the tests," she explains, "we'd have lost the opportunity to do the slow and thorough sifting that was necessary in this case. The tests would have been of a different character. At Penetang someone would see him for half an hour and if he was lucky he'd get a CAT scan, and that would be it. As it was, we got a full neurological work-up in a first-class teaching hospital and lots of detailed analysis." Furthermore, the results of those tests would be available to Marlys, with Ken's consent, and not readily to the Crown.

Marlys proceeded as if it were unassailable logic that a man accused of murder could be sent to a general hospital for such tests. Bureaucracy rarely is logical, however, and her request was most unusual. She was prepared to argue that the state has a right to detain an accused person in custody, but it has no right to interfere with an accused person's access to medical and psychiatric examination. She put this view to Dr. Paul Humphries, head of medical services for all provincial jails. A persuasive detail was on her side. The tests had been *ordered* while Ken was in Sunnybrook Hospital and would have been completed there if Ken had not been delivered prematurely to the Don Jail. Dr. Edmeads, the neurologist, had arranged the appointments. Why couldn't Ken be taken to Sunnybrook under guard to have the work done?

Humphries thought her request was a reasonable one. He granted it.

One of the peculiarities of the year that Ken spent in prison awaiting his trial was that the Crown showed little interest in Ken's mental state. Police homicide officers saw the Parks case as one of the easiest of their lives. Apart from the puzzling detail of the accused's claim to remember nothing, it was a classic open-and-shut case. They had a confession even before they had a body. The Crown seemed to share the feeling of comfort. An argument for not guilty by reason of insanity could be expected, but the Crown made no move of its own to examine Ken's mental state.

A degree of complacency seemed to prevail, perhaps because Crown lawyers at that period were notoriously overworked, underpaid, and deserting the ship. If Crown officials were aware of the doctors, psychologists, and psychiatrists who shuttled in and out of the prison to examine Ken at his lawyer's request, they showed no interest. A search warrant, executed to obtain Ken's earliest tests at Sunnybrook Hospital, was not repeated.

Ron Billings had two visits with Ken in the Don Jail, one on June 4 and the second a week later, for a total of three hours. He found his patient depressed, but only to a degree appropriate for a man in his dire situation. The psychiatrist could detect no evidence of delusional thinking or paranoia. When Ken spoke of his in-laws, for instance, he didn't present them as unfriendly or hostile to him in any way, as a paranoid person might.

The doctor ruled out psychosis; Ken Parks was a sane man. In the second interview, the doctor concentrated on the possibility of an antisocial personality disorder, a state he describes as affecting people who have not developed a conscience. Such people, sometimes called sociopaths, have no remorse about exploiting others for their own good.

Ken didn't fit the pattern. Billings commented at the trial, "He attempted to please other people, to do things for other people, and did not put himself first. Someone with an antisocial personality has evidence of a conduct disorder from childhood. There was no evidence of that, other than the fact that he had skipped school sometimes in the early years, which many of us I think have, and he had one episode where he stole."

He concluded, "There is just nothing to support a diagnosis of antisocial personality."

The doctor had another promising option. A condition known as temporal lobe epilepsy doesn't produce the typical seizures of epilepsy, but it can cause curious, impulsive, out-of-control behaviour. Billings would need the results of the brain work-ups to be sure, but he stalked the diagnosis by asking some pointed questions about Ken's experience with dissociative states such as black-outs, memory loss, and amnesia. Ken reported that there were none.

"Had you been drinking before this happened?" the doctor asked.

Ken grinned. "No, if you mean alcohol. Only Kool-Aid."

Billings saw Ken Parks five times for lengthy periods and came to like the young man. He testified a year later that he was impressed. "I felt that Ken was a very honest person," the psychiatrist told the jury. "He was not attempting to minimize. He was admitting everything he could remember. He was co-operative. I had no sense that he was not telling the truth. Never have I found that anything he has told me has contradicted anything before."

When she received Billings' report Marlys was stumped. If he wasn't crazy and he didn't have a personality disorder, she could only return to the original surmise that Ken somehow had managed to push the memory of the killing out of his head. She asked Billings, "Could this be psychogenic repression?"

Billings shook his head. "No. He doesn't repress the whole event. He remembers perhaps the most frightening part of the event."

"What is that?"

"Seeing his mother-in-law on the floor and the look on her face."

On June 16, 1987, Ken Parks was taken to Sunnybrook for brain tests to be conducted under the eye of Dr. John Edmeads. The neurologist began with a detailed medical history. He asked if Ken had any pains in his head, if he was subject to dizziness or loss of balance, if he had ever had a seizure, if he had any experience of numbness, or weakness, or paralysis? No, to everything.

Edmeads thought, "Well, nothing there to show neurological disease. But it's got to be something."

The physical examination started with Ken's eye movement, visual acuity, and motor responses. With a pin—"sharp end or dull?"—the neurologist checked for sensory awareness. He found nothing wrong with the young man except for the lack of sensation in his fingertips, the result of the cuts to his hands.

Edmeads moved to the CAT scan, a photographic X-ray capable of detecting shrinkage of brain tissue indicating trauma or various kinds of dementia, including Alzheimer's disease. If Ken had a brain tumour or brain abscess or a clot on his brain, the CAT scan would pick it up.

The scan, however, showed a completely healthy, intact brain.

The EEG, which charts brain function, produced the same results. Edmeads looked for a pattern in the electrical activity of Ken's brain that would show epilepsy and, particularly, the temporal lobe epilepsy that Ron Billings had wondered about. There was none. As he was to testify at the trial, he found Ken Parks "neurologically normal".

Marlys Edwardh, studying the results, thought, "Now what?"

Ken's first impression when he was admitted to the Don Jail was one of filth, of enormous numbers of people jammed into insufficient space, and of the callousness that mass confinement inspires. The medical range is dismal, but he was to discover that it is relatively luxurious when compared to the overcrowded cells elsewhere in that harsh building.

A prison doctor examined him cursorily and then he was left to himself in a bed in a cell with a door open to a barred enclosure that serves as a common room. His lunch was brought. A soft diet had been ordered, but no one offered to feed him. He struggled to hold a spoon between his bandaged hands but couldn't get a grip. His dinner came, the food cut in small pieces for his convenience, and he tried again but couldn't hold the spoon. This meal too was taken away untouched.

The next day another prisoner came to his rescue. If someone jammed the spoon handle between Ken's left thumb and the mound of bandage, he found he could hold it. It was awkward and unsteady, but he managed to get some food to his mouth.

Sam Ferracci, a kindly fraud artist in and out of prisons for some forty years, adopted Ken a few days later.

"Look kid," Sam said amiably. "You don't seem to know much about being in prison, am I right? Let me tell you some things. One is, don't whistle."

"Don't whistle?" Ken asked, not certain he'd heard right.

"Right," Ferracci nodded. "It sounds happy. There's something screwy about a guy who's happy in jail. The other guys will think you're crazy or something."

"What else?" Ken inquired.

"Never ask anyone what he's in for, not ever. You do that and you'll get beat up in the showers. I happen to know you're in for murder, but I would never ask you about it."

His new friend went on: "Don't get friendly with the guards. Guys will think you're ratting on them. Being a rat is about the worst, except for a rape hound or someone who molests kids. Those guys go into PC...."

"What's that?" Ken interrupted.

"Protective custody," Sam explained patiently. "If they get in the general population, they could be killed."

Ken discovered that except for sex offenders prison society takes an egalitarian view of crime. While guards were noticeably wary around him, knowing the young giant was accused of a particularly savage killing, his status as a murderer who faced a life sentence cut no ice with other inmates.

He learned the language.

"A fan's coming," Sam hissed one day.

"A fan?"

"Yeah, they're gonna do strip searches and toss the cells."

Ken underwent his first strip search, which means what it says and includes requiring the person to bend over to expose the anus. Having no other place of concealment, prisoners the world over wrap drugs or money in plastic and stow it deep inside their rectums. In the Canadian prison system the practice is called "suitcasing".

"You get drugs," Sam told Ken with a shrug, "you suitcase it."

Ken was revolted but politely concealed it.

"That's important to remember when you go down below," Sam continued. In answer to Ken's inquiring look, he explained, "Below means the federal prison. If you get more than two years, you go to Kingston or someplace like that. You want to take money with you so you can buy things, drugs, a hamburger, or maybe a TV."

Sam amiably went on with the lesson in "Prison 101". "Now, what's the worst thing you can call another con?"

Ken considered. Several crude possibilities occurred to him.

"I'll tell you," Sam informed him. "A goof. You call someone a goof, that means you want to fight."

Sam had other valuable tips. "Never touch another guy's stuff," he warned Ken. "If you steal from another guy in here, you're a box thief. In a federal pen, a box thief can get killed."

When he showered, Ken wore plastic bags secured with elastics on his hands to protect them, and another prisoner shampooed his hair. Other prisoners helped feed him and assisted him to the toilet. Ken was touched by the kindness and civility he encountered. To his surprise, prison society is full of such gestures. One time he watched inmates befriend a Korean-Canadian, a man of eighty-nine who spoke no English, and another time he saw great consideration for a Chinese-Canadian man of seventy-six. Inmates looked after the old men, making sure they had lawyers and learned how to roll cigarettes.

"You'd think it would be everyone for himself," Karen marvelled when he told her about it.

He nodded. "You'd think so, but it isn't that way. People here help one another."

"In a lot of ways," she commented thoughtfully, "they're better than regular society. They aren't judging you. They aren't convicting you."

Marlys meanwhile was baffled. The Sunnybrook tests showed that Ken didn't have a life-threatening brain tumour, which was the good news, but left her with no explanation for what had happened. How could Ken have forgotten driving fourteen miles to Scarborough from Pickering, killing his mother-in-law with a knife and tire-iron, and stabbing his father-in-law almost to death?

She studied the records of her interviews with Ken. It was heartening to her, thinking ahead to how he might conduct himself in the witness-box, that Ken's story never changed. Indeed, his consistency was a remarkable feature of her notebooks, given the great stress he was enduring. His calmer recollection of the fragments in his memory never varied from the story he gave police while he was in a state of wild confusion and horror. Ken became more coherent as time passed, but no detail of what he remembered ever altered.

Marlys marvelled at the uniformity. Something else also struck her as curious. In every interview Ken described the moment of seeing his mother-in-law's tormented face the same way: "I woke up and saw my mother-in-law's face." *Woke* up? Could he have been asleep? Was he sleepwalking? It was such a wild idea that she put it to one side.

She wondered if Karen Parks had some insight into Ken's situation. Perhaps there was a pattern of memory loss. Marlys noted that Karen was visiting Ken regularly, which was encouraging from the defence point of view, but it was ominous that Karen was frosty and distant whenever Marlys spoke to her.

"I had a low opinion of defence lawyers," Karen confesses. "That they weren't nice people. I thought Marlys would ask me if I intended to testify for the Crown, and I didn't know the answer. I believed Ken and I supported him, but I wanted to stay neutral. I wasn't inclined to help the Crown, but I didn't want to help her either."

Marlys telephoned and asked if Karen would see her.

"No," Karen said coldly. "I don't think I want to do that."

Marlys was very careful.

"There are a few things I'd like to know that would help me, and perhaps you have some questions too."

Karen was silent. "All right," she agreed, "but only if Ken is there too."

She was asking something almost impossible. Prisons allow only people who have business with prisoners to have open contact. The category includes lawyers, social workers, doctors, and psychologists and is not usually extended to relatives. Somehow Marlys, a polite woman who gets on well with administrators, managed to surmount this obstacle. A few weeks after Ken was placed in the Don Jail, the lawyer was seated with Karen and

Ken in an open area monitored by guards where they talked for almost two hours.

Marlys opened the discussion by detailing the results of the tests that showed Ken had no sign of brain disorder.

Karen had a burning question to put. A debate on capital punishment was raging in the country, with the House of Commons about to hold a free vote to decide on the reinstatement of the death penalty. Was it possible, she asked Marlys, that Ken could be executed? Marlys assured her that even if the abolitionists lost the free vote and even if Ken was convicted of first-degree murder, he would not be hanged. The death penalty would not be retroactive; it would apply only to murders committed after it was enacted.

That information flashed through Ken's family. Lil Hodge had been having nightmares in which she saw her grandson executed. A ten-year-old cousin, Phillip Hodge, Glen's son, had written a letter to Ken full of his fears that Ken would be killed.

"If he isn't going to be killed," Karen asked, "then what is the penalty for first-degree murder?"

Marlys looked at Ken, who was staring into the distance. "A life sentence with no right to parole before twenty-five years," she answered. As Karen stiffened, Marlys added quickly, "But the charge is almost certain to be reduced to second degree, which allows lighter penalties. The Crown doesn't have enough evidence of intent on Ken's part to sustain a first-degree charge."

Karen thought she'd rather be executed than spend twenty-five years in prison. Ken didn't agree. He'd been full of morbid thoughts about being hanged. Prison was better than dying, he reflected, even if it meant twenty-five years in a cell. He'd be out before he was fifty.

"As for the trial, there are two ways this can go," Marlys continued. "The Crown probably expects that we'll plead not guilty by reason of insanity, but maybe there is some other explanation. We still aren't sure. I'm going to get some people to examine Ken. One of the things I want them to look at is the possibility of automatism. It's possible Ken was in some state beyond his control, like sleepwalking."

Marlys expected Karen to be skeptical and was intrigued that she wasn't in the least.

"That's what I think," she said firmly. "That's the only thing that makes sense."

"Well, we'll certainly look into it, but it's a long shot," Marlys warned them. "I've never heard of sleepwalking being used successfully as a defence in a murder charge. I'll have to look around and see if I can find any precedents. In any case, I'm not sure what that would get you if we did prove sleepwalking. It might not result in an acquittal, I just don't know. I'll have to search the law to find that out. Maybe sleepwalking is equated with insanity."

Karen said, "I still think that could be it."

In fact, Karen also had noted that Ken always said, "I *woke* up and saw your mother's face." The attack had occurred in the middle of the night after Ken might have fallen asleep, not the next day when the visit was planned. Even her friend Connie Sullivan had thought he might be sleepwalking. Once when each was making wild guesses about what might have happened, Connie suddenly said, "Maybe he was sleepwalking. I have a friend who knows someone who did something really crazy while sleepwalking."

Even Ken's friend at Revere had said when she called, "It is so unlike Ken to hurt anyone. Do you think he was sleepwalking?"

Karen was warming to Marlys, but she dropped none of her wariness. When Marlys asked about Ken's relationship to Karen's parents, she tersely confirmed what Ken had said, that they had been on the best of terms.

Ken listened almost indifferently to the discussion. He was showing a remarkable lack of interest in how his defence would be conducted. What interested him more was finding an explanation for Barbara's death. He was positive someone else had done it. His theory was that another person for some reason had drugged him and taken him to Barbara's house. Once inside the house, Ken thought he must have started to revive from the drug. In a semi-conscious state, he had realized that the stranger was trying to kill Barbara. In the struggle to protect his mother-in-law, Ken's hands were cut.

He had to admit the scenario had problems. Who would want to do that? How did the person get into Ken's house to drug the Kool-Aid? Who was strong enough to carry him to his car, and why? It was very far-fetched, he thought, but not any more far-fetched than not being able to remember driving fourteen miles from Pickering and then attacking Barbara and Denis.

When he tried these conjectures on Marlys she listened sympathetically, but he could tell from her face that she didn't think his "other man" theory was feasible.

He longed for a magical resolution. Maybe he had forgotten driving to Scarborough. Maybe he was so groggy from the drug he thought he'd been given and two nights without sleep that he had forgotten that part, but maybe when he got there he had found someone attacking Barbara and Denis. He would have tried to defend them. That would explain how he got the cuts on his hands and arms, but why wouldn't he remember that? The suggestion that he was sleepwalking, however, caught his attention.

"My grandfather was a sleepwalker," he ventured.

"Really?" said Marlys, sitting up straight. "Really!"

Marlys consulted Graham Turrall again, who agreed that sleepwalking was a feasible explanation and worth pursuing. She asked him to use his connections in the field of psychology to find her North America's top experts on sleep disorders. He placed a call to the Center for Narcolepsy at Stanford University in California, where he had done some work.

"I need to consult with someone who is a recognized authority in the field of sleepwalking," Turrall asked. "Can you direct me to someone who is the best, the very best?"

The Stanford authority said, "Well, you've got one of the world's leading experts in sleepwalking right there in Canada. He's in Ottawa and he's Roger Broughton."

At about the same time, Ron Billings, the Sunnybrook psychiatrist, said to Marlys, "I've exhausted every possible explanation for this. I've gone systematically through a list of the major psychiatric diagnoses that could apply here. There's just nothing that fits. I think we should look at sleepwalking."

She grinned. "We are."

The casts on Ken's hands were removed at Sunnybrook Hospital and were replaced with a plastic brace and splints. He tried to curl his fingers but found he couldn't. Looking at his mutilated hands, Ken wondered how he could have sustained such frightful injuries without knowing who inflicted them.

Doctors at Sunnybrook told Ken that his wounds would have to be cleaned twice a day to prevent infection. When he mentioned this to a prison nurse at the Don, she handed him a bar of soap. Ken protested to Marlys Edwardh, who got in touch with the medical supervisor again, Dr. Paul Humphries. After that Ken's stitches were properly sterilized each day by the head nurse.

Karen came twice a week, all the visits he was allowed. Both found it hard to communicate through the noise around them and the bad telephone connection, but it was stabilizing for her to see him looking himself, the good man she had married, the man she had loved, nothing different about him at all. Except that she had never seen anyone in such pain. It touched her heart, and she could see that without her visits he might fall apart utterly.

Marlys warned them that the visitor phones in the jail were tapped, so they avoided talking about the case and were too self-conscious to discuss their feelings in any depth.

Karen's family knew she was visiting Ken, she was sure, but the subject was never discussed. She appreciated their tact in allowing her to deal with her turmoil in her own way. She figured her family was thinking that Ken would be sent away to prison for a long time, so she was seeing him while he was nearby. It was a temporary situation: eventually Ken would be gone and Karen would make a new life for herself and Melissa.

Maybe she would, she thought, but she still didn't know.

On the occasions when Karen was in contact with Marlys about such matters as Ken's medical needs, she was friendlier. Still she kept the lawyer at arm's length. Her tone said plainly, *back off!*

"I wasn't strong at that point," Karen confesses. "I still didn't know if I would take the stand for Ken. I knew if I did it might be something my family would never forgive."

For Ken the trips to Sunnybrook for tests and to have the casts removed were welcome breaks from the tedium and stresses of staying in his cell all day, alone with his despair. He was not cheered by the good news that the brain tests were negative. What did it matter? He had no future anyway.

After six weeks in the Don, he was transferred to the Metro East Detention Centre, primarily a holding jail where people are kept to await immigration orders or trial appearances. Inexplicably, it is built along the lines of a maximum-security prison. Doors are sheet steel and close with a chilling clang. First offenders, women, illegal immigrants, and teenagers caged there find it horrifying. Most inmates are people awaiting trial, technically innocent and often so found. For most, the crimes for which they are awaiting trial are minor ones, and those serving sentences are confined for relatively brief periods such as weeks or a month.

Almost since Metro East opened it has been crowded beyond capacity. Cells designed for two people to sleep in bunk beds often hold three, the hapless extra person assigned to sleep on the floor with his head near the lidless toilet.

Prisoners are locked in their cells to eat and at other times spend the day in a common area on each range. The low time of the day is between eleven and one when they are put in their bleak cells for the noon meal. The two hours seem endless. The common area where they congregate is furnished with three metal-topped picnic tables bolted to the floor. Recreational facilities and programs are almost unknown, since the premise is that no one stays very long. Ken Parks, however, spent almost a year in Metro East. Inmates call it "dead time", since it isn't subtracted from the sentences that follow trial and conviction.

Ken observed a substantial population of black men in Metro East awaiting trial. As someone whose closest friends, the Ramanis, were black, Ken expected to mix easily with inmates of any colour and was surprised to encounter prison's segregation. When he attempted to make conversation, black prisoners rejected him coldly. Many of them seemed to have their own rules, which conflicted with the traditional prison etiquette of white inmates. Many, too, talked a rapid-fire patter that other prisoners couldn't understand.

Ken's initiation to "the East", in fact, was a challenge from a big black man who threw a sucker punch at him. With his bandaged and tender hands, Ken was helpless to protect himself or retaliate. He looked to the guards for assistance but encountered only bemused stares. The attacks continued. Ken's size seemed to threaten the man, who was the acknowledged leader and bully on that range. To Ken's alarm, his oppressor was armed with a "shank", a home-made knife. Ken began to fear for his life, but he didn't dare step outside the unwritten rules against complaints to guards. One of them, noting the situation, suggested that Ken could request a move to another range.

"No," said Ken shortly. "Thanks."

Sam's paternal advice had been, "No matter what happens, don't ask for a transfer to another range. They'll think you're chicken."

The man persisted in tormenting Ken, who confided one day in Karen. She promptly went to the authorities. To Ken's relief he was moved immediately to another range.

Psychologist Graham Turrall visited Ken almost weekly. His long, thoughtful, probing interviews were designed to unearth clues about Ken's behaviour and to detect discrepancies in his account of his activities. He found only consistency and candour. Marlys, too, came and went, an oasis of calm and assurance that belied her growing anxiety. Every avenue she explored to explain Ken's memory loss either fell apart completely or was shot full of conflicting detail.

Her mind kept turning to sleepwalking. It fit the situation better than anything else she had explored, but she hesitated. Whenever she mentioned it to colleagues, the response was a variation of "Aw, c'mon! You mean he drove fourteen miles in his sleep and attacked two people without waking up?" She inquired if anyone had ever heard of sleepwalking as a defence: none had. A search of the appellate record showed no sign that it had ever been used successfully in a Canadian trial. A search of the annals showed no report of a sleepwalking defence. She couldn't find a single case in Canada where sleepwalking was used. The jury was certain to be very suspicious of such a unique and bizarre defence.

That left her with a defence of not guilty by reason of insanity.

"What are the odds of me going to prison?" Ken asked her one day.

"About thirty-seventy," she replied.

"For whom?" he asked, to make certain he had it right.

"For them," she replied levelly.

CHAPTER TEN

Preliminaries

One of Canada's most eminent criminal lawyers, Arthur Martin, served with distinction for many years as a high court judge on the Ontario Court of Appeal. In 1977 he wrote a judgment that has had considerable impact ever since on trials involving the defence of insanity. This landmark case, *Regina* v. *Rabey*, concerned a man who was devastated by the break-up of a relationship. In what was demonstrated in court to be a distraught state of mind, he attacked and injured someone with a rock. The defence argued that Rabey had suffered a "psychological blow" that put him in a dissociative state.

It is a fundamental principle of Canadian criminal law that in order to obtain a conviction the prosecution must prove beyond a reasonable doubt that the acts of the accused person were voluntary. As Marlys Edwardh explains it, "Voluntariness, in this sense, means that the physical act in question must be a product of the person's will."

The evidence was compelling that Rabey was incapable of knowing what he was doing. Accordingly the judge acquitted Rabey on the grounds that he was in a non-insane state of automatism at the time and therefore not responsible for his action.

The Crown, alarmed that the decision set a precedent of tolerance for reprisals by lovesick swains, appealed on a subtle point full of legal implications. The Court of Appeal was asked to substitute the lower court's verdict of "not guilty" with the verdict "not guilty by reason of insanity". The Crown argued that a dissociative state due to a psychological blow is a "disease of the mind" within the legal definition of insanity. The Ontario Court of Appeal therefore had the unenviable task of drawing a legal distinction between automatism that is sane and automatism that is insane.

Mr. Justice Arthur Martin had developed strong views about insanity pleas. His landmark decision to alter the verdict had a significant impact on the legal definition of "disease of the mind". He expanded the legal definition of disease of the mind so broadly that very little escapes it.

Marlys Edwardh, along with other criminal lawyers who frequent such pleas, is no fan of Martin in the *Rabey* determination. She considers his views on insanity as unfortunate for the defence. "Mr. Justice Martin cast too wide a net," she says tersely. "He set out far too broadly who gets caught in the insanity net."

However, in two sentences that might even have been an afterthought, Mr. Justice Martin stated: "Sleepwalking appears to fall into a separate category. Unconscious behaviour in a state of somnambulism is non-insane automatism."

Marlys spent a lot of time studying *Rabey* as she proceeded to put together the case for the defence of Kenneth James Parks. She decided it helped her case—that is, the two sentences about sleepwalking did—but also helped the Crown because it sternly put most automatism into the category of insanity. The Crown might well argue that this particular sleepwalking incident resulted in behaviour so violent it could only be described as insane automatism.

Martin began by admitting that "the term disease of the mind is not capable of precise definition". He went on to say that the evidence of medical authorities has no bearing on the matter, although judges can pay attention to such evidence if they are so disposed. In the end judges are left with the sole responsibility to fit the situation within a legal definition of mental disease.

That said, Martin decided that Rabey was suffering from a "disease of the mind" when he struck his victim, and therefore the judge should have returned a verdict of "not guilty by reason of insanity" rather than a simple acquittal. Rabey, in short, had suffered a bout of insane automatism, not non-insane automatism.

Regina v. *Rabey* was appealed to the Supreme Court of Canada, which upheld the Ontario Court of Appeal decision. Mr. Justice Brian Dickson, later chief justice of the Supreme Court of Canada, wrote a dissent helpful to the Parks case. He noted, almost offhandedly, "The defence of automatism is successfully invoked in circumstances of a criminal act committed unconsciously; and, in the past, has generally covered acts done *while sleepwalking* or under concussional states following head injuries" (emphasis added).

Marlys began to lay out her strategy. Speed, she decided, was an imperative. When Ken appeared in court to hear the two charges, murder in the first degree and attempted murder, she entered a plea of "not guilty" to both and asked the judge to set a date for the preliminary hearing as quickly as possible. The Crown was astonished. Normally, lawyers preparing for a murder trial prefer long delays, especially when a complex argument involving insanity is contemplated.

Marlys, however, was in a hurry to meet the Woods family to take their measure. Moreover, she wanted their testimony on the record before grief and anger coloured their recollection of events. Once their accounts were frozen in a court transcript, it wouldn't matter so much if bitterness deepened and reshaped their memories.

"The importance of the preliminary, especially one that occurs very rapidly after the arrest, is that people's stories haven't had a chance to change, to develop," Marlys explains. "As months pass in the slow wait for trial it is natural and very human for people to alter their views. When that happens at the trial you need to be able to confront the witness with the statement made at the preliminary."

Preliminary trials, which are designed to protect citizens against mischievous or malicious arrest, are an admirable safeguard in the justice system. The Crown is obliged in a preliminary trial to show a judge sufficient evidence to obtain the judge's agreement that the charge is warranted. The advantage for the defence is the preview of what the Crown will be presenting in the trial and an opportunity to cross-examine the Crown's witnesses.

A notable example of the value of the process is the case of Susan Nelles, the nurse at Toronto's Hospital for Sick Children who was held responsible for the deaths of babies on the cardiac ward. The evidence produced by the Crown at her preliminary trial was so weak that the judge ruled that she would not have to endure a trial.

The judge at Ken's arraignment fixed a date early in August for the preliminary trial. With that done, Marlys had another request. She asked for a court order against publication of the proceedings of the preliminary trial. This was done to ensure the purity of the trial jury. Preliminary hearings do not present the defence case and therefore are forums for the Crown. The public, reading accounts of a preliminary trial, can draw one-sided conclusions. Since the right to a fair trial is the cornerstone of justice, such requests for media embargo usually are granted and Marlys obtained the protection for her client that she asked.

She also obtained an arrangement vital to the preparation of the case for the defence. By acting so swiftly, she reduced the likelihood that the Crown would move to have Ken remanded to Penetanguishene's prison for the criminally insane. He could remain at Metro East Detention Centre until his trial. Marlys Edwardh had easy access to her client and so did experts she retained—and their reports went to her, not to the Crown.

The summer passed, a pretty one in Ontario. The Crown office, short-handed and desperate, protested that the August date provided too short a time to prepare. The earliest date that could be fixed was October. The Crown's case was assigned to Cathy Mocha, then twenty-eight, who had been called to the bar only a year and a half earlier. Born in Philadelphia and married to a Canadian engineer who settled in Toronto, Cathy Mocha is tall and elegantly thin, with sharp classical features, a heavy mane of reddish blonde hair, and green eyes. She would be trying her first murder case; in fact, since women lawyers rarely choose the criminal bar, it was startling that the historic Parks case would be argued by two women.

Cathy Mocha received the brief and read the facts. She couldn't guess what the defence would be, but she knew Marlys was not planning a plea of guilty. That left "not guilty by reason of insanity", but there was something odd about the statements the accused was making. Cathy Mocha's first thought was, "This sounds like a case of automatism of some kind." She started to read the case law on automatism.

The preliminary opened early in October, and continued for two days before being adjourned until later in the month for reasons related to the availability of participants. It continued for one day late in October and adjourned after that until two days in November. The hearings finally ended in December.

Karen Parks called the fragmented sessions "a waste of time". She corrects herself: "I have to say it was a learning time for us. We didn't know anything about the court system."

The preliminary trial was by no means a waste of time for Marlys Edwardh and Delmar Doucette, who had their first look at the case they would be facing. Marlys was particularly curious to see Denis Woods, who was one of the Crown's first witnesses. Marlys was as struck by him as she had been by Karen.

"Denis is a remarkable man in the same way that Karen is a remarkable woman," Marlys says. "Like her, he has total devotion to truth. I had a strong sense at the preliminary and again at the trial that he would not allow himself to mis-state anything, even if it helped Ken. When people reconstruct their recollections in hindsight, it almost never happens that they remember it exactly as it was. Denis did that. He has a strong sense that the way to live in the world is to live in truth."

The Crown's case began with police evidence and some ghastly exhibits, a knife, a tire-iron, bloody clothes, photographs. The grisly testimony was followed by a parade of the Woods family. At Marlys' insistence, all the children testified.

When Pru and Emma spoke of hearing Barbara screaming, Ken was shocked. He was unprepared for it. Karen had told him very little of what her sisters had experienced that night.

"I didn't want to make him feel worse," Karen explains, "and I knew that the visitors' phones are bugged. So Ken heard all that for the first time at the preliminary trial."

Their account of hearing Ken running up the stairs towards them was particularly appalling. He cringed as they told of hiding terrified in the bedroom while he, panting and grunting like an animal, prowled the upstairs hall. He had only a little memory of that, but in his recollection he was trying to help them, not to hurt them.

The low point for him at the preliminary was the testimony of Samantha Woods, who declared that she and Ken had never been close. Her denial of their warm association was painful to him, and he also was shattered when Denis Woods testified that the day before the killing, when he heard that Ken was still gambling, he told his wife he didn't want Ken in the house again.

"That really hurt me," Ken says, gripping his hands together and cracking his knuckles. "I didn't know until then that he felt that way. And I thought that me and Samantha were really close."

Marlys made careful notes. The evidence given by Pru and Emma conflicted in several ways, which was understandable in the horrifying circumstances. One sister spoke of the lights being on, the other of the lights being off; they didn't agree about whether one went down the stairs or both remained at the top of the stairs. As for Denis, he could provide almost no information.

Karen, sitting by herself in the courtroom in order to preserve her neutrality, listened attentively to the police testimony. Despite the minor differences in their recall of the hectic moments after Ken burst into the police station, they painted a clear picture of a man in a state of utter confusion. She kept thinking, "That doesn't sound like someone who's just knowingly committed a crime. It sounds more like a person who has been sleepwalking, waking up from a bad dream."

On the other hand, she noted pieces of evidence that made sleepwalking seem unlikely. "Nothing fits absolutely perfectly," she sighs. "We need a little bit more information before we can really put it together but we can't get it. We'll never get it. The police really didn't do a very good job of taking fingerprints or analysing blood."

"The police thought they had an open-and-shut case," Ken explains. "They found bloodstains on the doorway and thought it was mine, but it could have been Karen's mom, or it could have been anybody's. They didn't have it tested."

For Ken's part, he heard nothing in the preliminary trial that shook his conviction that another person was in the house that night and that he had been drugged. The evidence all pointed that way, he told himself, especially his confusion in the police station.

At the end Marlys rose to argue that the Crown had not proved the necessary element of intent to kill and therefore the charge of first-degree murder couldn't be sustained. She declared that there was no evidence that Ken Parks planned the murder of Barbara Woods. No evidence of premeditation had been produced. The Crown had offered no proof that when Ken drove from Pickering to Scarborough that night he had murder on his mind.

Intent is a mighty word in law. A premeditated killing is first-degree murder, punishable by a life sentence with no possibility of parole for twenty-five years. When it is shown that the homicide was intentional but there was no planning or deliberation, that's second-degree murder. The penalty is also a life sentence, but parole is possible in ten years.

The judge ruled against Marlys Edwardh's request that the charge be reduced. He committed Ken for trial on a charge of first-degree murder. Marlys sprang to her feet and civilly announced that she was moving to appeal his decision.

The appeal to quash the judge's decision at the preliminary was heard in the Supreme Court of Ontario. Marlys argued there that the Crown had an obligation to adduce enough evidence to warrant a committal for trial on the charge of first-degree murder but had failed to do so. She made a cool, lucid presentation but she lost. The Supreme Court decided that the Crown had made a sufficient case for a first-degree charge.

Ken was staggered but Marlys appeared undaunted.

"It was worth the try," she assured him, "but it really doesn't matter all that much. It doesn't change how the defence will be presented, and it puts a heavy burden on the Crown to prove premeditation, which is going to be difficult since everyone agrees that there was no bad feeling between you and Karen's parents."

In the chill, bleak days of March 1988, Marlys reviewed the Sunnybrook tests exhaustively, determined to be certain that there was no pathological element lurking in Ken's brain. The results were analysed over and over by neurological experts, but every assessment came to the same conclusion. Kenneth James Parks had a completely normal brain.

"That's how I got on the doorstep of Roger Broughton," Marlys says. "Sleepwalking fit the circumstances like a glove, and it had to be looked at carefully."

Dr. Roger Broughton heads the sleep disorders centre at the Ottawa General Hospital. As the Stanford University professor had assured Marlys, he is one of the world's most impressive authorities on sleep disorders. A physician, he holds an M.D. from Queen's and a Ph.D. in neurology and neurosurgery from McGill. He has a certificate in neurophysiology from the University of Marseilles, France. Significantly for the Ken Parks case, he has considerable expertise in electroencephalography and epilepsy. At the time of Ken's trial he was a professor of neurology at the University of Ottawa, a career investigator awardee with the Medical Research Council of Canada, research co-ordinator in the division of neurology at the University of Ottawa, and medical director of the department of clinical neurophysiology at the Ottawa General Hospital. He also functioned as head of the Human Neurosciences Research Unit of the University of Ottawa's Health Sciences Centre. His expertise in sleep disorders was reflected in his membership on the Nosology Committee of the American Sleep Disorders Association, which is an internal commission updating the classification of sleep disorders. He is also a member of the Scientific Advisory Board of the Center for Narcolepsy at Stanford University and the Canadian liaison person to sleep societies of the American Electroencephalographic Society, the American society involved in brain wave studies, and he has honorary memberships in sleep and neurological societies in Cuba, Czechoslovakia, Brazil, and Latin America. He is a past president of the international Sleep Research Society and the founding president of the Canadian Sleep Society and has written more than two hundred articles on sleep.

Finally, Broughton, along with Professor Henri Gastaut of Marseilles, France, had performed the original sleep studies in sleepwalking and was a noted authority on Ken's particular sleep disorder.

When Marlys Edwardh reviewed his credentials with him at the Ken Parks murder trial, the recital covered twelve pages of transcript.

Marlys contacted Roger Broughton and outlined what she knew about Ken's strange behaviour. She mentioned the repetition of Ken's constant mental image of *waking* to see his mother-in-law's face.

"Could you kill someone while sleepwalking?" she asked.

"Sure," said Broughton. "Sleepwalkers can be violent, especially when someone attempts to waken them."

"Bingo," Marlys thought.

"The Crown had no idea we were switching from a plea of insanity," Marlys says with relish. "No one had an inkling what we were doing. We hadn't asked for a remand. We had gone into the provincial court system and set the date so quickly that there was no Crown around to say, '*Wait a minute*, we want this guy sent to Penetang.' We managed to keep all of what we were doing outside the bailiwick of the Crown. All the Crown knew, if they bothered to check, was that there was a parade of people going in and out of East Detention to see Ken."

The silent struggle between Marlys and the Crown was not only about the case. At the centre of the trial stood the enigma of Karen Woods Parks and whether she would testify on her husband's behalf.

"I felt there were very powerful forces pushing her away from Ken," comments Marlys. "Some of them were her family, some of them were police."

Karen confirms this. In her family, Samantha was the one most openly hostile to Ken and the one least likely to observe the family's code of silence when Karen was around. One day Karen was hurt to the quick when her brother Jonny lost control and screamed at her, "I hate you and I hate your husband." She also noted that the police had a way of dropping comments that disparaged Ken's family. She was told, for instance, that Ken's father "hung around with bikers".

Cathy Mocha didn't approach Karen directly to ask what she planned to do. In fact, Karen says there was no contact with the Crown attorney at all.

Karen has an inbuilt ability to resist pressure. Something in her nature flares when she feels herself being pushed in a direction she's not prepared to take. That quality enabled her to keep a neutral perspective while visiting Ken twice a week and at the same time maintaining close contact with her bereaved family. When she saw Ken her heart twisted inside her. He was clearly in pain and he was losing weight alarmingly. At least fifty pounds had dropped from his big frame. He said the food was wretched and he wasn't sleeping well. He was getting a sedative every night, he said, and it helped a bit. On the other hand, when Karen was with her motherless family she saw their great grief and noted the suffering in her father's eyes.

She had never been so alone. She couldn't ask her family to share her concern for Ken, or seek comfort from Ken in her sorrow over losing her mother. She couldn't talk to Ken's family either. They made friendly advances, but she felt their awkwardness with her. She still wasn't sure what she felt about the crime. Until she had an explanation she could trust, she didn't know where she belonged. She instructed herself sternly to keep an open mind. It wasn't fair to judge Ken until the facts were known.

In November she marked her twenty-third birthday. Her mother always pulled together a family party with sandwiches and cake and, Karen's favourite, meringues. Denis tried to fill the gap, but meringues were beyond him. The gallant attempt at normalcy depressed them all.

She seemed to be processing her life, not living it. She plodded between home and prison, took Melissa for walks, and cooked dreary meals that she ate alone, always with a sense of being disconnected from what she was doing. A flyer came to the door advertising a social event at Dunbarton-Fairport United Church. On an impulse she called the number and was invited to meet the assistant minister, who was touched by Karen's plight.

195

Karen welcomed the kindness and became a regular member of the congregation.

"It gave me strength and hope," Karen explains. "I also got peace of mind to think that my mom is somewhere nice. I don't know actually how to explain it...she's actually better off? She's somewhere warmer and nicer than where we are. When the minister talked, a feeling came over me, a warmth. I felt that someone was hugging, holding me. A strong, warm feeling, almost like my mother was there. I've never been that religious before, but it helped me a lot."

The minister's sermons about forgiveness struck home with great poignancy.

On Sundays she went to the early service and then donated time in the nursery during the second service. She went to Bible study once a week and had Melissa baptized.

"I don't believe you have to go to church to be a good Christian," Karen says, "but the church meant a lot to me that year Ken was in prison."

She made a friend in the congregation who sometimes hired Karen to baby-sit. Karen decided she had an obligation to be honest. She explained her situation, but the woman didn't withdraw from her as Karen had feared. So many others suddenly became remote when they learned about her.

Ken's grandmother Lil Hodge says, "It was a year of hell, but Karen was strong. She was so strong. She'd break down every now and then, but mostly she was strong. She knew in her heart that Ken didn't know what he was doing."

Sometimes Karen's confidence faltered. Tossing at night alone in the queen-size bed she had shared with Ken, she would wonder if she really knew him at all. The gambling, the stealing, the lies, for instance. Were they the real Ken Parks? His younger brothers were rough men, and Ken played an aggressive game of rugby. Maybe she was badly mistaken to view him as a gentle and honourable man.

She reviewed every detail of the few hours that had preceded his attack on her parents, looking for clues that Ken had planned it. He had refused to sleep with her that night. Perhaps he wanted to stay on the living-room couch because he was planning to sneak out of the house and kill her parents. Maybe that sweet nature was really a façade under which there was a man full of homicidal rage.

Those were the doubts of the night. When she saw Ken, her confidence in his essential gentleness returned. He was so abject and tormented it touched her heart. She felt that she knew him thoroughly. He had killed her mother, but he wasn't a murderer. She couldn't throw away six years of loving him.

Once Ken said awkwardly, "If I get a sentence of twenty-five years, I want you to get a divorce right away."

Karen started to protest but he stopped her.

"You can't waste your life waiting for me," he told her steadily. "Melissa will need a father. You're young, you'll find someone else. You can't put your life on hold for twenty-five years."

She said stoutly, "Don't even talk like that. Marlys thinks she can get the charge reduced to second degree. That's ten years. Ten years isn't so bad."

Ken said, looking bleakly at his prospects, "Yeah. Ten years isn't so bad."

Her existence revolved around those visits and her flailing attempts to cope with her grief. Thinking back on that year, she can recall only bits of it.

"It passed in a blur," she says bleakly. "I don't remember too much of anything."

Karen's interest in her home had evaporated. She was indifferent to the dust that piled up in corners, the dirty counters in the kitchen, the laundry spilling out of the basket. A welfare social worker took in the situation and provided Karen with a homemaker who came three times a week to take care of Melissa for half a day and do such chores as vacuuming.

"It gave me a few hours by myself, so I'd go out," Karen explains. "I knew I was supposed to be thinking things through but I couldn't concentrate. I was in a daze."

When she and Melissa were alone together, Karen cared for the child with as much patience as she could muster, but she was often distracted and distant. When the child slept, Karen found she couldn't concentrate enough to read so she paced the floor. Many afternoons she stared leadenly at the soaps on television where beautiful people coped with disasters that were improbable by any standard other than hers. When bills she couldn't pay came in the mail, she sorted them out: when the Hydro was two months late with a warning note, she paid it, skipping the telephone bill; the next month she'd pay the telephone but not the cable television, and so on.

Often she ran out of food. Her pride hurt, but she went to a food bank operated by the Dunbarton-Fairport United Church for staples such as eggs, bread, and milk. The church, guessing her situation, allowed her food twice a week, or more if she needed it. She was embarrassed but realistic; she and Melissa had to eat. Street-Link, an organization that gives support to families of people in prison, provided her with clothes, and so did the always dependable Salvation Army.

Her father no longer offered her money, and she didn't ask.

She wished she could stop caring for Ken. If she could stop visiting, stop thinking about him, her family was waiting to take her in. Instead the strain was palpable when she went to visit them. Samantha was particularly withdrawn, and her father, the wounds on his head and neck plain to see, was kind but distant. The subject most on their minds, her continuing relationship with Ken, was something no one broached.

How could she abandon Ken? She put herself in his shoes, imagined that she went to sleep one night and woke up to find she had killed someone. She would want Ken to stand by her, and she could do no less for him.

She expected that she would always be alone. Ken certainly would be sent to prison for a long time. Despite all the talk about a sleepwalking defence, it was only realistic to expect the worst and prepare for it, but she couldn't summon the energy. She missed her mother. Barbara would have known how to help her.

"This time last year," she would think, "mum and I went to England." Or "This time last year, mum and Ken were playing cards at the hospital when Melissa was born."

Ken, twitching with insomnia in his prison bunk at night, tried to accept that he was a sleepwalker. Dr. Roger Broughton, the Ottawa specialist in sleep disorders, had told him so. In October, Marlys Edwardh had arranged for Dr. Broughton to see Ken in

Metro East to make an assessment. She provided the doctor with a transcript of the taped statement Ken had given police on the day of the killing.

Broughton asked Ken to describe everything he could remember about the night and was struck, as Marlys had been, by the continuing consistency in Ken's statements. Broughton's first thought on hearing about the bizarre events of that night had been that Ken Parks was a liar, but he couldn't see how even an accomplished liar could get the story exactly the same over many months of questioning. Besides, people fabricate stories in order to hide motivated behaviour. Ken Parks had no reason to kill Barbara Woods, none. Broughton told Marlys that he was struck by Ken's apparent integrity and his profound remorse and confusion over the events of the tragedy.

Broughton found it puzzling that Barbara's face, as Ken recalled it looming before him with a piteous expression, bore no wounds. He knew that when the police had found her Barbara's face was bloody. Possibly Ken's memory was so distorted he hadn't taken in Barbara's injuries.

Ken's memory interested him. Ken could not remember getting up from the couch that night, putting on his jacket, slipping into his loosely laced track shoes, picking up the car keys, and going out the door, leaving it standing open behind him, all of which he must have done.

Was any of that Ken's usual way of behaving? No, Ken said. He never went without underwear and socks, and he would never leave the front door open.

Ken had no memory of the twenty-three-kilometre drive to Scarborough, a distance that would take about fifteen minutes and that involved travelling along the six-lane 401 highway and making six turns before hitting a series of traffic lights. Had he made that drive many times? the doctor asked. Ken answered, "A hundred or more."

Ken could recall nothing of the attacks on Denis and Barbara or of how his hands were cut. After a period of blankness, Ken's memory became patchy. His first image had been Barbara's face. The next was of the children screaming and himself running up the stairs, calling out, "Kids, kids." He didn't remember going down the stairs and out the door, getting into his car, or putting the key in the ignition, but he had a piece of memory of being in the car and seeing the knife. He couldn't recall driving for the five minutes it would take to reach the police station. Awakeness didn't occur again until he was inside the police station.

It made eminent sense to the doctor. As he was to testify, following the period of no recall that is typical of sleepwalking—the period covering the assault on Denis and Barbara—Ken was going in and out of sleep, a phenomenon sleep-disorder specialists call microsleeps. Ken's spotty memories only reinforced Broughton's opinion that the entire episode occurred during sleepwalking, but he was not yet ready to rule out other explanations. He obtained the results of the neurological examinations, the EEG and CAT scan. Like Billings, he was looking for signs of epilepsy, because aggression can occur during seizures. He found nothing to indicate that Ken had epilepsy. He agreed with Dr. Edmeads' assessment: Ken's brain was perfectly normal.

He wondered if Ken had taken drugs that left his brain impaired. Edmeads had considered that possibility carefully and entered it into his records. There was no indication of drug toxicity and no history of drug-taking, not the night of the killing and not for years previous to that. Ken's fling with drugs in high school had been brief and the amounts of no great significance.

Broughton next considered the possibility that Ken was in a psychiatric fugue state, a condition of mental illness characterized by hysteria and possible memory loss. He saw no evidence of fugue either, which didn't surprise him. Fugues are exceedingly rare during sleep.

Like other pioneers in the emerging specialty of sleep disorders, Roger Broughton was aware of the phenomenon of rapid eye movement (REM) sleep behaviour disorder in which people get up and perform complex activities, often with a hostile component. He gave that possibility careful consideration, but had to exclude it, since the disorder arises only from brain lesions or some other form of neurological disease. None of those was evident in the brain of Ken Parks.

That left sleepwalking.

If Ken Parks was a sleepwalker, his habitual sleep patterns would be unusual. Broughton wouldn't have been surprised to find a pattern suggesting that Ken suffered from nocturnal epilepsy. It was unlikely that Ken would suffer seizures at night without having them by day as well, but it was necessary to check it out.

Broughton told Marlys Edwardh that he would have to test Ken's sleep patterns in a sleep laboratory. How could that be done, with Ken in custody? The lawyer secured a minor miracle. She made a request, and Metro East Detention Centre authorities agreed to allow Broughton and his associates to set up a temporary sleep lab in a parole office. It was far from an ideal setting. Ken, hooked by electrodes to a polygraph a few feet from his cot, was obliged to try to sleep with a technician in the same room watching him. The doctor wasn't happy with the arrangement, but it was the best that could be managed.

The technician monitored Ken's brain wave channel, eye movements, muscle tone, and blood oxygen and made a full respiratory assessment to see if Ken had a problem with loss of breathing (apnea) during sleep. The results were interesting. Ken's breathing was within the normal range, but his sleep patterns were abnormal. Two nights before the tests, at the doctor's request, Ken had stopped taking his sedative, which had the effect of suppressing what the specialists call slow-wave sleep, the deepest sleep. Broughton feared it would interfere with his ability to get a profile of Ken's normal sleep.

Deprived of the sedative and uneasy in the curious environment, Ken had more than his usual problem falling asleep. In the first hour or two after trying to compose himself, Ken was fully awake with a form of insomnia. After that came a period of an hour or so of drowsiness and then he descended the levels of sleep and reached stage four, slow-wave sleep.

The peculiarity in Ken's sleep pattern during the first session in the sleep lab was that he roused abruptly from stage four sleep, without any of the slow sliding out of that sleep state that most people have. Five times that night Ken reached stage four sleep, the deepest level of sleep, where there are no dreams and no mental activity, only to shift suddenly to wakefulness without passing through REM sleep.

Another and very significant finding was that the amount of deep sleep Ken experienced that night was roughly twice that of most adults and more closely approached that of a child. Children spend about 40 per cent of their sleep time in deep, slow-wave sleep, which is why sleepwalking is so common among children. Adults, however, spend only about 10 per cent of their sleep in stage four's deep sleep. Ken Parks, however, registered 20 per cent.

Otherwise Ken's sleep was normal. He showed no trouble breathing, he didn't exhibit any abnormal movements of his arms or legs, and no epileptic discharges were recorded in the brain wave channels.

Taken with the fact that Ken still had in his system the remnants of a sedative that impairs arousals from sleep, the finding that he roused so steeply from deep sleep was intriguing. Broughton was impressed by Ken's pattern of troubled, unstable sleep, but he wasn't yet ready to form a conclusion.

Four months later, on January 22, 1988, the sleep lab technician was back in Metro East to repeat the experiment. Again Ken was unable to sleep for almost two hours, after which he experienced the fragmented sleep he had displayed before. At one moment he would be in stage four of deep, slow-wave sleep, and then, abruptly, he would waken. This happened eight times in the night. This time Ken's slow-wave sleep amounted to 28 per cent of his sleep time. Not only was he having much more deep sleep than most people and an unusual rousal pattern, but his deep sleep was occurring later than usually happens. Most people have their deepest sleep soon after falling asleep. Towards morning, Ken was still having periods of deep sleep.

"Sleep-disorder people call that pattern of repeated brief awakenings micro-arousals," Broughton told Ken genially. Ken liked the doctor's friendly, unflappable nature. "You come out of stage four sleep without stopping at the usual stations of lighter sleep. Also you have a great deal more deep sleep than we usually find in people your age."

"What does that mean?" Ken asked.

"Taken with other precipitating factors, such as exhaustion and stress, you're a candidate for sleepwalking."

Ken's reaction was alarm. If he was a sleepwalker, maybe some night he would kill Karen and the baby. It meant he wasn't safe to be at large.

With the trial months away, Marlys was thinking of asking for bail. When Denis and others in the Woods household heard of it, they were alarmed. Karen told them not to worry.

"Ken has refused to let Marlys ask for bail," she told them. "He told her to drop it."

Ken explains: "I wanted to stay in jail, locked up, in case it happened again. I didn't want to put anyone at risk." He checked with Roger Broughton, who agreed with him. Ken might experience more stress and worry outside the detention centre, he thought, and such stress would increase the probability that sleepwalking would recur.

The discussion about bail was one of the few times Karen's family ever mentioned his name to her. With them she had the weird feeling that her husband didn't exist.

Prison made Ken a reader. He hadn't finished a book in his entire life, with the exception of those assigned in English classes, but loneliness and the idle hours in Metro East drove him to read. He started with westerns and Nick Carter detective stories. At the end he was reading Stephen King and Sidney Sheldon during lock-up times; during the time when the prisoners were allowed in the common room, he played Scrabble. Someone taught him bridge, which he came to enjoy. Often the men pulled together a poker game, the stakes being "snaps"—losers had to do whatever the winner suggested. Ken once ordered a loser to pull down his pants and run around the range quacking like a duck.

Prisoners at Metro East tend to be young. Ken, at twenty-four, was one of the older men on the range. He listened, fascinated, to prison shop talk. Men swapped stories of burglaries and how to rob a drugstore. "You go through the wall," he was instructed. "That bypasses the alarms."

"Through walls?" asked Ken, incredulous.

"Sure, it's only drywall."

He learned to be a team player when condoms containing drugs were thrown over the wall while the men were exercising. "If the buzzer sounds, you know the guards caught the play," Ken explains. "So everyone goes against the wall and drops their pants, pretending to stick something up. Maybe only two guys are really suitcasing, but it looks like everyone is."

To pass the time at the Don Jail, he had attended gatherings of a Christian movement aimed at self-improvement. He didn't continue the association in Metro East. Religion brought him no solace. "I know there's something there," he says, "but nothing's been proven to me. I have no religion at all."

At Metro East, Ken attended sessions of Gamblers Anonymous. It provided a diversion, but he didn't think he fit. His behaviour was that of a compulsive gambler, he had to admit, but he didn't miss gambling the way the others did. Gambling, prevalent in prisons, didn't interest him. If it hadn't been for his need to replace the money he had taken, he doubted that he would have gone to the track at all.

The cells were bitterly cold, which affected his hands. Some movement was returning if he worked at it, but blood circulation was poor. Karen got permission to bring him gloves but, to his indignation, a guard confiscated them. Karen protested in vain. He was advised to put socks on his hands.

Ken, friendly and co-operative by nature, came to be a favourite of the prison guards, who gave him the affectionate name of "Parksie". The couple noticed that they received more tolerant treatment than most inmates did. For instance, prisoners were limited to four photographs on their cell walls, but Ken decorated the area around his bunk with about twenty pictures of Karen and Melissa.

"We got to have longer visits, extra visits, stuff like that," Karen says appreciatively. "They knew he wasn't a bad person."

"Like, I had respect for them," Ken explains. "I didn't give them any hassle, so they didn't give me any hassle."

Melissa's birthday came and Karen wept that her mother wasn't there to see the child's delight in her cake and presents. Karen's first Christmas without her mother was even rougher. In the morning she went to the townhouse in Scarborough to exchange gifts with her family. All of them were depressed. The gift opening started bravely enough with the usual exclamations of surprise and gratitude, but by the time the family started to eat the ritual Christmas brunch, all were weeping.

Karen went straight from her family to see Ken, finding the transition, as always, a strange one. He reported that Christmas was a bitter time in prison. "The guys are missing their families," he explained. "The mood in here is pretty edgy. They've got us all locked up because they're afraid of a riot."

Karen had Christmas dinner with Ken's family. She didn't feel strong enough to keep her feelings bottled up through Christmas dinner with her own family. In Scarborough she had to pretend that Ken didn't exist. She didn't want to spend all of Christmas censoring herself. Her relations with Ken's family were warming, and she found relief in having someone to talk to about Ken and her fears for his future.

"We included her in everything that year," Lil Hodge says. "We were feeling so bad that Christmas. We couldn't even give Ken any presents."

Karen took practical stock of her situation. If Ken went to prison, she didn't want to continue living on welfare. Even a full-time job at the supermarket would not sustain a single mother very well. Working out the figures in the evening quiet of her house after Melissa fell asleep, she came to the conclusion that she needed job skills.

She reviewed her options. Going to university would take too long, and besides she couldn't afford it. What appealed most to her, she decided, was nursing. The prospect of making sick people comfortable and tending people in need appealed to her maternal nature. Karen discovered a registered nursing course in a community college, Durham College in Oshawa, and in January she applied for admission. The registrar told her she would be notified about acceptance in the spring.

Karen took home forms to apply for a government student loan, so she would be ready if she was admitted.

The mess Ken had made at Revere Electric remained to be addressed. Through intermediaries Karen made contact with Revere and offered a payment of $15,000 against the $32,000

Ken had stolen. She promised the settlement out of proceeds from selling their house in Pickering. Revere accepted and the house went on the market the next week, priced at $123,000. To clear title to it, Karen had to take back Ken's $10,000 bail on his fraud charge.

After paying Revere and some to Marlys for the specialists who were seeing Ken at Metro East, she wouldn't have enough to buy a new house in the Toronto area's hot housing market. In anticipation that she would be accepted at the nursing school, she started looking for something cheap to rent in Oshawa.

The Pickering house had a buyer within a few weeks of going on the market. The agreed closing was July 31 and Karen had occupancy until then, which gave her time to find another place to live.

By the middle of March, Marlys had two fascinating reports from Dr. Roger Broughton on the results of his tests in the improvised sleep lab at Metro East prison. The sleep specialist was confident that the only explanation for Ken's activities and memory loss was sleepwalking.

"How can you be sure?" Marlys asked.

He told her about the erratic patterns he had found. Moreover, everything else fit. The details of the episode, the marked pre-disposing factors of a past personal and strong family history of sleepwalking, sleep terrors, bedwetting, and sleep talking, and the presence of known precipitating factors such as extreme sleep deprivation and acute stress, all made the diagnosis very clear. Marlys was cautious.

"Let's pull together a few people and talk about this," she suggested. "Would you come to Toronto for a meeting with Ron Billings and Graham Turrall? Maybe we could get someone else who's good at sleep disorders. Any suggestions?"

"Sure," said Broughton affably. "Ask Rosalind Cartwright. She's in Chicago and she's good."

Marlys didn't share the doctor's delight in his diagnosis. It was asking too much of a jury to believe the twenty-three-kilometre drive, the bludgeoning and stabbing and strangling, all of it while asleep. Marlys talked to her colleagues in the big old house on

Prince Arthur Street that is shared by some twelve lawyers in a loose arrangement of partnerships and solo practices.

"In the Ken Parks case," she said in her crisp, sharply articulated way, "I'm thinking of a defence of sleepwalking."

She was met everywhere with incredulity. The reaction, phrased with varying degrees of skepticism and derision, was discouraging. Everyone echoed her own concern that it wasn't plausible that a man could remain sound asleep while he drove a car a great distance, entered a house, and attacked two people, killing one of them.

The lawyer went back to consideration of a defence of insanity with some sleepwalking aspects. She didn't like it. The pieces simply didn't fit together that way. Subject to the round-table consultations she was trying to arrange, it looked as though she had no choice but to plead Ken not guilty because of non-insane automatism—namely, sleepwalking. Sleepwalking was the only explanation that didn't fall apart on scrutiny.

The lawyer made a call to Dr. Wood Hill, a forensic psychiatrist with a formidable amount of experience with crimes of violence. At one stage of his distinguished career he was consultant psychiatrist to the Don Jail. During a period when he was in the forensic unit at the Clarke Institute of Psychiatry in Toronto, he did assessments of some 170 people accused of murder.

Marlys wanted to know if people who ruminate about killing someone can bury the impulse and then have it pop out while they are asleep.

He replied much as he did when asked the same question at the trial. He noted that many murders were committed at night following a day of wrathful thoughts, but that none was done after the person had fallen asleep and none without the perpetrator's having a clear memory of what had happened. He agreed to see Ken Parks and look at the mass of reports that Marlys had assembled.

She also contacted Dr. Frank Ervin of McGill University, who is an internationally recognized authority on the workings of the brain and has specialized for the last ten years in the study of people with pathological aggression. The Texas-born psychiatrist has held important positions in such places as the

Massachusetts General Hospital, Harvard medical school, the University of California, and the National Institute of Neurology in Mexico. As a consultant to the U.S. president he also gave advice on manned space flights and sat on a committee on violence. He too studied the reports. On April 24 he was at the door of Metro East Detention Centre to see Ken Parks. At the trial he stated his opinion that "he [Ken Parks] was in a parasomnia state, somnambulistic state, and that that parasomnia accounts for his behaviour."

In plain language, that's sleepwalking. Rosalind Cartwright, the sleep disorder specialist from Chicago, was sent all the information, including the sleep lab results. She travelled to Toronto and interviewed Ken independently, following which she talked to the family. At the end of the process she declared that she fully concurred with Broughton's conclusion that the only reasonable diagnosis was sleepwalking.

The sleepwalking defence was almost as tight as it was ever going to be. It was time to find out what role Karen Parks intended to play at the trial.

Marlys had been careful not to put pressure on the young woman. Karen's situation wrung her heart. She was caught between conflicting loyalties, and Marlys could appreciate her desperate attempt to stay neutral. However, time was passing. The trial was set for May, and the lawyer could wait no longer to discover whether Karen was willing to risk alienating her family by testifying for Ken. Marlys had to know if Karen was ready to commit herself.

Marlys first talked it over with Ken. Was Karen going to testify for him, or not? Ken said he didn't know and he didn't want to ask. He wasn't keen on having Marlys ask either. If Karen couldn't testify for him, he could understand that. He could live with it.

Karen was a lawyer's dream witness, intelligent and straightforward, with the added dimension of her poignant situation. Marlys sensed that Karen still hadn't made up her mind about Ken and was avoiding the moment when she would have to decide. That explained her continued unwillingness to sit down with her husband's lawyer. Except for the unusual meeting in the Don Jail, Karen had resisted every gentle attempt Marlys had made to draw her into a discussion of the case.

She decided she would inform Karen that Ken couldn't be held responsible for the attacks, and let Karen sort it out from there. Maybe when Karen knew the results of some of the tests, her confusion would be eased and she would be able to make her decision. Marlys hoped Karen would choose to support her husband rather than her family, but the plan might backfire. If Karen decided to testify for the Crown, she probably would tell the Crown everything the defence was planning.

Marlys decided she had to gamble. She called Karen and said it was imperative that they have a talk. Karen reluctantly agreed to come to her office.

"I was taking a chance that she would go to the prosecution with whatever I told her," Marlys admits. "There was risk in revealing to Karen what we were up to. I could see that the Crown was confident that we were going to enter a plea of insanity, and we wanted the prosecution to go on thinking that way. I held some things back in case Karen went to the other side, but for the most part I decided to level with her."

Karen sat in Marlys' elegant office, stiff and composed, and accepted a cup of tea. When the women were settled and the civilities completed, Karen said, "I'm only here to find the truth."

Marlys found that an astonishingly mature statement. Very cautiously, she began to tell Karen that she was looking at a range of explanations for Ken's behaviour just before dawn on May 24, 1987.

"I don't know for certain what we'll be presenting," she said carefully, "but every possibility that we study tells us that it isn't fair to hold Ken responsible for what happened."

Karen thought that over while Marlys studied her. Karen returned the inspection with level dark eyes but said nothing.

"We want you to know what we're doing and where we're going," Marlys continued. "We've been sending in streams of people to examine Ken, as you know, and the results are very interesting. All our research points very clearly to a defence that will show that Ken wasn't responsible, that he truly wasn't aware of what was happening."

"Was he insane?" Karen asked.

"No," said Marlys. "He wasn't."

The defence lawyer was now out on a limb.

CHAPTER ELEVEN

Putting It Together

"I had to take that chance," Marlys said later. "Once the trial started, Karen would not be allowed to sit on the sidelines as she had been. The position she had found halfway between Ken and her family simply couldn't be maintained. I couldn't go much farther in putting my case together without getting a sense of what she would do in that courtroom. Would she stand up against her family? It was time for her to make up her mind, and I wanted to give her the information and the tools so she could do that."

Karen made no commitment, but questions rushed to her mind. How could Marlys be so sure? She returned to the conjectures that had been swirling in her imagination.

"I wonder about a lot of things, little things," she said tentatively, her voice rising at the end of the sentence as it always does when she's uncertain. "Like, why didn't Ken come to bed with me that night? Was he planning to sneak out and go to my parents' house? And when I came in from work and he came over and kissed me, he took my purse out of my hands. He put it on the table. Was that so he could get the car keys?"

"Well, Karen," asked Marlys in a reasonable tone, "where do you usually put the keys?"

Karen's face cleared. "On the table. On that table."

Then she grinned.

Marlys has boundless respect for Karen. "I have been surprised by Karen Parks since the day I met her," she comments. "In theory she's a baby, a very young person who doesn't have a lot of worldly experience. She's had an ordinary, everyday kind of Canadian upbringing with nothing that would have told you that this woman was equipped with skills, social and otherwise, that make other people's skills pale. She's got determination. She's got a capacity to make decisions, to be reflective about what she's doing, to stand up for what she believes in the midst of enormous pressure."

Karen's total commitment, as Marlys discovered, indeed was to truth. "That's her moral peg," Marlys explains. "She's an extraordinary person. She wanted to understand what happened, what truly happened. She would take it from there, whatever the truth was, and make her decision. She wasn't prepared to come to Ken's side on an irrational basis. She made it clear she might work with us, but she wanted the truth. Always the truth."

With a better sense of trust established, Marlys was able to ask Karen what she knew of that night of terror. Karen had information that was new to Marlys, details that had not been part of the testimony at the preliminary. The lawyer learned for the first time that Pru and Samantha had heard grunting sounds from the intruder. One of Ken's memory fragments was of running up the stairs, calling, "Kids, kids." This was significant for a sleepwalking defence because sleepwalkers frequently utter unintelligible sounds when they think they are saying words.

The fact that the knife was kept in a sheath in a drawer apart from the other cutlery was also important. Most helpful was the information Karen provided that Denis Woods had heard nothing before he wakened with Ken's hands around his throat—no voice, no sounds.

"If Ken Parks had walked in and said to his father-in-law, 'I've always hated you, *take this!*' we would have been playing in a completely different ball park," the lawyer explains. "But the silence indicated that something inexplicable was going on. When Karen told me there had been no conversation between Ken and Denis, then all the pieces started to fall together."

Karen told Marlys about the two-hour interview that police had taped with her two days after the killing. Marlys knew about it and had been trying for months to get Cathy Mocha to release a copy to her. Karen's tape was done while the events leading up to that night were fresh in her memory, so Marlys wondered if there was something on it useful to the defence that Karen had since forgotten. Finally, exasperated by the Crown's lack of co-operation, Marlys secured a court order and was given a transcript. It proved a disappointment. After all that effort, there was nothing in Karen's taped statements that Marlys didn't already know.

Roger Broughton dropped a comment that caught the lawyer's attention. He said that scientists have found there is a genetic predisposition to sleepwalk. Sleepwalking, he told Marlys, seems to run in families. By the end of March, Marlys and Broughton were immersed in interviews with Ken's family. They asked each member the same question: Who sleepwalks?

The detective work paid off handsomely. The lawyer and doctor were regaled with stories about Hodge adolescents who wet their beds in their sleep, about the child who left the house in her sleep and crossed the street, and about the time when, as a boy, Ken almost dived out the six-storey window in his sleep. Most of all, and best of all, they heard about Stan Hodge slicing bread and frying onions while asleep, *making grunting sounds*.

Marlys met in three lengthy brain-storming sessions with Ron Billings, the psychiatrist from Sunnybrook, Graham Turrall, Roger Broughton, and a second expert on sleep disorders, Rosalind Cartwright, who heads the Sleep Disorder Laboratory at St. Luke's Presbyterian Hospital in Chicago. The experts had a marvellous time. Turrall and Billings were fascinated to learn about sleepwalking, and the sleep-disorder people loved the case they were addressing, one of the most spectacular and tragic examples of sleepwalking in medical history.

The experts bounced theories off one another, spinning skeins of conjecture and hypothesis against the scant store of facts and Ken's episodic memory of events. They took the same pieces of information and explained them every way they could invent. The brick wall they met every time was the inescapable proof that Ken had a normal brain, not a diseased one, and that he was a sane person, not a psychotic. A rational, truthful man had partially dressed himself, got into his car, driven twenty-three kilometres to Scarborough, gained entry to the Woods house, and committed violent acts when someone, almost certainly Barbara, tried to wake him.

Fascinated with the puzzle and stimulated by one another's company, the experts speculated freely, trying to put the sprinkling of known facts into a reasonable sequence. The psychiatric and neurological experts deferred to the sleep experts. Sleepwalking was almost unknown territory for them, and they were absorbed in the wonder of a new field.

Marlys participated with a judge's ear and a juror's eye: How could this happen? Can it happen again? What makes you so sure it wasn't an epileptic seizure? Since she lives with a psychologist and practises in the field of insanity pleas, the language was not foreign to her but she was picking up new phrases: "slow-wave sleep", the deep sleep also known as stage four sleep; "mentation", the activities of a mind at work directing action.

Frequently she had to haul the group back from fanciful tangents down which they wandered, entranced with the outer limits of the new field.

"We'd spend hours discussing where it fit that Ken thought he heard the noise of a telephone, or where the weapons came from, and then everyone would go away and think about it. When we met again we'd start back from scratch. People really struggled diagnostically with Ken's situation. In his case, there wasn't an easy category to slot him into."

She pressed them to help her explain to the jury how a sleepwalker could drive a great distance, presumably stopping at traffic lights, since he had attracted no attention. That alone would astound a judge and jury. Most people think of sleepwalkers as moving around with eyes closed and arms extended. The specialists assured her that sleepwalkers have their eyes wide open. Sometimes the eyes seem even to bulge from their sockets, as was usual in the case of Ken's grandfather. Moreover sleepwalkers process external stimuli while deeply asleep. They can find doors and put their hand on the knobs, they navigate stairs, they open windows. They follow familiar paths.

If the Woods family had moved from Scarborough, Ken probably could not have found them. As it was, however, he had been driving exactly that route with great frequency for two years. As with commuters who drive home from work on automatic pilot, the path to Scarborough had worn a groove of memory in Ken's brain.

The other element they explored was Ken's state of anxiety as he fell asleep on the couch. Worried about the meeting the next day with Barbara and Denis, his final thoughts would have been about going to Scarborough. Deep in sleep an hour or two later, he went through the motions he had imagined: dressing himself, taking the car keys, getting in the car, driving....

Could he be acting on a buried wish to kill Karen's parents? Marlys asked. That question, indeed, was put many times at Ken's trial. Cathy Mocha, the Crown attorney, asked it in her cross-examination of Broughton. She wanted to know if people in a state of deep sleep release barriers and act on feelings they normally repress. Broughton replied that that was a disputed Freudian view. "Freud suggested that barriers present in wakefulness are removed in sleep," he said, adding with emphasis: "Other people have said that sleepwalking can come out of a total mental void."

The trigger, Broughton maintained, was not a subconscious wish to kill but a prevailing state of high anxiety. Ken was on edge that night, exhausted and under great stress. He was acting in a "total mental void".

Marlys expresses it this way. "Even if he did have a fantasy to kill Denis," she explains, "the real Ken Parks would never consciously do that. Everyone in a bad situation gets fantasies of getting out of it. The fantasies might include thoughts of violence, but people don't act on those fantasies. On the way to law school thinking I'm not going to do well on an exam, I might think it would be nice if I broke my leg so I wouldn't have to write it but I don't throw myself down some stairs."

Broughton told the lawyer that the history of sleepwalking incidents shows no evidence that people act out of malice in their sleep. "How it works is from anxiety," Marlys concludes. "Ken went to sleep in a very anxious state, thinking that he was going to see Denis the next day. That's how the program got set. That's what put him in the car."

When she was sure of her ground on that one, she asked her experts another question she knew the Crown would put at the trial. It was, "How could Ken stay in deep sleep long enough to do what he did? He must have been in that state close to half an hour."

Broughton and Cartwright exchanged glances. "It's not exceedingly uncommon for people to be in a sleepwalking episode for forty minutes," Broughton replied. "The average time is about twenty, twenty-five minutes, but remember that deep sleep can only be observed under the unnatural conditions of a sleep lab. In a person's own bed, the episodes could stretch out."

Of all the people who had tried to tell Ken that there was no "other man" in the Woods house that night, it was Rosalind Cartwright, the sleep-disturbance expert from Chicago, who was finally able to convince him. She gave him what amounted to a classroom lecture on the nature of his sleepwalking, after which he bowed his head thoughtfully a long time.

"Yeah," he said heavily. "I guess that's it. I guess I did it."

He was still bewildered. He could accept that he had acted out of habit when he drove to Scarborough from Pickering and parked his car in a visitor's space, but that didn't explain how he got into the house. He simply wasn't accustomed to letting himself in with a key.

"If I rang the doorbell, how come my father-in-law didn't hear it, or any of the kids?" he asks. "If the police had taken fingerprints off the key, we might have known. I'd never used a key to get into the house, I always rang the bell. Karen would just put in the key and go in, but I didn't do that, except twice in all the years I went there. But the police didn't take the fingerprints so I don't know if I used the key."

If he rang the buzzer, and Barbara came to the door—as seems likely—he had a tire-iron in his hand. Ken's tire-iron was found in the bedroom where Denis was almost strangled. It had been in his car for months, stowed under the passenger seat ever since he had used it to fix some pot lights, but it wasn't the best weapon the car contained. In the hatchback he had an axe and two knives he used for electrical repairs.

216

"I'd fixed pot lights in a house that was similar to my in-laws' house," Ken muses. "Maybe I thought I was at that house and I was going to fix the pot lights again. Or maybe I had the two things mixed. My in-laws have pot lights in the TV room. Maybe I thought I was going to fix the pot lights in their basement."

Karen pictures her mother going to the door and seeing Ken there, looking strange, as sleepwalkers do. She would try to rouse him but her efforts caused him to become violent. He swung the tire-iron and hit her a glancing blow on the head. Then he went into the darkened bedroom where he started to choke Denis. Barbara recovered from the blow and ran upstairs to the kitchen, where she seized her sharpest knife in order to come to her husband's assistance. Ken took the knife from her, grabbing it by the blade and cutting his hands. Then he stabbed Barbara. She backed away from him, mortally wounded, into the television room, where he struck her with the tire-iron and she died. Maybe he returned to the bedroom and stabbed Denis after that.

"The kids think he ran up the stairs to kill them and then noticed that his hands were cut, so that's why he left," Karen says with dreadful calm. "They want to hate him anyway so it's easier if they make up a real good reason."

That almost fits the clues, but not quite. Karen says no scenario really puts the pieces together.

"One thing that's not clear is the phone the kids heard," Karen comments. "The beep-beep-beep sound a phone makes when it's off the hook...."

Ken interrupts, "Now if I'd taken the phone off the hook there would have been blood on it from my hands...."

"But they didn't take fingerprints from the phone," Karen says, "and there was no blood on it. So they can't tell who tried to phone, my mom or Ken. And another question is about the lights."

"One officer says he went in and no lights were on," Ken continues. "Another officer says the house was lit up, every room. Two officers came in at the same time...."

"The question is," Karen leaps in, "who got the knife? My mom or Ken? In my opinion I don't think Ken could have got it..."

"...because I didn't really know where it was kept," he finishes. "I went in the kitchen for maybe a glass of water, that would be about it. I didn't open the cutlery drawers."

"Basically he didn't know where the knife was kept," says Karen. "If my mom got it she wouldn't have intended to use it on Ken. She would have got it to threaten him, to make him stop choking my dad."

Ken listens to this quietly, his face sad.

"Yeah," he says. "It could have been like that."

Marlys Edwardh was puzzled about quite another element in the Parks case. Marlys had expected Cathy Mocha to move for trial in August, when it was clear that Ken was fit to stand trial, but Cathy didn't do that and Marlys was unable to reach her to ascertain when the trial date could be expected.

Letters to her were not answered, and phone messages went unreturned. Marlys found it curious that Cathy Mocha didn't ask what the defence would be presenting at the trial. Marlys was sure that Cathy Mocha was banking on a defence of not guilty by reason of insanity, despite the unusual amount of activity that was happening at Metro East.

Marlys likes to play with possibilities, as many as she can imagine. A possibility that made her blood run cold was that Cathy Mocha would hear of the sleepwalking defence that was being constructed, and after investigation would decide that it was valid. Then she might offer to consent to the defence argument that Ken was sleepwalking, obviating the need for a trial on the circumstances of the case, if Ken Parks and Marlys would concede that sleepwalking was insane automatism rather than non-insane automatism.

"I think I would have taken the offer," Marlys said later. "Ken was facing first-degree murder. I don't think I could have recommended to him other than that he accept. But having to make that choice was my worst-case scenario."

The offer didn't come.

Finally, the date was chosen for early May.

In late April, with the trial only weeks away, Marlys at last received a letter from Cathy Mocha. The prosecutor asked if the defence would be relying on medical evidence regarding psychiatric issues. Marlys, unwilling to tip her hand about the sleepwalking, responded cautiously that she was not raising a defence of insanity. When she received no response, she wrote a second letter to say she would be calling psychiatric evidence.

Cathy Mocha asked Marlys for permission to have a Crown-appointed psychiatrist, Dr. Brian Butler, see Ken. Marlys couldn't refuse because her lack of co-operation would have made a poor impression on the jury. Besides, she has great respect for Brian Butler, who is an experienced forensic psychiatrist. "He's very thorough," she comments admiringly.

Brian Butler called Marlys to ask, as a professional would, what was going on with Ken Parks. Marlys told him it was possible that Ken was sleepwalking during the incident. Brian Butler, highly skeptical, relayed this information to the Crown. He told Cathy Mocha, "If this is truly sleepwalking, it has to be very unusual."

Ken Parks, notified that the Crown was sending a psychiatrist to see him, was terrified. He has a horror of being seen as insane, which he regards as a greater stigma than prison.

"Brian Butler is one of the few psychiatrists the Crown could have chosen who would be able to see sleepwalking as credible," Marlys said with relish. "And he did."

Brian Butler examined Ken, heard about the family history of sleepwalking, checked his own sources, and concluded that Ken Parks had been sleepwalking. Marlys found out that Butler agreed it was sleepwalking even before the Crown did. Butler tried to notify Cathy Mocha first, but she didn't return his call for a few days.

"I can't see any way to shake a sleepwalking defence," he told her.

Cathy threw herself into intense cramming about sleepwalking. Despite a heavy work load in the courts, she assembled and digested every piece of information she could find on sleepwalking. She found the slim trail of cases where juries had acquitted people of murder on the grounds that they were asleep when the killing occurred. In time she had five boxes of books, medical papers, law books, magazine articles, and clippings. Her primary argument would be that the sleepwalking defence stretched the bounds of credulity, she decided, but as a fall-back position she would try to persuade the court that sleepwalking in the Parks case fit within the legal definition, as outlined in *Rabey*, of insanity.

"By the time I got to the trial, I was something of an expert on sleep therapy," she commented with a chuckle.

The problem for Marlys Edwardh and Cathy Mocha was that sleepwalking had never been used in a Canadian trial, so far as either could discover. The Parks trial would be cutting new ground.

"It was terrific fun for that reason," Cathy Mocha stated, her face lighting up. "It's something that you study in law school as a theoretical area, and you sit back and think, 'Well, this will never come up.' And here I was, all of a sudden, dealing with it. It's something lawyers wait a lifetime to get, and I get it two and a half years after my call to the bar. I can't imagine a trial that would have an issue that is more novel and more exciting than the Parks case."

CHAPTER TWELVE

Trial

As the trial approached, Ken's panic increased. He had no appetite for the jail food, and the weight loss that had been so pronounced during his incarceration in the Metro East Detention Centre became alarming. He noted, without caring, that he had lost about sixty pounds since his arrest.

A man who schooled himself to be agreeable and who detested confrontation, he appeared placid and good-natured for most of the prison experience. In the weeks leading up to his first appearance in court, however, he grew tense and edgy. One evening he exploded. Two prisoners were anxiously waiting to use the common room's only telephone in order to arrange bail, but a young prisoner chose to tie up the phone while he enjoyed a reggae concert. The two men begged and pleaded as Ken watched, but the man kept the receiver blissfully to his ear and ignored them. Ken's sense of fairness was offended. Suddenly he rose up in wrath and snatched the telephone receiver from the startled music lover. A fight broke out, which guards speedily ended. Ken was left shaking in the aftermath of his adrenalin rush.

Another time, when he was switching television channels, an irate prisoner, a newcomer, called him a goof. Ken ignored this most heinous insult in the prison lexicon, but the man repeated it. Ken felt obliged to retaliate or lose status, so he hit the man a few times. Ken was pulled off by prisoners who said they would take care of the man the next day.

Everyone cooled down until it was time to be locked in the cells. The next morning, Ken used the seniority he had gained through his long incarceration. He warned the guards to move the man.

"If you don't," he said, "I'm afraid he'll get hurt." The man was removed from harm.

Karen was instructed by Marlys not to tell anyone that the defence would be that Ken was sleepwalking. She was tempted however to hint at it with her friend Connie Sullivan, because Connie had thought from the beginning that sleepwalking was a plausible explanation for Ken's irrational behaviour.

"I think it should be part of the trial that Ken was sleepwalking," she said casually to Connie. "If he was sleepwalking, he's really innocent."

She was not prepared for Connie's reaction.

"That would be terrible," she gasped. "That would mean he'd go free."

"Well, if he's not responsible for what happened, why shouldn't he go free?" Karen asked.

"He isn't safe," Connie said. "It just isn't safe to let him out. I'd worry that he'd come after someone else—me for instance."

"What would you want them to do with him?" Karen asked stiffly.

"Well, maybe he shouldn't be locked up," Connie conceded. "But how do we know it won't happen again?"

Karen said indignantly, "Anything's possible I guess, but it's also possible that you can walk across the street and get hit by a car. You could drown in a swimming-pool. There's so many possibilities in life. The chances of it happening again are so, so, so slim."

Marlys Edwardh, marshalling her expert witnesses, ran out of money to pay travel costs and fees. Ken's family, but mostly Lil Hodge, had provided the funds for the costly psychiatric examinations of Ken in Metro East. In all, eight specialists had seen him, and now the money was gone. In fact, except for the initial retainer of $5,000, she and Delmar Doucette had not been paid themselves and were acting without a fee.

Marlys appealed to Lil and Glen Hodge. If she didn't have another $10,000, she told them, she couldn't bring Ervin, Cartwright, and Broughton to Toronto, and she couldn't pay witness fees to Edmeads, Billings, and Hill.

The valiant Lil Hodge went to her bank, secured a loan, and gave the money to Marlys.

Marlys has boundless admiration for Ken's grandmother. "We couldn't have done the case without her," she says.

Karen prepared for what Marlys said would be two weeks or more of trial by arranging with a friend to baby-sit Melissa, with welfare compassionately providing the money. The toddler had grown to be an enterprising, inquisitive, bright-faced eighteen-month-old charmer. Karen became a commuter, catching the GO train every morning to Union Station and walking the six blocks or so to the courthouse.

The trial of Kenneth James Parks on a charge of the first-degree murder of Barbara Ann Woods was scheduled to begin on the morning of May 2, 1988, before a jury. The presiding judge was the Honourable Mr. Justice David Watt of the Supreme Court of Ontario, a man rated by lawyers who appear before him as one of the most intelligent and fair-minded on the high court bench. The trial took place in the dignified district courthouse on University Avenue, a relatively new and handsome edifice with a pleasant courtyard filled with pools and sculpture. The courtroom, a vast, windowless, wood-panelled cube, the largest courtroom in the province, is illuminated from the ceiling with pitiless cold light, and the air is stuffy to breathe.

Ken Parks is subject to eczema in times of stress. During the weeks before the trial, it had broken out in a pink rash that ringed his nose and covered his chin. Pale as milk and lightly sheathed in sweat, he was delivered to the courtroom in handcuffs each day, wearing his only suit, a light blue herring-bone weave much too large for his gaunt frame.

Marlys Edwardh, thirty-eight at the time of the trial, wore the black gown and white wing collar required of lawyers appearing in high court. She gave the appearance of calm as she studied her notes. Beside her, keeping in order the reference material she would need, was Delmar Doucette, then thirty-three, lanky and bearded and excited; his call to the bar had occurred only two weeks earlier. Cathy Mocha, twenty-nine, austere and composed, sat at the other end of the table with Staff Sergeant Bobby Adair of Metro homicide beside her.

To Karen's surprise, her family wasn't notified that the trial was scheduled. She was the one, in fact, who told them the court dates and, well schooled by Marlys, explained the arcane ways of the criminal justice system. She informed them that they were entitled to have the transcripts of their testimony at the preliminary hearing. Her father was anxious to prepare himself for the trial by refreshing his memory, so he tried to contact Crown lawyer Cathy Mocha to request the transcripts.

A week before the trial, they still had not arrived. Karen told Marlys, who volunteered to copy her own set of transcripts to help him.

"The family had been very fair-minded in their testimony at the preliminary," Marlys explains. "It was in our interest to have them give their evidence the same way."

Marlys is meticulous in preparing her witnesses, so Karen had ample explanations for the ritualistic procedures of a formal court and became the family's legal consultant. She provided reasons for such matters as why witnesses had to sit in sad little rooms waiting to be called when they would rather watch the trial, and why the jury sometimes was excluded. As the trial unfolded, Denis found it simpler to ask Del Doucette directly what was happening and what he could expect next. Though an odd one, the relationship between the Crown's most compelling witness and the defence lawyer was no more strange than any of the other tangled relationships in the extraordinary case.

Karen sat alone. Ken's grandmother Lil Hodge, mother, and brothers sat together, and Denis Woods sat with his other children. Karen moved between both groups, on good terms with everyone but belonging to neither.

"I wanted to make a statement for the jury that I was independent," she explains. "I didn't sit with Ken's family and I didn't sit with my family. I sat by myself."

She found it unbearable to look at Ken, so thin and ill-looking. It was painful to be so close but not to be allowed to touch him.

She hated the handcuffs on his wrists that his escort removed after he was brought into the courtroom.

There was also the awkward moment when Del Doucette gave Ken a belt to hold up his too-large pants, which otherwise would have fallen. Since Ken was not allowed a belt in the cells, it was a ritual that Del repeated every morning before the judge arrived. Every afternoon when the court recessed for the night, Ken removed the belt and returned it to the lawyer.

Karen watched without expression. She kept her dignity but she wept inside.

On May 2, the trial started with two pre-trial motions presented by the defence. One was to exclude Ken's second taped statement to the police, made after he said he couldn't afford a lawyer, and the other to exclude statements made to the police by Karen and by Ken's mother, Betty Parks. That took three days; Marlys succeeded in convincing the judge on both motions. Judge Watt's decision on the motion that the second tape was inadmissible found its way to the Supreme Court of Canada almost two years later, where Mr. Justice Lamer, on behalf of a unanimous court, ruled that justice is not done when an accused person isn't informed of the right to be represented by a publicly funded lawyer when the person is unable to pay for legal services.

On the afternoon of Thursday, May 5, selection of the jury began and proceeded briskly. The Crown used its options to exclude such people as nurses, teachers, and social workers, who might be expected to have some experience with the bizarre potentials of human behaviour. Teachers are a favourite of defence lawyers because they have a reputation for compassion and comprehension. Marlys, allowed fewer refusals than the Crown, was obliged to guard her challenges carefully and was so frugal with them that at the end she had two left over.

"No questions are allowed by either side," Del Doucette explains. "We had their names, their ages, and their occupations. Beyond that all we could do was look them in the eye and decide if we wanted them or not."

Marlys was looking for intelligence and signs of the varied life experience that would be needed to know that truth often is stranger than fiction. Since the defence rested on a bedrock of scientific evidence, Marlys wanted people who would be able to understand the technical language of the sleep-disorder experts. She was also looking for mature adults, rather than young people inexperienced in the complexities of relationships.

Two people were excluded because they knew Ken. One was a friend of the Hodge family and the other dated a girl he knew.

"You look at the jury and it's scary," says Karen. "You think, these people are going to decide Ken's life. This whole year that we've been through comes to these people. What they decide changes Ken's life, it changes my life, it changes Melissa's life. It's really scary."

Karen, always keen on what's fair, was indignant to discover that the Crown was allowed many more refusals of prospective jurors than the defence. She thought it should be even. "Basically the Crown gets to pick the jury, because the defence runs out of refusals."

Cathy Mocha called the first witness, Denis Woods, and to the horror of the defence asked him about insurance. She wanted to know if the family had ever talked about taking out insurance, and he replied that the subject had been discussed.

The Crown left the exchange hanging there while Marlys sat still, enduring a storm of feeling. "It was one of those horrible moments for a lawyer," she said later. "It happens every once in a while. I couldn't get up fast enough to stop the question because it just popped out. Once it was out, I couldn't protest because the jury would think that there *was* insurance."

The possibility that Denis and Barbara had insurance from which Ken would benefit was one of the first concerns addressed by Marlys when she started the case, because such a policy would establish a motive for the killing. She had learned that no such arrangement existed. The family had discussed insurance briefly one time after Melissa's birth, when Ken and Karen thought of insuring themselves and making Denis and Barbara beneficiaries to raise their child in the event of their deaths, but nothing had been done about it.

No mention of insurance had been made at the preliminary hearing. Cathy Mocha's question planted the suggestion in the jury's mind that Ken might benefit from the death of Barbara and Denis Woods. From the defence point of view, the well was poisoned, though Marlys in her cross-examination of Denis was careful to draw from him the true facts.

Still, the jury was left with a very damaging innuendo. When Denis Woods finished testifying, the court adjourned for the day and Marlys and Del sat down to prepare a motion for mistrial.

The next morning, however, the motion was pre-empted. One of the jurors asked to be excused on the grounds of hardship to sit on a trial that was expected to last for three weeks. After a great deal of discussion it was agreed by all parties to start again the following Monday with a new jury.

The second jury of twelve, eight men and four women, included a pilot, a data-entry officer, a bookkeeper, an executive assistant, a driver, a keyer, an engineer, a supervisor, a technologist, an expediter, a real-estate agent, and a consultant. There was a great range of ages. Two were black, both women. The jury foreman was the expediter and looked the part, a confident man with a decisive air.

"They were average-looking, everyday people," Karen commented.

Ken felt more comfortable with the second jury. He liked their looks, all of them intent and serious. Karen, too, studied their faces, looking for clues as to how they felt, but all developed masks that she found inscrutable. "I didn't get any feeling watching them which witnesses they believed and which they didn't, who they liked and who they didn't like," she sighed. "They showed no emotion at all."

She liked watching the pilot best. He really slouched in his chair, which was in the front row, closest to the benches where the spectators sat, and sometimes he almost disappeared from sight. "His posture was awful," she comments, grinning.

The trial began again on Monday, May 9, 1988, with prior agreement from Cathy Mocha that there would be no more mention of insurance.

The Crown attorney opened with a brief summary for the jury of what she intended to prove. Kenneth Parks, she said, drove twenty-three kilometres from his home in Pickering to the home in Scarborough of his wife's parents, entered through a basement door, tried to strangle Denis Woods, hit Barbara Woods with a tire-iron, got a knife from the kitchen, and then stabbed them both, Barbara Woods fatally. Afterwards he went to a police station and said he had been sleeping and woke to find a knife in his hand.

The jury listened impassively. A court reporter yawned: nothing much to this.

Cathy Mocha then called her first witness, Gregory John Schofield, a police draftsman. He provided the court with diagrams of the townhouse at Unit 85, 25 Brimwood (exhibits 1 and 1A). There was an intake of breath and craning of heads when she called the next witness: "Denis John Woods."

Denis Woods, then forty-six years old, a reserved, inward man whose head bore the scars of knife wounds, took the stand calmly. He answered the attorney's questions with a deliberate, considered manner and even tone. Before she began the part of her examination that would deal with Ken's relationship with the Woods family, Cathy Mocha turned and gave Del Doucette a significant look. Del twisted around to catch Karen's eye, and Karen nodded and left the courtroom. At the request of the Crown, Karen was to be excluded when any of her family testified about their feelings for Ken.

Denis maintained his composure through a long series of questions about the family's relationship with Ken Parks.

To one such question he replied, "Well, when he married into the family, we treated him like a son from that point of time."

"Did your relationship with Mr. Parks change?" asked Cathy Mocha.

"I wouldn't say so, in the sense that we were always on speaking terms up to, I suppose, when we became aware of Karen's problems.... Karen tended to come round just as frequently, but he wasn't with her."

"Could you describe for the members of the jury how your wife appeared to get along with the accused?"

Denis answered, "Again, just like a mother to him subsequent to the marriage, as far as I saw."

"About how often would Karen see your wife?"

"I would think four or five times a week."

Denis was in the stand most of the day. Late in his testimony, Cathy Mocha showed him a knife sheath and a Wilkinson stay-sharp knife (exhibits 3 and 4), which he identified as the one Barbara kept in a kitchen drawer near the stove.

The questions Marlys asked in cross-examination emphasized that Denis Woods had had no warning that someone was in the room before he woke in the dark to find someone straddling his body and trying to choke him. That was done to remind the jury of the strangeness of the situation.

Her questions about the knife brought out another point. She established that it was kept in the same drawer with a bread knife, that it was kept sharpened, and that it was in a sheath that made it difficult to recognize as a knife. A person seeking a knife but unfamiliar with the cutlery would be more likely to seize the naked bread knife than the one in the sheath.

Inference: Ken Parks didn't take the knife out of the drawer. Barbara Woods did.

She moved to the area of Ken's place in the Woods family.

"From your perspective did you feel he was a positive influence on Karen?"

"It appeared to settle Karen down, yes," Denis nodded. "She became a more normal daughter in the household."

"She went back to school? She completed her school?"

"That's correct."

"And you felt during this time that Ken was a hard-working young man?"

"Yes."

"And, indeed, he and Karen had done quite well..."

"Yes, indeed."

"...given their position and how long they had been married?"

"Yes. Yes."

Marlys found it remarkable that Denis was so willing to be fair to Ken, despite the opportunity he had to cast doubt on the young man's character. Most people who suffer great loss as a result of someone's action are not inclined to frame their views of that person in other than a nasty light.

Denis was forthcoming even about Barbara's affection for Ken.

"She had a pet name for him, did she not?" Marlys asked.

"She always used to call him the gentle giant," he replied steadily.

The children testified next, and Karen was shuffled out of the room by Del just before they spoke about their feelings towards Ken. Prudence, fifteen years old and nervous, led off, followed the next day by Emma, twenty, who spoke in such a soft, frail voice that she had to be cautioned many times to speak up. Jonathan, seventeen, was next. When he described the marriage of Ken and Karen Parks, he made the jury smile. "When they came over they always seemed to be laughing and not too uptight," he said earnestly.

Samantha, twenty-two, closest in age to Karen, was the last. It was hurtful to Ken when she said her relationship with him was "distant".

The testimonies developed a rhythm, the Crown attorney drawing from the young people the chronology of that night of horror, the defence attorney concentrating on the good relations Ken had had with the Woods family. To the jury's puzzlement, both spent considerable time asking about the parking arrangements for cars belonging to the Woods family and their visitors.

Marlys and Del were confused by the Crown's fascination with the subject of parking. They couldn't imagine why it mattered so much to the prosecution to establish where visitors usually parked. They concluded that Cathy Mocha was going to argue in summation that Ken had parked in an unfamiliar slot, thus indicating that he was conscious when he drove to Scarborough that night, but the truth was that Ken and Karen often parked behind townhouse 77. Mystified, but anxious to take nothing for granted, Marlys in cross-examination also dealt with parking, until the jury was saturated with information about the guest parking slots at 25 Brimwood.

Similarly, the Crown appeared anxious to establish which lights were on in the household. Marlys couldn't see where that would take the prosecution, but she defended against all possibilities by asking a blizzard of questions herself about the lights. She succeeded in establishing that no one agreed which lights were on when the police arrived and which the police had turned on themselves, reflexively.

"I didn't know what she was trying to do with the lights," Marlys explains, "so I set out to confuse everybody. We got so many versions about the lights, all different, that we nullified whatever she had been planning to do."

Late on Tuesday morning the parade of police witnesses began, leading off with Richard Wiszniowski of the Metro Police identification bureau. He told of following a trail of blood from the counter in the police station to a red Capri parked outside. Patrick Sayer of the Durham Police identification section then brought pictures of the empty garage beside the Parks townhouse in Pickering and of Ken's cluttered workbench; these solemnly became exhibits 10 and 11.

Constable Clarence Blake, who drove the route between the Parks townhouse and the Woods townhouse several times, testified that the distance was 23.3 kilometres. Sergeant Ian Mann of the Metro Toronto Police identification bureau brought the knife sheath, blood-stained sheets, blankets and pillowcases, and a stack of colour photographs of Ken's car and the interior of the Woods townhouse. The jury looked with dismay at pictures of bloodstains on walls, a kitchen drawer sinisterly agape, a telephone off the hook.

Two photographs were of tire-irons, one found by police behind a box in the blood-drenched master bedroom and another in the back of Ken's car. The exhibits now totalled fifty-two.

John Mustard, a forensic engineer in the attorney general's department, testified next. His job was to establish that the jack found on a dusty shelf in Ken Parks' garage belonged to a Chevette, a model of car Ken had once owned. Before he could begin, Marlys Edwardh protested that she could not see the point to his testimony.

The jury withdrew while Marlys Edwardh and Cathy Mocha gave their reasons to the judge with the elaborate politeness required by courtroom etiquette, though both were actually quite irritated. The dispute found a simple resolution. Marlys consulted with Ken, who said the jack indeed belonged to his old

Chevette. He had forgotten to replace it in the trunk when he sold the car.

The character of the early part of the trial was established. Cathy Mocha, whose style is cool and distant, was taking an aggressive approach, pushing the Crown's case to the edge of admissibility at every turn. Marlys Edwardh was playing the role of a blocker, protesting whenever the Crown strayed from a path that she thought the evidence supported.

The skirmishes always were conducted with the jury absent and went more often to the defence than the Crown. For instance, Marlys was able to exclude ghastly photographs of Denis Woods' fresh wounds, images that most certainly would have been seared into the memories of the jury when it came time to discuss the verdict.

Denis Woods came every day. Sometimes during the recesses he chatted with Lil Hodge, who staunchly maintained her position that both families were civilized people who had no cause to be rude to one another. Many days all the Woods children were there. Karen talked easily with them in the corridor outside the courtroom, but they stuck to inconsequentials and avoided speaking about the trial.

Judge Watt, regarded as one of the brightest and most promising young judges in the country, showed himself an amiable, relaxed man. When the jury had been dismissed late Tuesday afternoon, he asked Cathy Mocha if she could tell him when the case for the Crown might be completed.

"Yes, my lord," she replied. "The Crown's case is moving along much more quickly than I anticipated."

"It sometimes does," he replied drily.

She smiled back and said that she hoped to finish by Friday.

He asked Marlys Edwardh when she expected to finish.

"I'm such a terrible estimator," she confessed.

"Well," the judge sighed, "I'll bear that in mind."

She reflected and told him she might finish in five days. The judge reminded the lawyers that the first long weekend of the summer was looming. He didn't want to instruct the jury just before a three-day holiday and oblige them to be isolated from their families over that period.

When they caught his point, the lawyers promised that they could not complete their presentations until after the long weekend.

Cathy Mocha began on Wednesday morning, May 11, 1988, with a General Motors employee, Alick MacLean, who established that the car jack in the Parks garage and the tire-iron found in Denis Woods' bedroom came from a Chevette, models 1976 to 1987.

Heidi Turner, the night clerk in the 42 Division police station, then described Ken's dramatic entrance just before five o'clock on the morning of May 24, 1987. Though she had been in a witness-box only once before, at the preliminary, and was fearful, she provided a graphic glimpse into the chaos of those moments after Ken's arrival at the station.

Describing the frantic scene as Ken's hands were being crudely bandaged, she said breathlessly, "I was asking whether I should call an ambulance, and the phones were ringing, and I was answering the phones and trying to check out his name on our computer system and answering our police radio, and I also went and locked the front door."

For a moment, the scene leaped to life for the jury. Marlys Edwardh was to use that glimpse into the reality of the chaos to suggest that none of the police witnesses could be certain what they heard Ken say and, certainly, it was unlikely that any one of them had stepped back from the confusion to take notes, as they solemnly claimed they had.

"It's simply ludicrous to say that they were taking notes," Marlys comments. "When Ken stumbled into the station he was trying to make sense of the pieces of distorted memory he had. He had the mystery of Barbara's face and the fact that he couldn't remember Denis. Putting that together with finding a knife in his hand, he thought he could have killed someone. To say, as he is reported, 'I have killed my mother-in-law and my father-in-law,' is inconsistent with amnesia. He assumed he had done something, that something horrible had happened, possibly a killing. Then he noticed his hands, which hadn't even hurt him to that point, and he said, '*My hands*,' as one would to see wounds gushing blood."

The police on duty that morning appeared next in the witness-box, starting with Sergeant Henry Flavelle. The courthouse gossip was that Flavelle had claimed credit for solving the case on the grounds that he had heard Ken's confession. When questioned by the Crown he gave a rather bland picture of his own deportment in the few minutes after Ken's arrival and suggested that Ken's behaviour was coherent. Checking her transcript of the preliminary trial, when Flavelle did not know that sleepwalking would be the defence, Marlys Edwardh reminded the officer that he had testified then that Ken's state of mind appeared to be one of amazement.

"You said," she reminded him, " 'The tone of his voice was...uh...amazement. Like 'I've really done this?'...'"

The sergeant didn't like the direction in which the defence attorney was taking him. Finally he conceded that he had had an impression that Ken was full of amazement.

Constable Frederick Palmer came next. He had been in the police car that followed Sergeant Flavelle to the Woods town-house, and he was the officer who had stayed with Denis Woods until the ambulance arrived. His testimony and that of the officers who followed him, Larry Webb and Cecil Gerrard, gave slightly different accounts of the tumultuous minutes when the officers tried to stanch the flow of blood from Ken's hands and then abandoned the effort and drove him to the hospital.

Marlys Edwardh, cross-examining each briefly, ensured that the jury appreciated the heightened excitement of those few minutes and the unlikelihood that anyone's memory was entirely accurate.

"The jury needed to understand that everyone was getting the gist of what Ken said," she explains, "but no utterance was faithfully recorded. Their recollections simply weren't reliable."

That ended Wednesday's witnesses. On Thursday, Cathy Mocha led off with Sergeant Colin Arthur Ashton. He offered something new. When he took Ken's arm in the police station, he said, he thought the man might collapse from the amount of blood he was losing. When Marlys asked him if he made notes about the moment when he was holding Ken, the officer said that note-taking was not a pressing concern at the time.

"The problem being the situation we were faced with," he told her honestly. "It was out of control."

Constable Brian Penwarden followed. He was there to testify that when the officers ran out of the station to investigate what had happened in the Woods townhouse, Ken said to him helpfully, "They'll need keys to get in." On the front counter next to a huge pool of blood, Penwarden found bloodstained keys on a key-chain with a miniature wrench and gave them to Sergeant Flavelle, who was just about to pull away in a cruiser.

Eric Puusa, the police officer who had stayed by Ken's side for five hours in the Scarborough Grace hospital emergency room, presented the notes he had made of Ken's disjointed statements. Constable Murray Grills, on patrol that night with Puusa, followed. Ken Parks, he said, was sobbing in great distress.

After lunch, David Montgomery, a forensic scientist, took the stand to present the blood analysis evidence. He explained in some detail why the Woods case presented problems for him. Some samples were blood type AB, which might mean that they came from a person with blood type AB, a relatively rare type, or that they were a mixture of the blood of two people, one of them A and the other B.

Ken's jacket, for instance, was stained with blood from his type, blood from Denis Woods' type, and blood that belonged to neither Ken, Denis, or Barbara Woods. The other garments provided the same confusion. The blood found in the garage and the car, however, was Ken's. Human blood stains found on the kitchen drawer didn't belong to Barbara, Denis, or Ken but might have been a mixture of Barbara's and Ken's blood. The blood on the telephone, however, seemed to be from Denis Woods.

As his explanations grew more technical, the jury began to look thoroughly baffled. One part of his evidence, however, stood out. Ken's blood was found on the bedding in the bedroom. It seemed that during the second attack on Denis Woods, Ken's hands had already been cut by the knife.

Next was Dr. Ernest Salmon, the surgeon at Scarborough Grace hospital who examined the wounds sustained by Denis Woods and Ken Parks. He was on the stand for more than an hour, after which the jury knew the details of the injuries to both men: Ken's fingers had been cut severely, and Denis Woods had numerous knife wounds to his head and back.

That ended Thursday's testimony. When the jury had filed out, Judge Watt asked Cathy Mocha if she was proceeding on schedule and she said she was. She expected to finish the next day. Marlys Edwardh had given notice that she was going to file an application to the court in the absence of the jury. As everyone knew, she intended to ask that the charge be reduced from first-degree murder to second-degree murder. That effort had failed at the preliminary hearing and failed at the Supreme Court level, but she was undeterred. She firmly believed that the Crown didn't have any evidence that Ken had planned and deliberately carried out the killing. She warned the judge that her application might require the entire afternoon.

On Friday morning, Cathy Mocha advised Judge Watt that she was calling additional witnesses. The schedule was about to be derailed.

After four days of police, doctors, and forensic scientists, the jury was refreshed to find that the first witness that day was a youth, Martin Liss, a twenty-year-old York University student who lives at unit 81 on 25 Brimwood Boulevard and is a neighbour of the Woods family. For reasons that baffled the jury, he simply testified that on the night in question he parked his father's Volkswagen van in the Liss family's space in front of the basement entrance to their townhouse.

Marlys was stunned by this. What was the Crown doing? Had she missed something crucial about the parking space?

Then, while perplexity hung in the air, Sergeant Ian Mann was recalled. Cathy Mocha wanted him to tell the jury about the trail of blood he had followed from the basement door of unit 85. He testified that the trail led from unit 85 to a space behind unit 77. A photograph of the location became Exhibit 68.

Marlys thought she understood. Cathy Mocha was preparing to tell the jury in her summation that Ken had parked in an unfamiliar place and then ran there directly after the killing, showing that he was fully aware of what he was doing. Marlys, however, remembered Karen telling her that the trail of blood went in one direction and then another, as if Ken hadn't been sure where the car was.

The defence lawyer was rough with the sergeant. She asked him sharply if he was trying to follow "a true trail" of bloodstains. He replied that he was.

"If you were documenting a true trail," she continued implacably, "in the ordinary course would you not have counted the number of droplets and measured their consistency, their frequency, and also exactly where they were?"

The officer looked annoyed. "Perhaps I should have, but I did not do it in this case."

"You didn't do that," Marlys echoed, to make sure the jury got the point that police work had been casual in the Parks case.

At the end of a series of questions, she pounced.

"All I would really like to suggest to you, sir, is that, although it is clear that you may have seen a pattern of drops going down to unit 77, or in that direction, what you cannot say to the ladies and gentlemen of the jury is that you measured with any precision to see whether or not the person, for example, was moving four or five feet each way or whether the person may have stopped and turned back for one step and gone forward. That wasn't the kind of analysis you did?"

Sergeant Mann, thoroughly irritated, replied tersely, "No."

The Crown's next witness that Friday morning was Paul Longo, a Bell Canada employee. He said that the Woods household had one Bell telephone in the kitchen and that three phones elsewhere in the house were connected to the Bell line. He provided the information that when one phone was off the hook, none of the phones would be operable. The jury then was treated to a recording of dial tone, then the familiar loud beep-beep-beep of a phone off the hook, lasting eighty seconds, and then a metallic voice pleasantly asking the caller to replace the receiver.

Marlys thought this was pointless. She assumed that the Crown was trying to lay the groundwork for saying that Ken had taken the kitchen receiver off the hook in order to prevent a call for help. Since police had testified that the kitchen phone was on the hook when they arrived on the scene, this premise didn't make sense. Ken would have had to replace the phone after the killing, in which case there would have been copious amounts of blood in the kitchen and on the telephone. The logical explanation for why the phone was off the hook, Marlys thought, was that the bedroom phone had been knocked off the table during the struggle and the investigating police had inadvertently put it back on the hook.

"The police who went to the Woods house that morning weren't trained to do homicide," Marlys observes. "They were responding to an emergency in which human life was involved. It was more important to see to Denis and to look for more victims than to think about preserving evidence. The only fingerprints found in the place were those of the police. They handled everything."

John Cowan, a police constable with traffic division, then described testing the two routes from Ken's house to the Woods townhouse. Taking Highway 401, as Ken always did, the trip clocked at 23.3 kilometres and involved making six turns and observing two stop signs and fourteen traffic lights. Another route, slightly shorter, included nine turns, two stop signs, and twenty-nine traffic lights. The time elapsed was about sixteen minutes.

After a recess that morning and before the jury was recalled, Marlys Edwardh objected to the next witness Cathy Mocha was planning to call, a traffic engineer who would testify to the timing of the traffic lights over the route that Ken drove. The defence lawyer declared that the evidence would be hearsay. Cathy Mocha said her witness would only discuss which lights were operating before dawn on May 24. Marlys Edwardh continued to protest.

"Well, is this a real big issue or something?" the judge asked.

"Well, it is becoming one," replied Marlys grimly. "I don't think it would assist the jury at all."

The judge seemed to agree, "Will they really be assisted by an engineer who might talk in language that some of them will be unable to understand?" he inquired of the prosecution lawyer.

Cathy Mocha accepted defeat, asking instead that she be allowed to show the jury a map of the route with the traffic lights marked.

Looking at Marlys Edwardh, the judge commented drily, "I wouldn't think you would have much dispute about where roads are in Metropolitan Toronto."

She said quickly, "There is none."

The road map of Scarborough became Exhibit 72.

Cathy Mocha then called Dr. Emil Orsini, a resident in orthopedic surgery who had performed the operation on Ken's hands in Sunnybrook Hospital. The jury learned again that on Ken's right hand the tendons and nerves of three fingers were severed, with the little finger cut the deepest. On the left hand, tendons and nerves were cut on the ring and little fingers. Pictures of Ken's hands five weeks later showed an extra laceration on the index finger of the right hand that had been missed by Dr. Orsini and Dr. Salmon in their preliminary examinations.

Cathy Mocha asked if the injuries were consistent with someone holding the knife in one hand and accidentally sliding his other hand along the blade. The doctor said that was possible. If the injuries were inflicted that way, Marlys Edwardh asked in cross-examination, wouldn't the doctor expect to see all the fingers cut instead of only three? The doctor agreed. Marlys then asked if the injuries were consistent with someone mindlessly trying to grab a knife away from someone else. Her point was that no mentally alert person would seize a sharp knife by the blade.

"It's possible, yes," he said.

The next witness for the prosecution was Staff Sergeant Bobby Burns Adair, the Metro Toronto homicide detective who had headed the Parks investigation. He gave an account of his inspection of the Woods townhouse, the appearance of the body of Barbara Woods, and his meeting with Ken Parks in Sunnybrook. He brought with him the tape (Exhibit 73) of his interview with Ken. Because Ken's gasping responses were sometimes difficult to understand, the Crown provided the jury with a transcript to help them follow along.

Ken's voice alternated between a breathless monotone and emotional outbursts as he told police that he could remember nothing after falling asleep in front of the television after watching *Saturday Night Live*.

"All I know, I woke up and I saw her face and her face looked so sad. I don't know how I got there. I don't remember." Asked on the tape if he could remember stabbing two people, he replied, "I just remember seeing her face. I ran." He said he thought he ran to the telephone in the kitchen to call the police, but he wasn't sure about that. He talked disjointedly about his marital problems because of his gambling on the horses.

"I have a gambling problem and my wife.... It was my fault. I gambled away all the money.... I lost all the money I saved after I stopped working there, and I lost all the money we had in savings."

Ken, sitting in the prisoner's box, bent over and put his hands over his ears.

When her turn came to cross-examine the witness, Marlys began aggressively. She wanted to know why police hadn't seized the screwdrivers, a knife, and a hand hatchet in the hatchback of Ken's car, since these were potential murder weapons. Adair said uncomfortably that there might have been "some confusion" because two investigative teams were working at once.

She asked if he had tested the other keys on the key ring used by Ken. He had not.

Marlys had been chipping all week at the degree of sloppiness in the police investigation. She was hoping the jury had not missed it.

The Crown's final witness for the day and the week was Dr. Hans Sepp, the forensic pathologist who had performed the autopsy on Barbara Woods. Marlys was shocked that the Crown hadn't warned the Woods family that this evidence would be painful to hear. She dispatched Del Doucette to tell Denis that the testimony would be grisly. He gravely thanked the defence lawyer and sent his children out of the courtroom.

Marlys comments, "Pathologists are always detached. They make death seem meaningless, like a cucumber on a shelf."

With the predicted lack of emotion, Hans Sepp described Barbara Woods as a forty-one-year-old woman, five feet four and a half inches in height, weighing one hundred and fifteen pounds. She had been stabbed five times, once to the heart. This wound had killed her, but there were four more to her chest and back. In addition she had been struck on the face and head with a blunt instrument or, possibly, had come into forceful contact with the wall. A single blow had broken her nose and skull. The doctor, shown the tire-iron that was Exhibit 5, agreed that it could have been the weapon.

Also, some ribs were broken. The doctor thought those injuries came from the body's being pressed against a hard surface. Marlys Edwardh elicited from the doctor the startling information that Barbara Woods could have walked upstairs despite the broken ribs (to the kitchen, perhaps, for the knife) and would have lived and been conscious for some twenty minutes after the wound to her heart. The blow to the head, however, would have caused almost immediate unconsciousness.

A dreadful picture was being drawn of Barbara screaming while being stabbed, certainly in the bedroom to judge from the quantity of blood found there, and then stumbling into the next room where she was struck on the head and abruptly silenced.

That ended the case for the Crown. Thirty witnesses had testified to the death of Barbara Woods; seventy-four exhibits had been entered and a number of admissions. It was mid-afternoon on Friday, May 13, 1988, and a tired jury left for the weekend. At three minutes to four, Marlys buckled down to work. She moved for an acquittal on the charge of first-degree murder. She said, as she had on two other occasions, that there was no evidence that the murder of Barbara Ann Woods was planned.

"It has not been shown," she insisted, "that there is any calculated scheme or design carefully considered by the accused in advance of his homicidal act. The evidence discloses no pre-existing intention to kill; indeed, it is the very antithesis of such intention when one considers the nature of the relationship between the accused and the deceased, more particularly the lack of enmity or animus. It is acknowledged that the accused took a tire-iron with him, but such circumstance, whether viewed singly or in combination, affords no evidence of a pre-existing plan nor its implementation."

Cathy Mocha protested that a jury, properly instructed by the judge, could find the murder to be planned and deliberate. The evidence, though circumstantial, could support such a view.

"He took a weapon to the house of the deceased," she argued. "He had two sets of keys and a flashlight. He was there in the early hours of the morning on the day there was to be a discussion of the accused's gambling problem at a family meeting. He drove some distance to the scene. He didn't simply arise from sleep and strike out at the first person he met."

Further, she added, the Crown was not required to show a motive in order to establish that the murder was planned. The apparent absence of motive was irrelevant.

Judge Watt listened patiently to both lawyers and announced when they finished half an hour later that he was reserving his decision.

On Monday, May 16, 1988, in a courtroom still empty of the jury, he was ready with his ruling. In the suspenseful preamble, Judge Watt noted that the test for a charge of first-degree murder included "that the murder which the accused committed was planned and deliberate". If a reasonable jury could not find such intent, the accused would have to be found not guilty of first-degree murder. The judge might even direct the jury to acquit. He quoted the applicable statutory provision, which reads: "Murder is first-degree murder when it is planned and deliberate."

Citing many legal definitions of deliberate—"not impulsive", "slow in deciding", "considered"—the judge ruled that the murder of Barbara Ann Woods did not fall under the definition of planned and deliberate.

"There is not, in my respectful view," he declared, "any evidence upon the basis of which a reasonable jury, properly instructed, could conclude that the accused's murder of the deceased was planned and deliberate in the sense required by the authorities....The application, accordingly, succeeds."

Before the judge could call in the jury, some minor hitches arose. Ken's trial for fraud was scheduled in a downstairs courtroom, and Marlys was obliged to hustle there and ask for an adjournment. Cathy Mocha had a problem of a different kind.

She was trying to find a sleep-disorder expert to counter the authorities that Marlys would be producing. She hoped to call a sleep-disorder specialist, but was having trouble getting in touch with him. She asked the judge to adjourn until after lunch.

"My lord," said Marlys, "with the greatest of respect to my friend's dilemma, I am really quite speechless at the notion that her expert has vanished into the night.... In any trial of this kind, my lord, a great deal of work gets done, and an enormous amount of stress rests upon Mr. Parks. He expects us today to do an opening and then he will proceed, as best he can, to put before you and the ladies and gentlemen of the jury his position and understanding of what happened that night. To ask him to defer is, in my opinion, extremely unfair and almost a little inhumane."

She continued, "We have a number of experts who are coming in from different cities. Some of them can only be available at certain times."

Her anxiety was real. Roger Broughton, her star witness, was leaving for Italy in two days. To her relief, the judge agreed to adjourn only until eleven.

With that he called in the jury and explained that his responsibility as judge was not to infringe on theirs, but he was obliged to make rulings on points of law. He described the requirements for first-degree murder charges to succeed and informed the jury that he found an absence of proof of "the essential ingredient", which was planning and deliberation. Accordingly he was instructing the jury to find Kenneth Parks not guilty of first-degree murder.

He suggested pleasantly that the jury didn't have to retire to consider his instructions. The members could discuss it in the jury box.

The jury foreman said with prompt spunkiness, "We wish to retire."

A few minutes later the jury returned. With dignity the foreman announced that the jury found Kenneth Parks not guilty of first-degree murder. Without being relaid, the charge would stand as second-degree murder.

Ken was swept by relief. Instead of twenty-five years in prison, he was looking at ten years. Ten years wasn't so terrible; Karen might wait for him. He appreciated that it was still a life sentence with only the *possibility* of parole after ten years, but he preferred to think of it as only ten years.

Marlys comments, "All it gave him is a little light at the end of the tunnel. With twenty-five years, there's no light."

Marlys made her opening remarks to the jury, outlining her case. She began by saying that there was a warm and loving relationship between Ken Parks and his wife's parents and, accordingly, that there was a total absence of motive. She would be calling expert witnesses, forensic psychiatrists, psychologists, neuro-psychiatrists, and experts in the field of sleep disorders. The accused man is not mentally ill and he does not have a disease of the brain, she declared. At the time of the killing he was in a state of somnambulism, a sleep state where there is no will and no conscious mind. The defence would establish the history of sleeping disorders in the Parks family, she went on, and show that, on the date of the killing, Kenneth Parks was suffering from severe stress, had been sleep-deprived for some weeks culminating in two nights without any sleep, and had exhausted his body with strenuous exercise that morning—all of which contributed to his state of protracted deep sleep during which the activities occurred.

The jury showed no emotion, but idle spectators all over the courtroom sat up in astonishment. Then Marlys called her first witness: "Kenneth James Parks."

As Ken moved to the witness-box, Karen Parks stood up to leave the courtroom. She knew she was allowed to stay, but she was scheduled to testify later and she wanted to make it clear to the jury that she wasn't parroting Ken's testimony. It had been Marlys' suggestion that it would be better if her testimony looked independent, and Karen agreed with the reasoning. Besides, it would be difficult for her if it happened, as it often does in marriages, that she and Ken did not recollect events exactly the same; she'd rather present her version without having to worry about what he had said.

She made her way out the courtroom door as conspicuously as she dared.

Marlys took Ken through his life story while the jury studied the huge man. His nervousness was appealing. In the first few minutes of his testimony Ken said he was "a very trudiant kid", when he meant "truant". It was apparent that he also had been a very lonely kid. "I was—I never really confided in anyone," he explained when Marlys asked about his earliest relationships. "I was always a self-supportive person."

He stumbled through testimony, sweating and anxious. The transcript in some places is incoherent. Asked whether Barbara Woods ever was critical of him, Ken said painfully, "Never. She never. She never spoke—she never said anything to me or I never felt anything. She always just gave me support and love."

Marlys probed in that area, asking if Karen's parents ever criticized him or were angry with him. Ken replied, "No. They were always supportive of me and I loved them and assumed they loved me. I knew they loved me and I was like a son to them."

In a typical exchange, when Marlys was asking about his gambling, she asked about his intentions towards his employer.

He said, "Well, I had intended on—if I got the big win, I was waiting for the big win and when I got the big win I would pay them, like pay them back, pay them, like pay my account, pay them back, pay—just get everything just all straightened out again. I had my daughter coming."

And again, when Marlys was asking about the effect of stress on his work at Revere, he said, "My work was—I was having a lot of pressure at work and my work, like slided.... I put a lot of things off, kept putting them off.... Like work that had to be done and then there's another work and I would put this one away and start the other one and the pile would just start building and building higher and higher."

The sentences weren't perfectly constructed, or even grammatical, but a portrait emerged. Ken Parks, isolated as a child, truly loved Karen's parents and for months before the fatal night was over his head in trouble. He was working twelve and fourteen hours a day and rushing to the track two or three times a week to try to get his money back.

Then came a discussion of his deteriorating marriage. The lawyer asked how his wife accepted his gambling.

"Karen would be quite upset, as expected. She would be very upset and yell at me."

"What did you do when she yelled?"

"Listen."

Marlys wasn't sure she had heard the answer. "Sorry?"

Ken cleared his throat and tried again. "Listen, because I deserved it. I deserved being yelled at. Like, I gambled away the money. I did it of my free will and, like, I just—I deserved it, so, you know, what could I do? I had to take it. I had to face up to it."

"Did you ever yell back?"

"No, never."

Sometimes his humour showed, as when Marlys asked him about rugby. He said the position he played was second row lock, which he explained as, "I do all the running around chasing after the guy with the ball, tackling him, and we do all the dirty work and the backs get all the glory."

Another time when Ken was being cross-examined by the Crown, he made the jury laugh out loud.

Cathy Mocha asked him to name his medication. When he did, she asked him to spell it.

Ken considered. To apologize for the slowness of his reply, he drawled, "It's a two-dollar word and I only have a dollar."

Late Monday afternoon, Ken Parks slowly, heavily, began to tell the story of the night of the killing. He recited the memory fragments he had, beginning with Barbara's face, the screams of children upstairs, starting up the stairs calling, "Kids, kids, kids," maybe trying to use the phone in the kitchen—and maybe not—and sitting in his car with a knife in his hand.

He ran into the police station, he said, thinking, "What have I done? Why am I here? What happened?"

Then he saw his hands gushing blood.

"Have you ever had any memory of hurting or injuring either Mr. or Mrs. Woods?" Marlys asked.

Ken shook his head adamantly. "No. I would never do that. I loved them. I would never hurt them. I would never *ever* hurt them."

His lawyer's final question to him was, "Did you ever apply for bail?"

Ken answered, "No, I was scared, scared. I didn't know what I had done and I was scared of myself and I could feel how my father-in-law must feel. Like, he was really scared, what was happening to him. He's scared and I'm scared, just scared. I didn't want to scare—I didn't want to hurt anyone. What if it happened again and I hurt someone? I didn't want to hurt anyone."

Ken was on the stand until the adjournment Monday afternoon and took the stand again Tuesday morning, May 17, for Cathy Mocha to finish her cross-examination. Though the Crown counsel asked sharply if Ken could remember using the telephone, or seeing Denis Woods, or turning on lights, his testimony of what he did remember didn't vary in the slightest from the previous day.

In one exchange with the Crown attorney he gave a better picture of his state of mind in the police station than the jury had yet heard. She asked him, "You thought all this might be a dream?" and he replied, "Yes."

"Why did you think this might be a dream if you had never remembered any of your dreams before?"

Ken replied, "Because, why was this happening? What was happening? I don't know what was happening. I had a knife. Why would I have a knife? I threw it down in the car. Why? I don't know. I was just confused. I was trying to sort things out. I was in shock. I didn't know what's happened and I was trying to piece everything together, what everyone said. They charged me with murder, and all the police saying this and this and this, and hearing them outside the door and, I don't know."

"At the hospital do you remember telling the police you wanted some help?"

"Yeah," Ken replied. "I wanted to be put out so I could go to sleep and wake up and everything is over and, like nothing has happened, wake up back on the couch. I don't know what's happened. I'm just in a state of confusion. I'm in shock. I'm shaking and then I'm hot and he's bringing me ice chips and he's bringing me blankets and I'm just really shaking and I don't know what's happened."

Karen thought Ken's appearance on the stand was a major asset to the defence. "The jury saw him, right? They knew who he was and what he was about," she says. "And they knew he wasn't a monster."

Karen Woods Parks testified next. Her apprehension about this moment had been so great that psychologist Graham Turrall met her that morning over breakfast to help her steady her nerves. She had made her choice. Between her family and her husband, she had chosen Ken. The die was cast.

Small, sturdy, quick-witted, and decisive of manner, she went over the now-familiar ground of Ken's warm relationship with her parents, his unfamiliarity with the Woods kitchen (Barbara Woods, it seemed, not only cooked big meals for her family without assistance but also did the clean-up alone), more detail about where visitors parked, and a good deal of testimony about Ken's sleeping habits.

After Melissa was born, she said, "Ken would come to bed with me. We would get into bed. We would both be tired and he would end up getting out of bed again half an hour later and just tell me he couldn't sleep and he would go downstairs. He would go and watch some TV."

As time went by in the late winter of 1987, "there were more nights when he couldn't sleep."

Marlys asked, "In the weeks prior to the incident before your mother died, do you recall where Ken was sleeping most of the time?"

"On the couch."

Cathy Mocha spent only a brief time on the cross-examination. Karen Parks wasn't a witness who could be rattled.

After the lunch break, Marlys Edwardh advised the judge that later that day she might be calling two men confined in the cells downstairs. She had mentioned them before to the judge because she was anxious that they remain available to her rather than be returned to Metro East. The two, Wayne Thompson and Michael Bellis, were cell-mates of Ken's, and both could testify to witnessing Ken's disturbed sleep patterns in prison.

"The ones who are at Her Majesty's pleasure?" he asked with a small smile.

"Yes," she nodded, "but I would ask that they not be brought through that door in leg-irons and handcuffs."

The judge's smile disappeared. "No," he said emphatically. "They will be brought through this door without leg-irons or handcuffs, unless there is some specific security risk of which I am made aware and of which I am not presently aware."

"Thank you, my lord," said Marlys. "I appreciate your consideration."

Her concern was not entirely for the dignity of her witnesses. Marlys was anxious to show the jury that Ken's sleep problems, particularly his difficulty in falling asleep and later his sleeptalking, were normal to him. She was expecting that Cathy Mocha would challenge Ken's family, who were soon to testify that Ken had a history of sleep disorders, and she wanted some extra money in the bank.

At the same time she worried about the prison context that she would be putting around Ken. The jury, seeing his two cell-mates, might unconsciously see Ken in a different light, as someone who associates with criminals. "The connection with them was accidental and would never have happened in Ken's normal life," Marlys was thinking, "but still it might colour Ken."

That kind of shift in perception is deadly when a jury is finely balanced between conflicting views of an accused person's credibility. Marlys couldn't made up her mind whether she needed to risk it, but meanwhile she wanted her witnesses at hand.

The next witness was Ken's seventy-year-old grandmother, Lilly Hodge, who had been attending the trial every day, sitting very erect on the uncomfortable bench provided for spectators. Most of the time she was in such a state of fright that she couldn't draw a deep breath. She was trembling as she approached the witness-box. Throughout her testimony, lawyers and the judge pleaded with her to speak up, but she couldn't get her voice above a whisper.

Lil Hodge weeps when she recalls the trial.

"It was very devastating. Marlys and Del more or less kept us together, encouraging us to think that Ken would win. I had great faith in her, but it was an awful worry. It was terrible to see him in handcuffs, looking so thin, not able to talk to him."

Her role in the case for the defence was to establish that her side of the family, the Lokkens, had numerous members who engaged in sleepwalking and sleeptalking. The Hodge side of Ken's heritage had even more examples. All the males, it seems, were bed-wetters well into their teens and most of them had incidents of walking around in their sleep. She then described the bizarre somnambulistic cooking episodes that Ken's maternal grandfather, Stanley Hodge, often engaged in.

"He had lots of difficulties when he was asleep," Lil Hodge whispered. "He used to wake up, sit up in bed and jump around, his arms and that, and sweat a lot, and he would get up through the night and walk around through the house in his undershorts and he always had—his eyes were very stary, very bulgy, his eyes, and he used to get up through the night often, and he would go different places to the bathroom except to the washroom."

And then came a critical bit of testimony.

Marlys asked, "And at times on those occasions, did you endeavour to try and comfort him or console him in any way?"

"I used to try to get him to lie down and go back to sleep."

"And when you would do that, at the very beginning of your efforts to do that, were they effective? Could you console him?"

Lil shook her head. "No. He was always—just nudging me away. He wouldn't answer or anything. He would just try and push me away."

When Cathy Mocha questioned Lil Hodge, Marlys was relieved that the prosecutor didn't attack on what she feared was a vulnerable front, the fact that it isn't readily apparent to others when a person is moving around at night whether the activities are done in sleep or wakefulness. Marlys was braced for such questions in cross-examination as, "How do you know your husband was asleep when he went to the kitchen to cook? How do you know he wasn't awake? You're not an expert on sleep disorders." That didn't happen with Lil Hodge or with any of Ken's

family, all of whom went neatly into the witness-box and came
away unscathed.

Diane Hodge, Glen's wife, testified next and provided the
jury with a change of pace. Delmar Doucette, who had been
sitting quietly beside Marlys for a week and a half, making notes
and keeping an eye on the transcript of the preliminary trial,
conducted that examination. He had been called to the bar only
two weeks before, and this was his first time on his feet in a
courtroom as a full-fledged lawyer.

Questioned by Del Doucette, all business and concentrating
fiercely on his responsibility, Diane Hodge described the sleepwalking and bed-wetting of her male children, her husband's
habit of being difficult to rouse in the morning, and her observations of Stan Hodge's sleepwalking at the Balsam Lake trailer
park where he and Lilly spent the summer.

Del Doucette asked her what she did to wake her sons.

"I usually shake them," she replied. "I find with my oldest boy
as he got a little older, he occasionally would kind of fling his
arm or kind of strike out at you and he would just roll over and
go back to sleep again."

Her husband, Glen, is also difficult to rouse, she explained,
but she doesn't shake him. "I've got wise and stood beside the
bed and just called out to him and just hoped, you know, that he
would wake up."

"What do you mean, you've got wise?" asked Del.

"I've had a couple of occasions where he's actually struck out,
you know, and doesn't even recall doing it when he's woken up."

Marlys then questioned Betty Parks. In contrast to other
members of the family, Ken's mother spoke in a voice that was
loud and uninflected. As tactfully as she could, Marlys obtained
from the witness a promise that she would not pretend to hear
what she couldn't follow. The most dramatic part of Betty's
testimony was the description of Ken, at age eleven, almost going
through a six-storey bedroom window while completely asleep.
All her sons were like that, she said, bed-wetters until their teens
and almost impossible to wake in the morning.

Glen Hodge followed with much the same testimony. Court
adjourned until the next day, Wednesday, May 18.

Marlys and Del went straight to her office where they made coffee, laid out their notes on a low table, and crouched around it trying to reconstruct what had happened on the night of the sleepwalking. They needed a hypothesis that she could present to witnesses for their response. Around midnight, groaning, Marlys left Del to finish and went home, where she worked on the pattern of questions she would put to Roger Broughton the next day. Around four in the morning, Del completed the hypothesis and drove wearily home to bed. A secretary came at six that morning to type it and make copies for the court.

Later it was entered into the record. It began:

Shortly after falling asleep at between one and two in the morning, Ken rose from the couch. He was already wearing track pants and a T-shirt that he had put on to sleep in, but had no underwear or socks on. He put on a windbreaker and a pair of running shoes, which he could slip into because they were not fully laced. He put on neither underwear nor socks, which was quite unusual since he had never before left the house without them. He picked up a set of keys from an end table, one of the usual places keys were placed, and walked out the front door of his townhouse, leaving it open, which was unusual since he always closed and locked it when leaving the house. Ken opened the garage and got into his car. He then drove twenty-three kilometres to his parents-in-law's house. It was Ken's custom to drive the route to the Woods' residence via the 401, a large highway. This route involves making six turns. Upon leaving the 401 or exiting the 401, the route proceeds directly up a street on which there are some eight traffic lights, and he may well have encountered at least two or three red lights. The total travelling time for the route customarily took him ten to fifteen minutes in light traffic. Upon arrival at his parents-in-law's townhouse, he drove into the underground parking lot, the normal route of entry into their home, and parked in a space he had previously used. He took with him from his car a tire-iron, which was with a variety of tools that he kept in his car for part-time electrical work. Among those tools were also a hatchet and two knives.

Ken entered the townhouse using a key. In order to enter he would have to ascend three or four stairs which were immediately inside the door. He went to the master bedroom, which is on the basement level of the townhouse. Some time thereafter he ended up on the bed on top of Mr. Woods, who awoke to find someone strangling him. Mr. Woods was rendered unconscious within five to ten seconds. Some time after, Mr. Woods sustained lacerations to the head and upper back area. These lacerations were consistent with cuts from a sharp knife. All but one of them was in the head. At some point Mrs. Woods sustained a variety of serious injuries:

1. five stab wounds, one to the chest and four to the back, the first of which entered her heart and was found to be the cause of death, for which a kitchen knife from the Woods' kitchen was the weapon, or was consistent with being the weapon;

2. a skull fracture, with associated injury to the brain, consistent with a blow from a tire-iron or, as well, with hitting the corner of a wall;

3. other blunt injuries to the head, consistent with one or more additional blows beyond that causing the skull to fracture; and

4. pressure fractures to several ribs, not consistent with a blow but consistent with steady, heavy pressure.

As well, at some point Ken received severe lacerations to both of his hands; the flexor tendons and nerves were cut in three of the fingers of his right hand and two of the fingers of his left hand. Ken's first recollection after having fallen asleep on the couch was of being in his parents-in-law's house and seeing his mother-in-law's face. Her eyes and mouth were open and she had a "help me" look on her face. She looked frightened. Although she had sustained serious injuries to her head and face, Ken recalls seeing no marks or blood on her face.

At this time he heard the family children yelling from upstairs. He began to run upstairs calling, "Kids, kids." The children who were upstairs did not hear the words articulated but merely heard "animal grunting sounds or noises" from Ken. He does not remember running up the stairs to the upper level of the townhouse where the children were, but he does remember being on the landing at the top of the stairs and bracing himself.

The children heard Ken wander around on the landing for a short period of time. He was making some grunting noises, which eventually became quieter and then ceased. Ken never entered beyond the threshold of any of the rooms on that floor.

He vaguely remembers having tried the telephone, needing to get help but having a sense that the telephone was dead. The telephone may not have been used by him at all, but a phone was off the hook and a beeping sound could be heard from the phone during the time when the children were screaming out to their mother from the landing, or perhaps shortly prior.

Ken then ran out of the house and to his car, which was parked in the underground parking lot of the townhouse. He does not actually recall if he started his car or if it was already running. He then drove to the local police station, very near by, but he does not recall which of the two possible routes he took in order to get there.

Their star witness, Dr. Roger Broughton, arrived by plane from Ottawa and met them at seven-thirty that morning to go over his testimony. It had been decided that it would take the form of a lecture. Broughton explained to Marlys that the jury wouldn't be able to make an informed decision about sleepwalking without some understanding of the basics. He suggested a non-interruptible format in order to give him the room he needed to put Ken's strange episode of sleepwalking into the context of the body of knowledge in that field.

Marlys realized as well that the psychiatrist would be more comfortable giving a seamless classroom lecture. She could accommodate him—she would simply set up the courtroom like a lecture hall.

"Lecture was the style he knew best," she says. "He was at his most relaxed and compelling when teaching. So that's what he got."

Michael Code, a partner of Marlys and Clay Ruby, volunteered to coach Broughton through some questions he might encounter on cross-examination. Throughout the rehearsal, the neurologist remained composed. He wasn't accustomed to testifying in a courtroom, but he appeared at ease with challenges.

When Judge Watt arrived in the big courtroom, he was startled to find a slide projector and screen in place.

He commented affably, "Who has the popcorn concession?"

Roger Broughton, a dapper, grey-bearded man, proved an engaging figure. Marlys had expected that his testimony would take only the morning, but Broughton was not prepared to be brief on a subject that has absorbed him professionally for twenty years and that he finds endlessly fascinating. For almost two hours, everyone in the courtroom received a lecture on sleep and its disorders that would equip them to be parlour authorities for the rest of their days.

He began by explaining how he became interested in sleep disorders. He was working in France in the early 1960s with Professor Henri Gastaut, an international authority on epilepsy, he said, and they were studying epileptic children who were also enuretic—that is, bed-wetters. The doctors reasoned that either the children were wetting their beds because they were having nocturnal seizures, or they had co-existent non-epileptic enuresis. The distinction was important for a proper diagnosis and treatment. In order to determine if the children were having small seizures in their sleep, the doctors attached electrodes to monitor brain patterns while the children slept. They found, to their astonishment, that the children had normal brain patterns. The bed-wetting was occurring most frequently during their periods of deepest slow-wave sleep, the period in which sleepwalking also occurs.

Over the next few years medical papers poured out of Roger Broughton on the subject of sleepwalking, sleep terrors, and confusional arousals. With electroencephalogram graphs, he could read the physiology of sleep, and he began to explore what happens in people's minds when they sleep.

Then he launched into the familiar ground of a university-level lecture.

"Sleep," he said, "is a behavioural state of relative inactivity and relative withdrawal from environmental stimuli. Sleepers do not totally cut themselves off from environmental stimuli. They can waken with noises and, indeed, the nature of the stimuli is important. The cry of a baby or calling one's name will awaken people more often, more rapidly, than non-significant stimuli like a simple buzz.

"Sleep is controlled by the brain. It is not a sort of passive phenomenon that occurs when you withdraw from wakefulness and go into a quiet place. There are actually structures in the brain that actively cause sleep. In animal studies, if you damage those centres so that the normal mechanisms to induce sleep are missing, then there will be no sleep.

"We have known for many years that there are two different types of sleep. Sleep is not just a single phenomenon that just varies in depth. The two types of sleep are qualitatively different, as different from each other as either is from wakefulness.

"One is called, as I'm sure you're all aware, rapid-eye-movement sleep (REM), and the other one is usually referred to as non-rapid-eye-movement sleep."

The first slide appeared, showing six squares full of zigzags. "On these six small chartlets," Broughton continued, "you will see the top two lines in each are eye movement, the next one is muscle tone, and the bottom three are brain wave recordings from different sites of the skull. This"—he pointed to the first one—"shows a segment of wakefulness. There are eye movements because the person was looking about with eyes open. There is no waking alpha rhythm. When the eyes are closed, or during quiescence or wakefulness, there is usually a very abundant rhythmic activity in the back of the head referred to as an alpha rhythm.

"The measurements are taken by electrodes fastened to the scalp for brain reading, and near the eyes to catch eye movement, and under the chin for muscle tone. The messages go through a machine that amplifies the signals, increases their voltage and causes a paper write-out. The part of brain activity which is recorded is in the cortex, the outer rind of the brain.

"Most of the higher functions of the brain and of the mind are related to cortical activity. What the cortex can accomplish depends a lot upon how activated it is, how aroused it is as an organ, and the controlling influences of that mainly come

256

from structures in the base of the brain that regulate sleep and wakefulness.

"These charts I'm showing you are twenty-second samples showing different sleep stages that are chosen from a whole night of sleep. Approximately one thousand pages of paper go into the average overnight sleep study, so these are just samples of different things that occur in the night.

"As a person falls asleep, rapid eye movements disappear. There are often slow-rolling eye movements, and you have a transitional EEG, as you see in these three channels, and then as sleep deepens you get these brief transients, which are called K-complexes, and the beginning of isolated slow waves, lasting a second or two in duration. These become more and more abundant as sleep deepens and one progresses through these deeper stages of sleep that, because of the abundance of slow waves, are often called slow-wave sleep. So these four stages are all different levels of non-rapid-eye-movement or non-REM sleep, that is, the type of sleep that the brain does other than the REM sleep.

"The deepest level of sleep in which the threshold of wakening is the highest—that is, it's hardest to waken people because the ability to return rapidly to wakefulness is most impaired—is the deep three and four stages of sleep. People rouse more easily from the other stages of non-REM sleep, which are often called light non-REM sleep.

"And then from time to time, this sleep state disappears during the night and the body goes into what is called rapid-eye-movement sleep. The brain waves get lower in amplitude and get faster and muscle tone is suppressed. There is normally a body paralysis during the rapid-eye-movement sleep state. The highest incidence of reported dreams occur after awakening from rapid-eye-movement sleep. On average, between eighty and ninety per cent of REM awakenings will be followed by a report of a dream. The incidence is substantially lower in the non-REM sleep stages, and generally, in most studies but not all, the lowest in slow-wave sleep.

"These are the two types of sleep. Animal physiology, bio-chemistry, and endocrinology studies—and indeed almost all approaches to study them—indicate that they are very different states of the body. They are seen in man at all ages and, in fact, in all mammals.

"Normally there is an alternation—non-REM sleep and then some REM sleep, non-REM sleep and REM sleep, a periodic recyclic event with each cycle lasting about a hundred minutes in young adults. Individuals at all ages show most of the deep slow-wave sleep in the first part of the night. In young adults this is more or less concentrated in the first two cycles of sleep. Significant amounts of either stage three or stage four deep slow waves are really quite rare in the second half of the night.

"Young children have sleep patterns that differ from adults'. Their sleep cycles are much shorter, averaging about forty-five minutes in comparison with an adult's ninety or one hundred minutes. Young children also have much more slow-wave sleep and are deeper sleepers than adults. Young children might spend as much as forty per cent of their sleep in deep, slow-wave sleep.

"In young adults, for whom an average full night's sleep is between six and a half and seven and a half hours, the amount of slow-wave or deep sleep rarely exceeds twelve to fifteen percent. This normally occurs in the first three hours of sleep. Wakenings in the first couple of cycles are relatively rare, normally. The two or three awakenings in the night tend to occur as sleep lightens later in the night, usually happening during REM sleep. Spontaneous awakening from slow-wave sleep in the first part of the night in young normal adults is quite rare.

"There is natural ageing in sleep. At about fifty-five to sixty years of age, there is very little slow-wave sleep and usually more frequent awakenings.

"If you waken people in REM sleep or in the light sleep stages of one and two, particularly in the latter part of the night when lighter sleep stages are more abundant, people tend not only to awaken easily but they are quite clear in their mentation. They know where they are and they are not confused. When you waken people from slow-wave, deep sleep, they may be quite confused and occasionally are disoriented. They may do inappropriate things. They are still half asleep in a way. This particular carryover effect is often called sleep drunkenness. The person is sort of drunk with pressure to remain in sleep or to go back to sleep.

"These different effects between awakenings in the two sleep stages have been the basis of a number of studies trying to see what the brain's responses are like, particularly during this confusional state. I'm going to show three slides and three studies to show that people are in a very different state usually when they are awakened from slow-wave sleep as opposed to REM sleep."

A new slide appeared. "The first slide," Broughton explained, "is what happens if you look at the brain's response to strobe flashes. We show subjects the strobe flashes before they fall asleep, and then we wake them both in REM sleep and in deep slow-wave sleep. During the next few minutes after they are roused and put on their feet, they are told to look at the flash.

"You can see the brain's response in this dotted curve. In the thousandths of a second after the flash occurs after REM sleep you see that the curve is essentially the same as in the pre-sleep waking period. In the awakening from stage four, deep sleep, you see that each one of the deflections is occurring much later in time. The response is much later and it's much lower in amplitude. The brain is sluggish. It isn't fully awake."

The next slide appeared. "This chart shows the pre-sleep wave form in different individuals. Here we have the potentials two minutes after arousal and five minutes after arousal. You can see the brain is still not responding normally after two minutes. It responds in a partially asleep manner. These effects can linger for a number of minutes in normal people. After REM sleep, however, the awakenings immediately show a wave form similar to wakefulness.

"The second slide shows the ability of subjects to do a performance test when they are wakened from either REM sleep or from slow-wave sleep as compared to wakefulness. In this test they had to respond to either a blue or a white flash as quickly as possible by pressing a key. They not only had to respond to the flash but they had to decide which was the right stimulus to respond to. It's called the decision time, or DT. If they respond either not at all to a flash or extremely late—that is, after over a second—that particular response is called gaps.

"By this test the reaction time in wakefulness, prior to going to sleep, was 400 milliseconds. When people wakened from REM sleep they were at 440 milliseconds, only 40 milliseconds later, which is not statistically different. When they wakened from slow-wave deep sleep the reaction gap was half a second, and there was a doubling of the number of gaps.

"We know now that people cannot perform as quickly after non-REM sleep awakenings. Rousing from deep sleep, people either respond exceedingly late or not at all."

The light in the darkened courtroom flickered as the next slide dropped into place. "The third slide comes from a study on memory function in the two states. Normal subjects were wakened either from REM sleep or non-REM sleep and were given lists of words as a memory test. They were tested several minutes after for their ability to recall the words and again the following morning. They also were tested at the same times during a night when they didn't sleep at all.

"The figures, as you can see, are essentially identical between REM sleep and no sleep. After REM awakenings, subjects function much as they do in full wakefulness. After non-REM sleep, however, subjects recalled many fewer words. They showed significant impairment of memory.

"These findings are significant for understanding sleepwalking. In all the studies we have done, sleepwalking begins in deep, slow-wave sleep. It is in fact a disorder of arousal from sleep. The evidence in sleepwalking is that there is a very durable, very intense confusional state during which quite elaborate automatic behaviour can occur. When the sleepwalking episode is over, sleepwalkers normally can't recall anything that happened."

Dr. Broughton pressed the button and a new chart slid into place.

"I prepared some slides," he said, "that show when sleepwalking occurs and what happens during the sleepwalking episode. Sleepwalking is not a rare condition. Something like two to two and a half percent of normal adults will have one or more sleepwalking incidents. Only very few of these will regularly sleepwalk several times a week. In children the incidence of sleepwalking is higher: one to six per cent of children of the ages from six to twelve have sleepwalked. It is, in fact, quite common in children.

"Essentially, sleepwalking always occurs in the first two or three hours of sleep, generally from slow-wave or deep sleep. It almost never occurs in the latter part of a night's sleep. Quite complex acts can occur during sleepwalking. People can drive vehicles. They can go from one area of a house to another, open kitchen cupboards, take out a frying pan, put things in a frying pan, etcetera. They are all fully asleep and have no recall later. They can do any variety of quite elaborate acts. In habitual sleepwalkers, these acts are often repeated. That is, if someone does the cooking routine that I mentioned, many of the sleepwalking episodes, but not all, will involve cooking.

"A child who is sleepwalking may wander around and end up going into the parents' bed or something like that. Sleepwalking is almost a universal phenomenon in young childhood. Virtually all young mothers have seen sleepwalking episodes they have induced, most typically arousing their young children to go to the toilet before they themselves go to bed. The child walks over to the toilet, sits on it, uses it, and is essentially totally asleep.

"The ability to control what one does in the sleepwalking episode, however, despite its apparent complexity, is severely limited. There is really no evidence that people can consciously change their behaviour. In fact, they seem to respond poorly and sometimes even aggressively to efforts from people who try to stop them, for instance, from going into the kitchen.

"It is as though there is a preset program of behaviour that the sleepwalker wants to carry out in an automatic way rather like a robot or automaton. The behaviour may involve aggression. There are a significant number of cases of aggression during sleepwalking, well documented in medical literature, and even cases of homicides that occurred during sleepwalking.

"Sleepwalking can terminate in various ways. Some sleepwalkers simply go back to bed. They sometimes abort spontaneously. That is, the persons wake up, wonder why they are where they are, and don't remember how they got there. They can be wakened, sometimes by calling their name, though they usually don't appreciate being wakened from the outside.

"Most sleepwalking episodes last between ten and forty minutes, but there are well-documented cases that last much longer. Medical literature on sleepwalking contains reports of sleepwalking that lasted an hour and a half.

"When wakened the sleepwalker has no recall and no explanation for what happened. Occasionally you get a fragment of a visual image that is like a single snapshot, but these form only about five per cent of the episodes. There are no descriptions, really, of the elaborate dream activity that can occur. The rule is, there is no recall.

"Unique to sleepwalkers are episodes in which subjects sit up in bed and look around with their eyes open. To an observer, it looks like wakefulness, but when you try to communicate with them you find they are deeply asleep. The important thing is that the behaviour looks like wakefulness but in fact it isn't.

"There are three predisposing factors in sleepwalking. One is family history. People who have a family history of sleepwalking have a much higher probability of sleepwalking than the average person in society. The second is a personal history of sleep disorders other than sleepwalking. The third has to do with the nature of the person's habitual sleep.

"When you get a family history of sleepwalking in brothers, sisters, cousins, aunts, uncles, grandfathers, and so on, the likelihood of sleepwalking occurring in the individual is greatly increased.

"There is a second phenomenon called night terrors or sleep terrors, which also occur in deep slow-wave sleep, in which the person sits up, screams out, is confused and inconsolable, but has no recall of an organized dream. They are more common in the family members of sleepwalkers. Sleeptalking, as well, is more common in the family members of a sleepwalker. Also involuntary bed-wetting. These are all episodic behavioural disturbances that can occur in deep sleep.

"Bed-wetting usually ceases at four years of age when full control of the bladder is attained. Once a child reaches the age of between four and six and is still a bed-wetter, the family becomes concerned and goes to a doctor for an explanation. When it isn't successfully treated, bed-wetting is a great problem for children and adolescents, usually males, who want to go to summer camp or sleep over with friends.

"Because of the tendency for families of bed-wetting children to consult physicians, we have a great deal of material about them in medical literature. The important thing is that it is widely accepted that there is a genetic family predisposition to bed-wetting. If two or more members of the family, and certainly if three or more, had sleepwalking or sleep terrors or bed-wetting, you can safely say the family is predisposed to sleepwalking and children will quite likely be bed-wetters.

"Sleepwalking occurs in people who come from families in whom the majority of the members are deep sleepers, hard to waken, and show confusional episodes.

"The second factor that correlates with sleepwalking is the person's own sleep pattern. Individuals who have episodes of sitting up and screaming or bed-wetting or talking in their sleep have a higher probability than normal of being a sleepwalker. In recent years we have been finding a high correlation as well of sleepwalking and headaches, particularly migraine headaches.

"Sleepwalking, remember, is a *disorder of arousal*, a disorder of incomplete awakening, and not strictly speaking a sleep disorder. The group of phenomena which includes sleepwalking, sleep terrors, and confusional sleep-drunken episodes occurs exclusively during abrupt arousals from deep slow-wave sleep. It is not a disease. It is considered a disruption or an abnormality of sleep itself.

"It has no connection to mental illness. Sleepwalkers are totally normal in daytime. There is no necessary correlation either with mental illness or any specific mental illness. Also, there is no evidence that sleepwalkers have brain damage. It is not a form of epilepsy.

"In addition to these predisposing factors there are triggering or precipitating factors that will deepen sleep. Among the triggers that deepen sleep and impair the ability to awaken alertly, the most important is sleep deprivation. Very frequently, individuals who have sleepwalking episodes do them after they haven't slept well for a few nights.

"As well, sleep is much deeper after excessive exercise, except late-night exercise. When people exercise late at night, their hearts are still racing when they want to go to sleep. But people who exercise in the daytime tend to sleep more deeply that night.

"Drugs that depress the brain also make it difficult to awaken, especially sleeping pills, drugs called tricyclic antidepressants, alcohol, certain toxins; fever and head injury also make arousal more difficult. All may increase the need for deeper sleep.

"The important aspect is to note that deep sleep by itself does not give rise to sleepwalking. The person has to be aroused to trigger sleepwalking, and the factor which arouses them very frequently is stress. Children, for instance, often sleepwalk the night when there has been a fight in the schoolyard or the night before an examination.

"Stress is the most common triggering factor of arousal, though noises can also do it. When a door is slammed, the child who is a habitual sleepwalker may immediately get up and go through a confusional sleepwalking episode.

"In a normal person the factors of stress, excessive exercise, and sleep deprivation would be unlikely to trigger a sleepwalking episode. In someone with a family or personal history of such incidents, they can be significant precipitants. It is characteristic of sleepwalkers to have sleep fragmentation.

"As we can see, there are both internal and external arousals that precipitate sleepwalking.

"The brain waves of sleepwalkers when they rouse are not those of an awake person. Here's a chart of a person in a sleepwalking episode who was monitored by a forty-five-foot cable attached to a recording machine. It shows a sleepwalking episode of two minutes or so during which the person got up in slow-wave sleep, wandered around, got to the end of the electrode cable, yanked it, went back to bed, and remained in non-REM sleep. You can see that in the brain waves."

A new slide. "Here's the brain waves of a six-year-old sleepwalker child who was aroused and stood on his feet. He had to be held partially erect at first because he didn't have sufficient muscle control to stand on his own. About ten seconds later he's able to stand erect without any help. He is questioned, 'What are you doing? What is your name?' and he doesn't answer. Then in a minute the child left the bedroom in the sleep lab, went down the stairs, wandered about in a large room, turned around on his own, came up the stairs, still did not answer queries, and then went to bed. The researcher persisted in trying to communicate with him, and the child eventually responded, 'Jus' go away. I'm sleepy.'

"The important thing is that the brain waves are never those of wakefulness, even when the child responded. You don't get the alpha rhythm that occurs when awake with eyes open."

Another slide. "Here's another study of brain waves and eye movements of a young girl who was a habitual sleepwalker. Fifty minutes after she fell asleep she starts moving in bed. She sits up, looking to both sides as she's sitting up in bed. She's gazing around the room, eyes open, seemingly fully awake, and she lies down again. The duration of the behaviour is about twenty-five seconds. She's in stage four sleep throughout. The brain is asleep. When she is wakened, she remembers nothing of this.

"We have limitations on what we know about sleepwalking because of the lack of memory of sleepwalkers for their episodes. Nevertheless we're aware of a number of important features. It is impossible, for instance, that a person could formulate a plan before falling asleep and then carry it out while sleepwalking. The most striking feature of what we know of what goes on in the mind during sleep is that it's very independent of waking mentation. We cannot direct our minds in sleep as we do in wakefulness. In the waking state we voluntarily plan things— what we call volition—but there is no evidence that volition occurs in sleepwalking.

"In wakefulness people are always responding to what is happening around them. In sleepwalking there's a great impairment of ability to know what is going on. Sleepwalking persons usually are very unresponsive to efforts to get their attention or to alter their behaviour. It's as though they have a preset program that has to run out. The activity is quite mechanical and we describe it medically as automatic behaviour or as an automatism.

"In wakefulness much of our activity is directed to satisfying our needs and interests, whereas in sleepwalking there is no evidence that there is motivation toward a specific goal. In fact, often the behaviour is unrewarding. People may hurt themselves and cut themselves from windows, or may hurt other people.

"In daytime people's behaviour is fairly consistent. They may be quiet or they may be extroverted and outgoing, but there is a style of personality. In sleepwalking people can do things which are entirely inappropriate and which they would never do during wakefulness. The brain is not awake during sleepwalking.

"From the point of view of memory, we can remember most of our behaviour if we pay attention to it while we are awake. The sleepwalker, in contrast, however complex the behaviour, has absolutely no recall of what happened. Volitional control is not available to sleepwalkers. They do not have awareness or control of what they are doing while they are doing it.

"We used to believe that during sleepwalking episodes people were acting out their dreams. When we started recording brain-wave patterns we were very very surprised to find that sleepwalking occurs when there is the least amount of dreaming or mental activity."

Lights in the courtroom snapped on, momentarily blinding everyone, and Marlys returned to questions about Ken Parks.

She took pains to establish for the jury that Broughton had looked at every possible explanation for Ken's behaviour and absence of memory before he came to the conclusion that it was sleepwalking. Accordingly she asked the doctor to restate his findings about the condition of Ken's brain and asked particularly about nocturnal epilepsy. Roger Broughton, comfortably in his element, repeated that the brain was completely normal. She asked about mental illness.

"In the straightforward interview situation," he replied, "the things you normally look for in diagnosis of mental illness are inappropriate behaviour, poor contact with reality, hallucinatory behaviour, and so on. I observed no such features."

He worked through a list of Ken's activities that were consistent with sleepwalking: the time of the event, a few hours after falling asleep; Ken's belief that he was calling, "Kids, kids, kids," when actually he was making grunting sounds; the snapshots of fragmented memory; the stress, sleep deprivation, and heavy exercise, all of which were potential precipitating factors that had preceded his sleep that night; the family pattern of sleepwalking; Ken's own experiences of sleepwalking and difficulty with waking; his strange, disoriented, hyper state at the police station and hospital.

The doctor pointed out that Ken's horrified comments in the hospital emergency room were jumbled. He said at one point, "I killed two people," and at another, "I don't know if I killed anybody."

"I would think that Mr. Parks was trying to synthesize what he felt must have happened," Roger Broughton observed. "He was very uncertain about it, and the comments he made changed from moment to moment because, in fact, he didn't know."

The lawyer asked how a sleepwalker would respond when Barbara Woods, armed with her sharpest knife, attempted to interfere as Ken was assaulting Denis Woods.

The specialist replied, "The response would have been one of aggression, that is, fighting back."

Roger Broughton's testimony concluded with more slides, these showing the results of Ken's two nights in the improvised sleep lab in Metro East Detention Centre. One of the moments of high drama in the trial came when Roger Broughton, having prepared the judge and jury adequately with a two-hour lecture on sleepwalking, pointed out that Ken Parks spent an abnormal amount of time in deep sleep, a state in which his mental activity was near zero.

Marlys Edwardh asked a series of short sharp questions.

"Is there any evidence that mental activity in any way correlates to sleepwalking?"

"No, not to my knowledge."

"In your opinion, would Mr. Parks have intended to kill Barbara Ann Woods?"

"No, I don't think there's any suggestion of motive or intent."

"Assuming he was sleepwalking at the time, would he have the capacity to intend to kill Barbara Ann Woods?"

"No."

"Would he have appreciated what he was doing?"

"No, he would not."

"Would he have understood the consequences of what he was doing?"

"No, he would not."

"Would he have been able to stop what he was doing?"

"No, I do not believe he would. I think it would all have been unconscious activity, uncontrolled and unmediated."

"Do you know of instances of serious aggression that has taken place while people were in a state of somnambulism?"

"Yes. There are some thirty or thirty-five well-documented cases of homicide during sleepwalking episodes."

"In Canada?"

"No, no. It's well documented in reports from other countries, England, France, Australia, and so forth."

Next came more crucial questions.

Marlys asked, "Have you heard or read about or from your own clinical observations seen any situation where there was a recurrence of an aggressive or homicidal event during sleepwalking?"

"No," said the doctor with emphasis. "I went through the best bibliographic source of information on that over a large number of years. There are no reported cases. The probability of it occurring is not statistically significant. It is just absolutely improbable."

His testimony ended with his explanation of what he termed "sleep hygiene", a program to prevent a recurrence. It included: avoidance of the precipitating factors of stress and sleep deprivation, maintenance of regular bedtimes, obtaining sufficient exercise to tire the body but not exhaust it, and avoidance of obesity and alcohol. As well, he said medication was available to ensure that a subject would not become sleep deprived.

Finally, he stated firmly, "I am absolutely convinced in my own mind that the sleepwalking event occurred with homicide and there is no other medically acceptable interpretation."

As she faced the defence's most formidable witness, Cathy Mocha, the Crown attorney, seemed confident and not in the least intimidated by his astounding credentials or the esoteric lecture. Indeed, in recent weeks she had been poring over his medical papers and she was certain that his testimony contradicted some of the articles he had written on sleepwalking. The proposition she needed to wring from Roger Broughton was that sleepwalking was a dissociative state. With that as a starting place, she was on her way to nudge sleepwalking into the category of mental illness.

"A person who is sleepwalking is not able, as you indicated, to control his actions?" she asked politely.

"Mm-mm," said the doctor.

"And that would also be true of a person who was in a psychotic state?"

The doctor replied unhelpfully, "And also somebody who is just drunk."

To a subsequent line of questions about his personal experience with aggression during sleepwalking, Broughton answered that in the last five years he had known only three cases. None involved homicide, but in one case a man caused great harm to his wife asleep beside him, and in another the subject beat his hands on the wall with such force that he suffered injuries.

The prosecutor hammered his credibility. Had he ever personally witnessed a sleepwalker in an aggressive state? No, people who sleepwalk regularly have a much lower incidence of sleepwalking in a sleep lab. The chance of observing sleepwalking under such conditions was minimal.

"Is it possible that some part of the mind or personality operates during a sleepwalking episode?"

"I don't see how."

"Isn't it true that, in fact, in some of the literature it indicates that sleepwalking can be an indication of some underlying conflict?"

"Many people have conflicts, and sleepwalking is relatively rare...."

"What I asked, though," Cathy Mocha said impatiently, "I still don't think I have an answer."

Dr. Broughton was growing irritated. "I'm sorry," he said coolly. "I am trying to answer your question."

"I don't know that it needs anything more than a yes or no. Can sleepwalking be an indication of underlying conflict?"

"It could be, it could be. Yes."

The relationship deteriorated. Marlys Edwardh, appalled, appreciated what was happening. Her star witness found it incomprehensible that he was being questioned in a way that obliged him to give replies that would leave a misleading impression.

"He was deeply troubled to be exposed to a style of questions which undermined the truth," she explains. "He couldn't control his responses because yes and no answers weren't real answers. I simply hadn't prepared him well enough. The preparation I gave him wasn't what he needed."

At one point Cathy Mocha snapped, ""Doctor, when I ask my questions I realize that there are a number of possibilities. That's why when I phrase my question I say, 'Is it possible'."

He said grudgingly, "Yes, it's possible."

Thoroughly out of sorts, the Crown attorney said, "If you could simply just answer my question when I ask, 'Is it possible,' it may save us some time."

"If I feel that it's really misleading," protested Broughton, "then I have a right to...."

"I'm sure my friend," with a curt nod in the direction of Marlys Edwardh, "will be happy to clarify that if I in any way mislead you."

The doctor said, equally miffed, "When you are quoting from my articles, I do recall what I wrote."

Marlys was making a damage-control estimation. Cathy Mocha was scoring points, she thought, and her star witness was being rattled, but she didn't think the situation was seriously impaired for the defence. The jury, which had been impressed with Broughton and his credentials, was still solid, she thought. Marlys suspected that the Crown attorney's belligerence and icy tone were alienating some jurors.

"I don't think she got the jury's sympathy," Marlys comments. "I think they could see that Broughton was struggling because he didn't want her to put words in his mouth."

Still, Marlys jumped in shock when Judge Watt, normally a scrupulously neutral person in the courtroom, leaned forward and shouted at Roger Broughton to answer the question.

Later, when the cross-examination had subsided to a calmer level, Cathy Mocha asked, "Is it fair to say that the brain doesn't generally turn off? It just perhaps becomes less active?"

"It goes into a different state," Broughton corrected her, his stiff tone that of an affronted man. "That is the way I think most people would describe it."

"Can a person perform virtually any sort of act in his sleep?"

"I'm not sure," replied Broughton. "It depends what you mean by acts. There are lots of higher nervous function activities of discrimination or planning and so forth which are quite improbable during sleep."

"Is it fair to say that in a sleepwalking stage one generally has poor co-ordination?"

The doctor answered, "No. People can at times have quite co-ordinated motor activity. People have been found sleepwalking who have gotten up on rooftops and kept their balance and walked along and been totally asleep."

"Are you saying," she asked, setting a trap, "that sleep-walkers have perfectly functioning and properly functioning co-ordination?"

"I did not say that," he snapped. "You asked me whether they had major problems of co-ordination and I said, no, they did not."

"I don't believe the word I used was 'major'."

"I'm sorry," he said angrily.

"Poor?"

"No, I don't think they show poor, what I consider poor co-ordination."

"Perhaps lower co-ordination then?" she continued relent-lessly, her own temper showing. A great deal hung on this exchange for the Crown's case. Ken Parks' long drive from Pickering to Scarborough undeniably required considerable co-ordination.

The doctor was equally stubborn. "They may and they may not," he replied.

"Is it true that sleepwalkers are unlikely to have precision of aiming at something?"

"Well, I think it's unusual in watching a sleepwalker to see what I think you mean in any activity. Usually they get up and do rather trivial things, like wash dishes or dust the table, or whatever, which I would not consider aiming as part of it."

"All right," she said. "Well, perhaps I can ask you this. If there were a sleepwalker who had an object in his hand, would you expect that sleepwalking person to be able to go over to an object and strike that object and pick it out of a number of other objects and strike it?"

"He could," said the doctor. "Yes. Or she could."

"And the object was moving?" asked Cathy Mocha, her voice rising in incredulity.

"Mm-mm," murmured the doctor.

"Are you indicating that sleepwalkers are able to pursue something?"

The doctor plainly was uncomfortable. "That sleepwalkers are able to pursue things? I didn't mean to imply that."

"All right. I take it they would not be able to do that?"

Broughton was getting rattled. "No, I don't believe...." he began. Then he said, "I believe that they could, yes."

Later, when the Crown lawyer asked about Ken's inability to remember the attacks, there was another burst of fireworks.

It began when she said, "Again, what I asked was, are you indicating there's no possibility then that he actually recalled stabbing them and choking them?"

"I have no evidence that he recalled that."

"All right," she said with a hard look. "So in your opinion there is no possibility of that?"

"I did not say there is no possibility of it."

"That was my question, Doctor."

"I have no evidence that he did. The possibility, if it exists, in my mind it's extremely rare. If I might elaborate on that...."

"If you could just answer my question, Doctor," she interrupted coldly.

"Yes," he said wearily.

"We might be able to finish sooner."

"I'm sorry," he told her, steaming.

"Perhaps I can put this hypothetically to you," she went on, "that the accused when he went into the bedroom attacked both the mother- and father-in-law. He then left the room and somehow the mother-in-law managed to get to the television room. The accused then went up the stairs to the kitchen, took the knife, and at that point took the receiver of the phone in the kitchen off the hook, went back downstairs to the television room, where he went over to Mrs. Woods, the deceased, and proceeded to stab her. Is that consistent with someone who is in a sleepwalking state?"

The doctor held his ground. "It could occur. It's consistent, yes.... But I personally do not think that scenario could possibly have occurred."

The lawyer said, "Doctor, I'm not asking you whether or not you think that scenario was correct. Would a sleepwalker be capable of that sort of purposeful act?"

He said steadily, "The sleepwalker would be capable of doing that."

Towards the end of what must have seemed to Roger Broughton an extremely long day, an important exchange occurred, one that Marlys Edwardh was to quote in her summary to the jury.

Cathy Mocha was asking the specialist about the possibility of recurrence. He gave a different answer than he had given the defence attorney. He said it was unlikely, "based on the frequency of sleepwalking in the past of the accused and the fact that he is getting older. It's also based on the assumption that this wouldn't have happened if he had received appropriate treatment." When she received the transcript, Marlys Edwardh underlined that last sentence.

Broughton stepped down from the stand at four-thirty that afternoon after a gruelling day he would not soon forget. After the jury had left the room, the judge fixed Marlys with a quizzical look.

"What about the time estimate?" he asked with pointed politeness.

"I think I'd better take the fifth, my lord," she said ruefully, "but I'm actually still hopeful we will conclude the defence by Friday...with your lordship's assistance and the hours we are sitting. I think we are doing very well."

"All right," he sighed, "but I don't take full credit for it. We wouldn't do it without the jurors' permission. They don't mind, so nine-thirty tomorrow morning." He looked up sharply. "Accused removed."

Ken stood up and was led out, his shoulders slouched in despair. Marlys and Del were depressed as they drove back to her office. Marlys blamed herself for not preparing Broughton for the kind of questions Cathy Mocha had put to him. They tried to assess whether the jury had lost confidence in his testimony. They assured one another that the main body of Broughton's testimony was solid and undented, but neither could be sure.

Broughton went to the airport, as Marlys and Del met with two psychiatrists, Wood Hill and Ron Billings, to go over their evidence for the next day. Then they took Frank Ervin to dinner at the Park Plaza hotel next door to their office and lingered with him until nearly midnight, preparing him for his testimony.

Del Doucette, driving home later, was so tired he had to force himself to concentrate on steering straight.

Both were up at dawn to meet John Edmeads, the neurologist, to discuss his evidence. Two wan attorneys then pulled on their gowns and braced themselves for another day of expert witnesses.

The trial resumed that morning, Thursday, May 19, 1988, somewhat later than the judge expected. The spacious courtroom was booked for a host of lawyers to set the dates for cases proceeding to trial in the Supreme Court of Ontario. Some time after ten, the room was clear for the Parks case to proceed.

Marlys Edwardh began, as she did with all her expert witnesses, by referring to the lengthy hypothesis of what happened on the night Barbara Woods was killed. She felt it put a platform of facts on which testimony could comfortably stand. Marlys checked that all relevant people in the court had copies of it and then called Dr. John Edmeads, the Sunnybrook hospital neurologist. John Edmeads stated unequivocally that Ken did not suffer from neurological disease and had a healthy brain.

Keeping in mind that Cathy Mocha was attempting to establish that Ken's sleepwalking was in the category of mental illness, Marlys put a key question: "From the perspective of your discipline, is sleepwalking a disease, sir?"

The neurologist promptly replied, "No, it is not."

Cathy Mocha began with what she hoped would be a promising line of questions that would show that Ken Parks was taking a medication, Chlorazepam, which is prescribed for epilepsy. From that, the inference might be that doctors saw in him the possibility of epilepsy. The effort proved an embarrassment. It developed that she understandably had confused Chlorazepam with Chlonazepam. When that was sorted out, she had little more to say. The evidence presented by John Edmeads was seen by all sides to be clear and unassailable.

Dr. Ron Billings, Ken's psychiatrist, followed Edmeads into the witness-box. Marlys in her examination-in-chief established what she needed to have before the jury: Ken Parks was wholly sane, there was no evidence of temporal lobe epilepsy, and he did not suffer from hysterical amnesia or hallucinations.

After seeing Ken, he said, "this case was on my mind and it bothered me that I couldn't come to a conclusion. I was really thinking a lot about it. In the course of my psychotherapy practice patients told me of incidents that had occurred during sleepwalking. One patient particularly told about very complicated behaviour she had done. I began to wonder if this could be sleepwalking."

He read the literature, he continued, and learned that aggression could be associated with sleepwalking. He came to the conclusion that Ken had been sleepwalking when Barbara Woods was killed.

"Was there any other diagnosis that was left in your mind as a competing diagnosis?" Marlys Edwardh asked.

"Not at that point, no. To my satisfaction, I had ruled the others out."

"And today?"

"I still feel that way."

Ron Billings also offered some insight into Ken's gambling. "It is very important for Mr. Parks to do well and to be approved by people," the psychiatrist commenced. "He had been married for three years at that time and had bought a house, and I think had paid off the mortgage, paid off the loan. He had with his wife savings of $5,000 in the bank. To do this, he was working hard.

"He had his regular job, which he had been promoted in, and he was working on part-time work with friends as well to earn extra money. The house was very important to the family, particularly to his wife, and he wanted to help get that paid off more quickly. He wanted to be able to buy things for his wife that he knew she wanted, and he didn't earn a lot of money at his job. He had an idea he would like her to be able to take a trip to Australia, where she came from."

Ken was not a compulsive gambler, Ron Billings said, as the term is used in diagnosing a pathological addiction to gambling. Instead he was a youth with poor judgement and very high hopes.

"He always recognized it as being wrong," the doctor said. "Gambling wasn't something he was doing for excitement. It was something he was doing to get money to achieve the things he wanted, to continue to be thought of as having done well."

He said it was significant that Ken didn't gamble in jail, though gambling is rife in prisons.

In the morning recess, Marlys drew Frank Ervin aside for a final briefing. He looked at her and read the exhaustion.

"Marlys," he said firmly. "Carbohydrates."

She stared, uncomprehending.

Taking her by the arm and steering her to the escalator, he told her, "It is more important to this case that you eat than that you talk to me."

In the basement cafeteria, she obediently ate a sandwich.

Karen and her father fell into conversation during that recess. Denis Woods made a comment that Karen can't forget.

Looking long and sadly at his daughter, he said, "I don't know what to think. If he's convicted, I'll always think that there is a possibility that he's really innocent. And if they find him innocent, I'll always think there's a possibility that he's guilty.

I don't want to see him acquitted, but if what the doctor says is true, he shouldn't go to prison."

Karen gave his arm a loving squeeze.

When Karen repeated that to Marlys, the lawyer was moved. "Denis Woods came to the trial with the expectation that if he sat there every day and listened carefully, he would discover exactly what happened and why," she commented. "He came to realize that he would never know. For him there would never be closure. Even the verdict wouldn't end the mystery. I found what he said incredibly insightful."

After the morning recess, it was Cathy Mocha's turn to question Ron Billings. Using DSM III-R, an edition of the Diagnostic Statistical Manual physicians use to assist them in diagnosis of disorders and diseases, she noted a category labelled somnambulism.

"It is listed, I take it, as a disorder, is it not?" she asked.

Ron Billings replied, "The chapter is called 'Disorders of Sleep', and the second part of it is parasomnias. These are behaviour that can occur during sleep. Do you want me to mention what those are?"

"Yes," she said patiently.

"The first that is mentioned is night terrors and enuresis, and then sleepwalking and sleeptalking...."

"Right," the lawyer nodded. "And DSM III is a diagnostic manual, is it not?"

"Yes, basically it's..."

She interrupted firmly, "It's a diagnostic manual?"

"It is a diagnostic manual," Billings protested, "but it is expanded in order to help physicians, not just psychiatrists, to diagnose conditions from the clinical picture."

"All right," Cathy Mocha said heavily. "And the word 'diagnose' you used, I take it implies disorder or treatment, does it not?"

"No, it's not a textbook of treatment."

"I *know* it's not a textbook. I said the word 'diagnose'..."

Billings continued through her interjection. "...it does not imply a treatment."

The lawyer was incredulous. "Does not imply it?"

"No."

"The fact that there is a disorder which responds to treatment?"

"The response to treatment can help you with your diagnosis, but diagnosis in itself does not imply treatment."

There ensued a half hour of tense exchange during which the Crown attorney attempted to extract from Ron Billings agreement with her position that Ken's return to gambling after his arrest for embezzlement was evidence that he was a compulsive gambler. Billings insisted that it was not.

"If the accused were to resume gambling again tomorrow or some short period down the road, would you then have to reassess your opinion as to whether or not he was a pathological gambler?"

"It would depend on the type of gambling," Billings replied, "and if it was similar I would have to reassess, yes."

The lawyer moved to Ken's state of mind in the months that followed the tragedy. Billings had stated when questioned by Marlys Edwardh that Ken's depression was so severe Billings had prescribed a strong antidepressant for some two months. He called Ken's state "adjustment depression". Cathy Mocha, looking for an opening to assist her in identifying Ken's sleepwalking as a form of insanity, wanted to know how that differed from mental disease.

"It doesn't meet the criteria for a major affective disorder," the doctor replied.

She asked him to outline the criteria. When he finished she jumped on what he had described as adjustment depression, which Ken had suffered following the incident. She asked, "Would that form of depression, adjustment depression, be considered a disorder of sorts?"

"Yes," said the doctor.

Next the lawyer asked if hypnosis had been used to determine if Ken was suppressing memories of the killing. Billings said he was not a hypnotist.

"Would you agree with me," Mocha asked, "that with respect to seeing his mother-in-law's face, it appears that the accused certainly repressed the blood and injuries that were evident on her face?"

"No," answered Billings. "When a person is coming around from sleepwalking, they are in a confused state and their memory is not consistent and clear. It's patchy. What he saw, what he remembers he saw, may not have been what his eyes took in."

Mocha asked sharply, "Is it possible that there can be in psychogenic repression, repression of portions of events?"

Ron Billings replied shortly, "Yes."

Dr. Wood Hill, a forensic psychiatrist, took the stand next. While Wood Hill was quick to say he wasn't an expert on sleep-disorder problems, he knows his way around the legal definition of insanity as well as anyone in the country. Among the titles of his numerous medical papers and academic presentations are *The Borderline of Insanity* and *The Psychiatrist's Contribution in Mental Disorder and Criminal Responsibility.*

Wood Hill reported on his examination of Ken Parks and said he had come to the conclusion that the man was sleepwalking. "No other explanation, in my mind, is at all appropriate and/or can be legitimately sustained, at least from a psychiatric point of view, to explain how these two events, falling asleep, waking up and seeing his mother-in-law, could have occurred."

In other murders of his experience, "individuals give much more information and they don't fall asleep."

After the lunch break when the Wood Hill testimony resumed, Marlys took some time asking the psychiatrist why he believed that Ken Parks was telling the truth. He joked about giving away "tricks of the trade", and then presented some techniques for exposing fabrication. Ken Parks, he said, met every test for truthfulness.

"In terms of his character structure, in terms of his ethical stance on general issues, in terms of his concept of morality and right and wrong, I was comfortable that I wasn't dealing with an individual who has major defects in his moral attitude towards life, his perspective of what is right and wrong."

The defence lawyer asked the psychiatrist how it could be possible that Ken Parks remembered nothing of the attacks and yet in the police station and hospital made such statements as, "I stabbed..." or "I beat..." or "I choked...."

Wood Hill replied, "It does not reflect memory which was laid down while the behaviour of violence was being undertaken. It represents an individual who does have some information. He did not leave the premises immediately, so there would be some information going into his brain—among other things, the blood, the apparent awareness or recollection that he had a knife in his hand....Those are horrendous pieces of information to face one out of the blue with no context, and it is instinctive that one will try to make some sense of it....You go over it and try to find some meaning which can help you reduce the pain you are feeling."

He also testified that he found Ken Parks "consistently non-aggressive". He continued, "He is not a violent individual, and violence is not an active way of handling stresses for him."

As for the profile of a compulsive gambler, Wood Hill said that Ken didn't fit the diagnostic criteria. "He does not fit the personality style of such individuals."

Later he was asked what was emerging as the crucial question: "Is sleepwalking itself a mental disorder?"

"No. We don't consider it a mental illness."

"Is it viewed as a neurological disease?"

"The answer is no."

"And in your perspective, Dr. Hill, do you consider it, sir, a disease of the mind?"

"No, I do not."

Cathy Mocha tried a fresh approach with her opening questions. She noted that Ken maintained control of his emotions and kept his feelings to himself. Sometimes, she suggested, that kind of control conceals a violent nature.

That can happen, the psychiatrist agreed.

Leaving that hanging in the air, the lawyer moved quickly to compulsive gambling. The period of Ken's gambling extended over eight months, ending just before he was arrested, but was it not possible that if he had not been put in prison his gambling would have continued and it would be clear that he was a compulsive gambler?

Wood Hill shook his head. "He's a different bird. He would have become more and more panicky. It would have become increasingly an anxiety-provoking exercise for him and increasingly seen as a dead-end street for him. That's not gamblers. They, unfortunately, don't see it as a dead-end street. He wouldn't have slipped into that style."

A few minutes later she skipped to the ground she was building to argue that Ken was repressing his memory of the event.

She asked, "Is it possible that psychogenic repression could explain that situation of lack of recall?"

He replied, "Well, I think it always has to be considered. It's very possible that there is some degree of forgetfulness based on what we would call psychogenic repression. Psychogenic repression goes on in all of us to some degree after very frightening horrendous events."

Cathy Mocha said gratefully and with emphasis, "That's right. Thank you very much, doctor."

Marlys Edwardh rose to her feet to attack the tantalizing suggestion laid down early in the cross-examination that Ken might be at heart an aggressive person who usually held himself under control.

When asked about that, Wood Hill said he didn't think so. For one thing, Ken could watch television and forget his troubles, something not easily done by obsessive personalities. "The over-controlled individual is a different bird. They are very clearly on edge and to an outside observer they are a button waiting to be pushed. No, I don't think Ken Parks is overcontrolled at all."

Wood Hill was followed to the stand by McGill psychiatrist Dr. Frank Ervin, an authority on people with pathological aggressions. When his name was called and he rose from the spectators' section to move to the witness-box, he was the last person anyone in the courtroom would have expected to be Frank Ervin. Dressed in rumpled clothes, his hair and beard long and grey, he has the look of a dishevelled biblical patriarch.

He spoke in a voice that rolled like thunder. Judge Watt, a man of erudition, looked entranced. Frank Ervin reported that he had examined Ken Parks for almost two hours, studied the neurological work-up, talked to Ken's mother and grandmother, and reviewed the sleep recordings.

"And what is your opinion, sir, of the state he was in at the time of the death of Barbara Woods?"

Frank Ervin replied at once, "My opinion is that he was in fact in a parasomnia state, somnambulistic state, and that that parasomnia accounts for his behaviour."

He gave three reasons for his conclusion. One was that Ken was in a dissociative state during the incident—his behaviour was not characteristic and there was no evidence of rational thinking. This happens in homicide, he offered as an aside, but usually drugs or alcohol are involved. In this case, blood analysis showed no evidence of either in Ken's system.

The next two reasons were that Ken had no brain disorder and no psychiatric disorder. By the process of elimination, Dr. Ervin said, it could only be sleepwalking.

"We have heard evidence the last few days that sleepwalking is not a neurological disease," said Marlys. "We have heard evidence that it is not a mental disease. First of all, do you agree with that?"

"Sure."

"And we have also heard evidence that it's not causally related to a mental illness."

"Right."

"Nor is it part of a mental illness."

"Right."

"Do you agree with that?"

"Sure."

With that spike in the Crown's wheel, Marlys asked the expert to explain what happens in the human brain when the subject is sleepwalking.

"Okay," he responded cheerfully and told the courtroom how the brain works. It is an interconnected masterpiece, he said, constantly full of interplay. In a fully alert smoothly working brain, two levels constantly interact, the logical, rational brain and the non-verbal survival brain, which dictates such survival messages as hunger. The neocortical, thinking brain clamps down on the primitive brain, which is inclined to take furious action against slights.

In the REM state of sleep, when dreams occur, the doctor continued, the brain is very busy. "It is during that period that we have dreams that we remember. Problem-solving activities go on, old memories come up. Exactly why the brain wants to do that is not entirely clear, but it serves an important function because every animal from man down to the laboratory cat gets very disturbed if you disrupt REM sleep. It is an essential component of the day's housekeeping for the brain."

In slow-wave sleep, the brain is also busy, but differently. The growth hormone is released during deep sleep, for instance. Children whose deep sleep is constantly interrupted may suffer from dwarfism. Ken Parks, he said, has a genetic vulnerability to shift into deep sleep.

What Frank Ervin said next came to be a major part of the defence argument. In deep sleep, he told the courtroom, the thinking brain—the cortex—is essentially in a coma.

"It is very slow. It looks like ocean waves rolling along, suggesting that all those nerve cells are no longer doing their busy, integrated work. They are cut off. They are not working."

What is left? he asked rhetorically. "What is left are those deep structures evolved some time back, evolved very competently in lower animals." In short, the primitive brain, the fossil brain, the site where rage dwells.

Frank Ervin said he was particularly intrigued by studies of the brains of sleepwalkers because he was one himself until the age of twenty-one. "It's a universal capacity that seems to diminish in most of the population," he explained. "It occurs in about two-point-five per cent of the population.

"The rest of the brain is turned off but moving about, responding to familiar patterns, and is perfectly intact and ready to go as if everything is nicely put together."

He likened it to putting a new program in a computer. "You take out disc A and put in disc B."

Cathy Mocha opened cross-examination of the brain specialist with an important question.

"Are there any neurological differences in the sleepwalker who may commit a violent act in his or her sleep, assuming that there is no physical interference with the sleepwalker?"

"A very reasonable question," the doctor nodded, "and I don't know the answer. You're suggesting that in a dissociated state there are still drives that come out of the experience of the individual.... It's certainly not clear to me, and I don't know colleagues who have stated ways to make it clear."

When the Crown's cross-examination was finished, Marlys Edwardh went after that part of Ervin's testimony.

"Just so we understand your position, Dr. Ervin," she asked, "is the behaviour in sleepwalking an unconscious working out of feelings that you have?"

He was taken aback. "No. I didn't mean to imply that."

"To be more specific, is there any known connection between earlier thought and the specific behaviour engaged in by the sleepwalker, or earlier feelings and the specific behaviour, so that one could say that what one thought about or felt just prior to going into deep sleep had any relationship to the behaviour in the sleepwalker?"

Said Frank Ervin, "I don't think there's strong evidence of that kind. What you are both asking, obviously, is whether Ken was acting out an unconscious desire to kill his mother-in-law. Even though he didn't do it consciously and wittingly, now that his frontal lobe is turned off and his limbic system is turned on in his brain, with a mind of its own so to speak, was he free to go about doing that?"

The jury waited tensely for him to continue. "I don't think that's true. I don't think that's true for a couple of reasons. One, I haven't found a shred of evidence, and I'm sure I've looked as hard as anybody except maybe the prosecutor, for a good motive for him to do this. It just doesn't wash at the motivational level.

"When we move to the more theoretical level that says, 'Would it be possible ever for someone to have a kind of motive that is expressed in a sleepwalking episode?' I can't say no to that. I'm sure that's likely to happen sometimes, but I don't think this is borne out by it."

That ended the testimony for Thursday. Marlys Edwardh again assured the judge that she thought she could complete the case for the defence in about three hours the next day, Friday. Mr. Justice Watt informed the jury that it would take about a day for both lawyers to deliver their summations. That being so, he was reluctant to give instruction to the jury at that time. He preferred to hold it over until after the holiday weekend so that he could end in the morning rather than late in the day. The jury therefore would have an early start for its deliberations.

The next morning the account of the trial in the *Globe and Mail*, written by Thomas Claridge, began with a paragraph that caught the attention of readers across the country: "Four psychiatrists lent support yesterday to the finding of an expert in sleep disorders that a Pickering man was sleepwalking when he stabbed his mother-in-law to death."

Marlys and Del were elated as they drove back to the office. It had been a perfect day for the defence. "Mocha didn't lay a glove on us," Del beamed.

Marlys was thinking ahead. "I wonder if we need Rosalind Cartwright after all."

She climbed the narrow carpeted stairs to her office and stuck her head in the adjoining room where Clay Ruby works. She pulled up a chair.

"I'm thinking that I won't call Rosalind Cartwright tomorrow," she said. "Tell me what you think."

She went over the reasons that she had been turning over in her mind. She had planned to bracket her expert witnesses with the sleep-disorder specialists, Broughton leading off and Cartwright closing. Now she wasn't so sure. Cathy Mocha hadn't yet been damaging to the defence, except for rattling Broughton, but she had two days to bone up on sleepwalking and get a better focus.

Michael Code, a partner of Clay and Marlys, joined them, and the four lawyers went over the ground carefully.

"We've called all our expert witnesses except for Cartwright," Marlys explained. "The Crown doesn't have anything like our expert testimony to present. I don't think Mocha is going to use her sleep-disorder expert. He doesn't outweigh Broughton. And she can't use her own psychiatrist, Brian Butler, because Brian thinks Ken was sleepwalking."

Marlys had considered called Brian to the stand as a defence witness but dismissed the idea. It was over-clever, she decided, and Brian Butler was new to the field of sleep disorder. Cathy Mocha in cross-examination might hurt the case.

"Rosalind Cartwright is absolutely convinced that Ken was sleepwalking," Marlys went on. "There's no question of that. But her research on sleep disorders has led to some conclusions that are slightly different from those of Roger Broughton. If Mocha spots any discrepancies in the testimony of our two main witnesses, she could go to town."

"It wouldn't matter that the differences were irrelevant to the diagnosis," Clay nodded. "The jury would be confused."

"A really brilliant cross-examination would try to pit the experts against one another and nullify them both," Marlys observed. "I have a sense that our case is in good shape just as it stands. I called Broughton for an entire day. I called Ervin, I called Wood Hill, I called Billings, I called Edmeads. The case has been clearly put. I ask myself, do I need her? I think, no, I don't. I think Cartwright would be overkill."

Her colleagues agreed. The conference broke up, and Del went to the telephone to call Rosalind Cartwright in Chicago. Dr. Cartwright, he was informed, was on her way to Toronto.

Marlys left a message at the doctor's Toronto hotel. When she slumped back from the phone, she announced, "I don't think I'm going to call Ken's cell-mates either. We don't require any more evidence that he has sleep disturbances, because the family's testimony wasn't challenged. And I don't like leaving the jury with the impression that Ken hangs out with criminals. It's a red herring. We don't need red herrings at this stage."

Rosalind Cartwright picked up her message an hour later and called Marlys, who went to see her. Cartwright was disappointed to learn that she had made the trip unnecessarily, but was understanding. "I'm sure you know what you're doing," she told Marlys. "You have to decide what's the most effective way of handling your witnesses."

There was still time to catch the last flight that night for Chicago. Marlys put Rosalind Cartwright in a taxi and sent her off, with her thanks. Then she went back to the office: work to do. She had one more witness to think about, and she had to work on her arguments to the judge about his charge to the jury and develop her own summary to the jury.

The next morning Marlys Edwardh informed Judge Watt with a smile, "I've got good news, not bad news. I don't expect to be more than half an hour."

The judge wondered what that did to the schedule. The next step was the arguments of both counsel on the judge's charge to the jury. Cathy Mocha estimated that the two submissions would take half a day. That would be done in the absence of the jury. When the jury was present, the lawyers would deliver their summations and the judge his instructions. After that the case was in the hands of the jury.

Judge Watt asked Cathy Mocha how long her address to the jury might be.

"My address may be an hour to an hour and a half at the most," she replied.

"Ms. Edwardh?"

"I'm notoriously bad at estimates," Marlys admitted, "but I would hope that it would be within an hour or an hour and a half."

The judge considered. "So we would be able to get both addresses in before the lunch break, if we were to start at something like nine in the morning?"

Both lawyers agreed.

"Well, it may be that I'll instruct the jury on Wednesday," the judge said. Everyone was relieved that the long holiday weekend would not find the jury sequestered in hotel rooms.

As soon as the jury was seated, Marlys called her last witness, David Loucks, a team-mate of Ken's on the Ajax Wanderers rugby team. David Loucks, when he stood up, proved to be the only man in the courtroom as big as Ken Parks. Indeed it turned out that he played the same position, lock forward, on the Wanderers. Moreover, he was—every massive, handsome inch of him—a well turned out, well-spoken representative of the middle class.

"Rugby, after all, is a private-school sport," Marlys noted with a grin. "The jury might have been thinking it was a violent sport, a game for roughnecks, but our witness belied that. He showed it as a gentleman's sport. Since he was Ken's colleague, his presence enhanced Ken's position before he even said a word."

Loucks testified that the position Ken played, lock forward, was a strenuous one that requires the athlete to do a lot of pushing in the scrum. On a scale of exertion, he rated it almost at the top—"nine out of ten".

He said that on Saturday, May 23, 1987, when Ken played with the Wanderers, the weather was hot and humid. Ken played the entire sixty minutes, though he appeared to be out of shape, and at the end he looked very tired.

The judge asked, "Cross-examination, Ms. Mocha?"

"I have no questions, my lord," she said.

"Next witness?" Judge Watt inquired.

"My lord," said Marlys, "that completes the evidence for the defence."

It was Friday morning, May 20, 1988. The judge gave the jury a four-day recess until Wednesday, straddling summer's first long weekend with an extra day, Tuesday, thrown in. In the absence of the jury on Tuesday morning, he would hear submissions from the two lawyers. The jury foreman asked politely for assurances that the lawyers' addresses and the judge's charge to the jury would be completed in two days. The judge was startled but gave the requested assurance.

"It was a very uneventful ending, considering that I had planned to bring in Cartwright and the two cell-mates," Marlys muses.

What remained was for her to persuade the judge that the jury should be informed that it could return a simple verdict of not guilty because the situation was one of non-insane automatism. The prosecution, she expected, would be arguing that the jury should be instructed to choose between a verdict of guilty of second-degree murder or not guilty by reason of insanity. Marlys didn't think the issue of wilful murder should even arise, since there had been no evidence to support that view, not a shred.

The jury box was eerily empty as Ken was brought from the cells on Tuesday morning to listen to the submissions. Both lawyers gave the judge thick case-books bristling with tabs to mark the precedents they would be citing. Then Cathy Mocha led off for the Crown.

"It seems clear to me," she told the judge, "that there is no agreement as to what a state of somnambulism is in law." The matter of whether to classify sleepwalking as insane or sane was in the judge's hands and she urged him to consider the Arthur Martin decision in *Regina* v. *Rabey*. She conceded that in every known case involving sleepwalking, courts had deemed sleepwalking to be non-insane automatism rather than a form of insanity.

"I can't dispute the fact that all the authorities have indicated somnambulism is a situation of non-insane automatism," she admitted, but she declared that the cases occurred when sleepwalking was regarded as something supernatural.

"In fact," she commented, "it was believed that the person's soul actually left his body during sleep and that was why it was felt a sleepwalker could not be accountable for what he did."

She continued: "The abnormality that we are dealing with in this case is an abnormality of the sleep mechanism which, in my submission, is a functional disorder." Further, she said, the dissociative state that Ken was in should be characterized as a "disease of the mind" within the legal meaning of insanity.

"There is certainly leeway for you to take the position that, using the rationale set out in *Rabey*, that should be viewed as a situation of insane automatism."

She cited a decision written by Denning in the *Bratty* case, heard by the House of Lords in London, in which the English peer observed that "any mental disorder which has manifested itself in violence and is prone to recur is a disease of the mind".

When she finished Judge Watt inquired if there were any other issues that she wished him to canvas with the jury.

"The only other issue," she replied, "is the issue of manslaughter, whether or not that should be put to the jury."

"What is your position on that?" asked the judge.

She answered that she felt that second-degree murder was an appropriate charge, but the judge might consider changing it to manslaughter if he was going to advise the jury that the automatism of sleepwalking fell within the legal meaning of insanity.

When it was her turn, Marlys Edwardh began briskly. "In this case, my lord, only one defence should be left," she asserted. "It is the defence of non-insane automatism arising from the fact that Mr. Parks was sleepwalking at the time. Neither insanity nor manslaughter should be left."

She reviewed the expert opinions that a sleepwalker's activities are involuntary and done in an unconscious state, "and thus form classically part of the definition of automatism.... I concede for the purposes of this argument that automatism may be of two varieties, sane and insane, and that automatism resulting from disease of the mind is insane, but that sleepwalking has always been, and in my respectful submission is today, clearly viewed as one of the two phenomena that fall under a claim of non-insane automatism."

She continued, "This position is consistent not only throughout the Commonwealth, but with the greatest respect to my friend's characterization of all that 'old law', it is consistent for over one hundred and twenty-five years, including a case that was just recently dealt with in 1986 in England."

Mr. Justice Martin made a distinction in the *Rabey* decision, she said. She read the relevant sentences: "Sleepwalking appears to fall into a separate category. Unconscious behaviour in a state of automatism is non-insane automatism."

She said, "I take the view, my lord, that that statement, short of compelling reasons to the contrary, is one that your lordship should not in any way deviate from."

The lawyer added, "What the Crown counsel is inviting you to do is to take sleepwalking and put it *per se* into diseases of the mind. With the greatest of respect, that is an invitation to disregard history and tradition and jurisprudence in a way that is at least unusual."

She dealt at length with an element always pertinent in such cases, the risk to the public if the accused is released. "What is before you is evidence that the chance of reoccurrence is statistically insignificant," she reminded the judge. "There is no evidence from the examination of the literature that there has ever been a reoccurrence [of violent behaviour while sleepwalking]."

In reply, Cathy Mocha protested, "My friend made a comment that because I submitted that somnambulism should fall within diseases of the mind I was submitting that all cases of somnambulism should fall within diseases of the mind. That is not my position. My submissions were dealing with the accused before this court."

The presentations occupied more than two hours, but Mr. Justice Watt made up his mind quickly. As soon as both counsel finished, he said, "I propose to put the defence of non-insane automatism to the jury, not the issue of insanity."

Further, he would instruct the jury that if there was any doubt in their minds that the act was conscious and voluntary, they should find Ken Parks not guilty of second-degree murder.

He offered to write his reasons, and Marlys Edwardh replied that she would appreciate that. Judge Watt reflected, "I'm not sure that I can provide any clear insight, but it is a novel case."

Marlys Edwardh observes admiringly of David Watt, "He doesn't hijack the jury's deliberations. He's a judge who truly listens and he's very interested in legal theory and jurisprudence."

On the last day of the trial, Wednesday, May 25, 1988, the heavy scent of flowers on the spring air outdoors made the courtroom seem stuffy and unpleasant. Ken Parks was delivered to the witness-box with some extra baggage. Curled in plastic wrap in his rectum was three hundred dollars, a gift from inmates at Metro East Detention Centre against the possibility that he would be taken from the courtroom to a federal penitentiary and would need cash to purchase small comforts in the prison canteen.

The backbone of Marlys' address to the jury was that Ken had been sleepwalking when Barbara Woods was killed. Therefore, she emphasized, the necessary element for conviction—that it was a "voluntary and conscious" act—was missing. Also, sleepwalking was not a disease of the mind. "The prosecution has failed to produce any evidence, not a shred, to discredit the sleepwalking thesis." She skirted carefully around an arresting point: the Crown's psychiatrist who examined Ken Parks sat in the courtroom but had not been called to testify for the prosecution. Reason, by inference: he agreed that Ken was sleepwalking.

All the statements Ken gave the police were consistent with the experts' descriptions of the type of amnesia suffered by sleepwalkers while in a state of somnambulism. All the doctors—*all* the doctors—who had examined Ken were initially skeptical, but all ultimately concluded that sleepwalking was the only explanation that made sense.

When Marlys finished, Karen Parks slipped out of the courtroom. She didn't want to hear what Cathy Mocha said about Ken. Ken's old friend Richmond Ramani joined her. He didn't want to hear it either.

"That's another thing that isn't fair," Karen comments. "The defence should get to go last."

The Crown lawyer showed high scorn for Ken's statement that he didn't know what had happened, in view of his statement, "I killed two people."

"He knew that he had choked them," she said to the jury.

She emphasized that some of the expert witnesses had agreed that, if Ken Parks wasn't sleepwalking, it was possible he was repressing the memory. She saw in Ken's reluctance to join his wife in bed a desire to avoid detection when he left the premises later. The sleepwalking defence, she said, was "simply ludicrous". She outlined Ken's complex movements—turning off the television, putting on his jacket and shoes, picking up the keys, opening the garage door, finding the ignition key, starting the car, putting on the glasses that he kept in the car for driving, driving twenty-three kilometres, parking in a cramped space, arming himself with a tire-iron, selecting the key to the basement door of the townhouse, entering a darkened bedroom to strangle Denis Woods, getting a knife from the kitchen to kill Barbara Woods, returning to the bedroom to stab Denis Woods repeatedly.

Other members of the family of Ken Parks went through ritualistic, repetitive behaviour when they engaged in sleepwalking, she pointed out, while the activities of Ken Parks were so exceedingly complex they could only indicate a functioning brain.

"I appeal to you, ladies and gentlemen of the jury," she said, "to rely on your common sense."

She declared: "Permitting the accused to leave the court a free man would be an affront to the community's sense of justice."

The Crown counsel also commented disapprovingly on Ken's behaviour in the witness stand. He was, she said, "joking around". Ken thought that was unfair. He smiles when he is uneasy and only once, when he couldn't spell the name of his medication, did he make a small joke. "She made me out a monster," Ken comments gloomily.

Marlys noted that Cathy Mocha's customary cool and formal approach was maintained to the end. "She didn't try to convey the pain of the Woods family and invite the jury to enter that," the defence lawyer observed. "I thought she might, but she didn't."

In jury trials, the judge has the final word. At one-thirty, after the lunch break, Mr. Justice Watt began what turned out to be a very lengthy charge to the jury. He began ponderously, in a manner suited to the gravity of the situation: "Ladies and gentlemen of the jury, it shall shortly fall to you to commence the final aspect of your sworn duty to well and truly and a true deliverance make between our sovereign lady, the Queen, and the accused whom you have in your charge, Kenneth James Parks. It is now my privilege and duty to instruct you as to the principles of law applicable in this case, to refresh your individual and collective recollections of certain features of the evidence which has been here introduced, and to endeavour to demonstrate for you how to relate the applicable legal principles to the facts as you may find them to be, so that you may render a just and proper verdict....

"The duty in which you are presently engaged is the most important civilian duty a Canadian citizen can be called upon to perform. You occupy a position in the administration of criminal justice which is the equivalent of my job as a judge of this court....You are legal guardians of the rights of your community....You are equally the legal guardians of the rights of the accused....

"Ladies and gentlemen of the jury, considerations, sympathies, prejudices, or emotions should not be permitted to influence you to the slightest degree in your decision as jurors in this case. If such matters should influence you, justice will not be done.... I expect from you a judgment resting upon the evidence, law, good reason, and common sense, and unaffected by considerations of compassion or vindictiveness."

That introduction to the solemnity of their responsibility completed, the judge instructed the jurors on the legal principles involved in a charge of second-degree murder. The fundamental one, he declared, was the right of the accused to be presumed innocent until the Crown proves guilt beyond a reasonable doubt. "If the Crown should fail to prove guilt in respect of a particular crime beyond a reasonable doubt, then you *must* find the accused not guilty."

He explained what reasonable meant in that context and the difference between direct evidence and circumstantial evidence, and how to weigh the testimony of expert witnesses.

"Although the evidence of the eminent doctors who speak with authority bred of their great experience is important, and should be weighed carefully, you are not bound, without consideration, to it. You are not a rubber stamp. Secondly, the decision whether the acts of the accused were conscious and voluntary or unconscious and involuntary is a matter for you alone."

He then recited the chronology of events as they had unfolded in the courtroom during the two weeks of testimony.

He paused and offered the jury a break, which invitation was accepted. In the jury's absence Marlys Edwardh made a submission to the judge that in her address to the jury Cathy Mocha had made some statements that weren't true—for instance, the comment, "He knew that he had choked them." Marlys protested that the jury would have the "clear impression that some of Barbara Woods' injuries involved choking. There is no evidence."

Citing some other remarks she thought were at variance with the testimony, she asked the judge to rectify the errors during his charge to the jury. He made a non-committal response, after which the jury returned. He then listed the three questions it was to decide: Did Kenneth Parks cause the death of Barbara Woods?

If he did, has the Crown proved beyond reasonable doubt that the acts causing the death were conscious and voluntary? And if the acts were not conscious and voluntary, what crime has the accused committed?

Around three-thirty that afternoon, the judge adjourned until the following morning. People filed out of the courtroom in a suspenseful state of mind. Ken Parks, putting his hands behind him for the handcuffs, found it difficult to draw a natural breath. He was panting, his back wet with sweat.

The judge resumed the next morning.

"He spelled it right out," Karen recalls admiringly, "that there should be no question in the jury's mind. If they thought this, then it had to be this, and if they thought that, it had to be that. He repeated things *five times*, in different ways, so everyone would understand. He was really good."

A telling point came late in the charge when he said, "Before an accused can be held criminally responsible for conduct which constitutes a crime, he or she must be proven by the prosecution to have had, at the revelant time, the ability to control his or her conduct....We describe unconscious involuntary behaviour as 'automatism' and hold those whose conduct falls within such a state to be not criminally responsible and not guilty, however enormous the consequences of their behaviour might be."

At the end of the morning, Mr. Justice Watt presented the jury with two alternatives. One was to find that Ken Parks was conscious of what he did when Barbara Woods was killed and therefore guilty. The other was to find Ken Parks not guilty, since the evidence did not support findings of not guilty by reason of insanity or guilty of the lesser charge of manslaughter.

Among the most significant statements he made in the course of the long charge were, "One cannot plan to sleepwalk. One can't plan whilst awake and carry it out during sleep, as sleep is independent of waking mentation and there is no control over it....Volitional control is not available in a sleepwalking state. There is neither awareness of, nor control over, what a sleepwalker does."

"I heard," observed Karen Parks thoughtfully, "that the judge has a daughter who sleepwalks. That didn't hurt."

At thirty-two minutes past twelve that day, Thursday, May 26, 1988, the jury left the courtroom with sombre faces. The judge thoughtfully promised to notify the lawyers when the jury went out to eat, since this would release them to have a bite as well.

Karen's family waited for the verdict huddled together in one of the small rooms reserved for witnesses. Ken's family was in another. The strain was showing on every face. The civilities observed earlier in the trial were dropped. When they met in the corridors or washrooms, they nodded curtly or, in many cases, not at all.

Karen had no reason to remain alone. Her testimony had put her in Ken's camp, so she sat with Betty Parks and Lil Hodge. Her father and her sisters and brothers sat in another room. That evening, when word came that the jury had gone to a restaurant, there was an awkward moment when the two families almost collided as they went for dinner themselves.

Ken paced in a holding cell, watched sympathetically by a few others from his range at Metro East who were still awaiting transportation back to the jail. Around four o'clock these men were collected by guards to be returned to their cells. The large holding area was empty except for Ken and one other prisoner, a man also waiting for a jury to come in. Neither asked the other what charge he was facing. Around six the other man was taken to hear his verdict and didn't return. Ken was left alone.

He counted floor tiles to keep his terror at bay. He did push-ups and sit-ups, rested, paced again, did more push-ups. He was sweating so heavily that he took off his clothes to protect them. At dinner time, the guards brought him a club sandwich purchased from a nearby restaurant. Ken wolfed it down. He remembers it fondly as the best meal he had eaten for a year. As the evening wore on, a kindly guard gave Ken a book, and he tried to read it. He doesn't remember what it was about.

Darkness fell, a soft and lovely spring night, and the jury was still deliberating. In the harsh light of a witness-room, Ken's family sat playing cards. Karen paced. Marlys popped in and out to assure them that it was a good sign that the jury was taking so long.

"If they decided to convict him of second-degree murder, this would have been over quite quickly," she explained. "The delay shows they're really wrestling with this, which means they're looking at the sleepwalking defence."

Diane Hodge wasn't convinced. "I just know he's going to be convicted," she wailed.

"If he's found guilty, don't think it's all over," Marlys said soothingly. "I have the papers ready, and we'll file a notice of appeal at once."

"We all had lots of confidence in Marlys," Betty Parks says gratefully. "She knew what she was doing."

Often Marlys and Del sat by themselves. "You need to be alone," she says. "You give all you can, and then giving more is really hard."

Once, strolling in the corridor to have a cigarette, Marlys encountered Cathy Mocha. She used the opportunity to ask a question that had been on her mind.

"If he's convicted of second-degree murder," she said, "are you going to ask for more than ten years?"

Cathy Mocha gasped. "Do you think he'll be convicted?"

Marlys was taken aback. Cathy Mocha had seemed, throughout the trial, supremely confident. In fact, however, Cathy had felt her case lost when Judge Watt disallowed the element of insanity.

"I don't have a position on that," replied Marlys discreetly, "but I'm considering all the possibilities."

Marlys' colleagues gathered—lawyers from her building and others, such as criminal lawyer Diane Martin, with whom she has worked. Marlys was touched by their support and the spirit of camaraderie that brought them there. Clay Ruby came, exuding affection for her. He had stored champagne in the trunk of his car, to be handy in the event of a victory.

The jury had been out for more than nine hours. It was ten minutes to ten when the weary judge convened court again. He intended to ask the foreman if the jurors were close to a decision or whether they would like to be dismissed to resume in the morning.

A court officer popped his head in the door. "We got one!" he called. Karen started to pray.

Guards left hurriedly to bring Ken into the courtroom. They found him in his shorts doing sit-ups. He dressed himself with fumbling hands. He felt strangely calm; the ordeal was about to end. One way or another, in the next five minutes the suspense would be over. As he was led to the prisoner's box, he looked around at a packed courtroom for friendly faces but was feeling so disoriented he could focus on no one.

He waited to have the handcuffs removed, but the guards stepped back and left him with his wrists pinned together behind his back. If he was found guilty, they wanted control. The court usher, by curious coincidence a man also named Kenneth Parks, looked up sharply.

"Take those handcuffs off," he ordered.

Ken was accustomed to being guarded by two men, one on either side of the prisoner's box, but this time there were four, and all were tense.

Karen looked over at the area reserved for reporters and noted that it was full. Throughout the trial there had never been more than two people there, and usually only one. The Toronto papers had shown little interest in the Ken Parks trial, assuming it was a simple domestic crime, but word of the sleepwalking defence had electrified newsrooms, and people with notebooks overflowed into the spectators' area.

As the jury filed in, Ken couldn't look at them. He fastened his attention on the floor. Karen tried to read the jury's faces, but their expressions were closed. Ken shot a quick look at the judge, but he looked perfectly composed and unfathomable.

Ken was asked to stand. He got to his feet, swaying. His head felt detached from his body, swimming somewhere in a hollow, echoing space. He thought he might be sick. His mother, sitting next to Tyrone, was trembling. "Everything seemed to be in slow motion," she said.

But Karen was stunned by how quickly it was done. The judge said, "May we have the verdict."

The registrar asked formally, "Members of the jury, have you agreed upon your verdict?"

298

The jury foreman replied, "We have agreed on a verdict. We find him not guilty."

An audible gasp swept the courtroom and reporters ran from the room to contact their editors. Ken's eyes filled with tears.

The registrar intoned, "Members of the jury, hearken to your verdict as the court hath recorded it. You say the accused at the bar is not guilty as within charged. So say you all?"

The jurors, almost as one voice, said, "Yes."

The judge's aplomb was unshaken at the drama. He thanked the jury, wished them well, and discharged them.

Cathy Mocha concealed her disappointment under a professional's mask. Later she was to say, "Frankly, I can't say that the jury was incorrect in the decision, with what they had before them. I like to think, though, that if they had the issue of insanity before them, that there may well have been a different outcome."

When the jury had left, Marlys said she would be asking the judge to set bail so that Ken could be released pending his trial on a second charge, the attempted murder of Denis Woods. Marlys Edwardh had her course of action planned. She would challenge the legality of a second trial, since the circumstances in both charges were identical. Cathy Mocha protested that it was all too fast.

"I do not want to leave my client in custody any more than is necessary," Marlys conceded, "but I certainly understand that Crown counsel needs to at least assess the situation."

In truth, Marlys knew that it would be impossible to release Ken immediately. His bail on the fraud charge had been revoked when Karen needed to clear title so she could put the Pickering house up for sale. In any case, arrangements still hadn't been completed for a place for him to stay. Karen, she knew, was not ready to take him back immediately. The young wife wanted to keep her distance for a time. It seemed most likely that Ken would stay with Lil Hodge, but that wasn't yet certain.

"Ms. Mocha," Mr. Justice Watt inquired, "how long do you require to assess the situation?"

She replied that she thought she would be ready early Monday.

"She just said that to stall things," Karen comments bitterly.

"Does your client agree to that, Ms. Edwardh?" asked the judge.

Marlys stepped back from the table where the lawyers sit and raised an inquiring eyebrow to Ken. He saw what was happening: he would be kept in custody over the weekend. He supposed he could protest, but Marlys seemed to be signalling him to accept the situation. He nodded. After a year in prison, a few days more didn't matter much.

Out of consideration for her family, sitting stricken and weeping on their side of the courtroom, Karen was struggling not to look delighted. Samantha and Emma were sobbing loudly, and the whole family clung to one another in a tight circle and then suddenly broke and strode through the door with set faces. Karen made no move to join them. She kept her head down, her eyes squeezed shut, and said silently to herself, "Yes, yes, yes, *yes*."

She approached Ken and saw that he was crying. A guard glared at her, so she stepped back.

Outside on the sidewalk she saw members of the jury waiting for taxis. She had to control herself to keep from running to them with her thanks.

Lil Hodge, Betty and Tyrone, Glen and Diane, Richmond Ramani and his girl-friend, and Karen went to the bar of a nearby hotel, the Downtown Holiday Inn, and had a drink to celebrate. Then, "We telephoned the good news to everyone we knew," Betty recalls blissfully. "We were so happy."

Marlys Edwardh's friends followed her home for the victory celebration. They gathered in her hot tub, sipping Clay Ruby's champagne. Clay lifted his glass to Del Doucette, who had been a lawyer for less than a month. He said, "Del, hang up your robe. This is the pinnacle of your career. This is as good as it gets."

CHAPTER THIRTEEN
After the Trial

Ken, pale and tense, was released at the courthouse on June 1, 1988. His grandmother, Lil Hodge, posted bail twice, for $2,000 on the fraud charge and for $10,000 on the charge of attempted murder, both sums secured with liens on her house. Marlys warned Ken and Karen that a horde of reporters and photographers was waiting on the sidewalk outside the courthouse.

"It's a scrum," she told them. "They want to get pictures of you and ask some questions. My advice is to let them do that and get it over. Otherwise they'll only keep after you."

Karen was taken aback by the number of microphones and cameras that surrounded them as they came through the courtroom door. She and Ken posed awkwardly, trying to look pleasant but feeling acutely uneasy. Reporters asked Ken some questions about how he was feeling and what he planned to do, but words didn't come to him. He spotted Marlys in her car, waiting for them, and hurried Karen into it.

They drove to Marlys Edwardh's office for a discussion of his impending legal situation. Ken faced two more charges, one of the attempted murder of Denis Woods and the other of the fraud against his former employer, Revere Electric. Marlys said neither should give concern. Either the judge would rule that the second charge should be dropped in view of the first acquittal, or there would be a trial before Judge Watt that would consist of nothing but the lawyers' submissions.

Marlys had arranged to have the fraud charge heard on the same day. Ken would plead guilty, saving the courts the cost of a tedious trial. Since this was a first offence for him, and Karen had arranged to make restitution, the Crown would not ask for a prison term. Cathy Mocha had agreed to recommend that the judge grant a suspended sentence and parole.

The only danger on the horizon, Marlys told them, was that the Crown might appeal the jury's acquittal.

"Sleepwalking has never been used before as a defence in Canada," Marlys explained. "At least not successfully, so far as we have been able to discover. The Crown might not like the precedent."

"Can you appeal a jury decision?" asked Karen, confused.

"Only in Canada," Marlys told her. "Ever since Magna Carta, in every country which bases its jurisprudence on English common law, the jury has the final word. Once the jury speaks, that's it. But in Canada we allow appeals of jury decisions. The appeal judges could order a new trial."

Ken and Karen looked stunned.

"Don't worry," Marlys advised them. "The Crown has only a month to make up its mind what it will do. After that, it's over."

Marlys shrinks from painting too rosy a picture for her clients, but she had reason to be confident that the Crown would not appeal. That morning in the *Globe and Mail*, Thomas Claridge had written: "A Crown appeal is considered unlikely against the acquittal of a Pickering man who fatally stabbed his mother-in-law but was found not guilty because of doubts that he was awake at the time.

"An Ontario Supreme Court jury of eight men and four women deliberated about nine hours Thursday before acquitting Kenneth James Parks of second degree murder in the death of Barbara Ann Woods, 41.

"The verdict represented the first recorded instance of a Canadian successfully using a somnambulism (sleepwalking) defence in a murder charge....

"To reach a conclusion of guilty, the jury would have to accept the Crown's call to reject a defence theory that won unqualified support from five psychiatrists and went unchallenged by a Crown witness.

"Any Crown appeal of the acquittal would have to be based on alleged legal errors by Judge Watt, himself a former Crown who, in two and a half years on the bench, is considered one of the brightest minds in the Supreme Court.... Judge Watt's long charge to the jury was accepted as fair by both sides. One lawyer called it 'impeccable'."

In fact, Cathy Mocha already had put a request to appeal to the office of the attorney general and was awaiting a decision. She had decided that the important precedent of Ken's sleepwalking being ruled to be non-insane automatism, rather than insane automatism, should be subjected to judicial review.

Ken and Karen left their lawyer's office and took the subway to a restaurant, Mr. Greenjeans, for lunch. Hamburgers.

The next stop was to pick up Melissa. A friend had been caring for the eighteen-month-old child throughout the trial. Melissa was dressed in party clothes for the occasion, complete with frilly socks. When Ken stooped to talk to the little girl, she ran crying to her mother.

"That's your daddy," Karen told the toddler. "You remember, you talked to daddy on the telephone?"

Melissa hid her face and cried harder. Ken looked at his daughter helplessly. He hadn't touched her for a year, not since Karen had put Melissa on his chest in the hospital. It was to be several days before she would let him near her.

Karen and Ken had agreed on the wisdom of giving themselves some space before resuming their marriage. Lil Hodge invited Ken to live with her in Scarborough in the interim. It would give the young couple time to adjust.

"I'd been on my own for a year," Karen explains, "and there was a lot to sort out. Feelings about his gambling, about what happened to my mom.... I needed to know I could trust him again before I could even think about going on with the marriage. I had to get the trust back before we could share a bed together."

She and Ken spent every day together in Pickering, and at night he caught the last GO train back to Scarborough.

In mid-June Ken nervously went to court to face the twinned trials. Because Marlys Edwardh couldn't attend, he was represented by Clay Ruby, who got a postponement.

On June 28, the last day on which an appeal could be filed, the Crown went to the Ontario Court of Appeal to declare that Judge Watt "erred in law" in ruling that Ken's state of somnambulism "was not a disease of the mind within the meaning of the Criminal Code".

Cathy Mocha explained: "As I understand the delay, the Crown was waiting for Justice Watt to write his reasons. My request was put in right away after the trial to the Crown's criminal appeal division and I was advised almost immediately that the Crown would be appealing. The difficulty was that the Crown didn't want to appeal something without having read the judge's reasons. Finally they decided to appeal it blind just on the basis of what I had indicated in my notes of what the judge said. His reasons at the time were very brief, so it was difficult for the Crown to make that decision. The fact is that the point is so novel, and it never has been decided by a high court, and this finally swung the decision to appeal."

The Crown asked that the acquittal be set aside and a verdict of not guilty by reason of insanity be substituted. As an alternative, the Crown suggested, there could be a new trial.

Ken and Karen were aghast. Marlys Edwardh consoled them as best she could. All the psychiatric evidence made it clear that sleepwalking was not a form of insanity, she said, and everyone who had examined Ken agreed he was not insane. When the appeal court read the testimony and the reasons that Mr. Justice Watt promised to write, chances were very good that the appeal would be denied.

The issue to be tested was not whether Ken was in a state of automatism when the attacks occurred—that was conceded by all sides—but whether sleepwalking should be considered a form of insanity that should have resulted in Ken Parks' committal to a locked hospital for the criminally insane until the lieutenant-governor's Board of Review certified that it was safe for him to be free.

On July 14, 1988, Ken Parks was before Judge Watt again to face the charge of attempted murder. This time there would be no jury or witnesses: the judge had heard all the evidence that either side wished to produce at the previous trial. Cathy Mocha reminded the judge that the wounds to Denis Woods were superficial in comparison to those sustained by Barbara Woods. The explanation, she said, was that Ken Parks cut his hands while attacking Barbara Woods and subsequently, when attacking Denis Woods, was unable to grip the knife tightly enough to inflict fatal injuries. Her argument was that he was feeling pain in his hands, which meant he was awake for the attack on Denis.

The prosecutor told the judge, "In my submission it is open to you to find at that point when he attacked Mr. Woods he was no longer in a sleep state but was awake."

Marlys Edwardh protested. "Given the nature of the evidence of somnambulism," she said, "your lordship ought not to engage in speculative ventures to find a different verdict. The verdict of the jury in relation to this case or in relation to the murder, because the evidence is identical, ought to be the same."

She argued that the sequence of the assaults is a mystery and will so remain. "To take a splice of one assault and invite a different verdict is nothing short of inviting your lordship to bring in a verdict which is inconsistent with the first verdict."

Further, she added, the wounds to Denis Woods were far from superficial: some were to the bone. No conclusion could be drawn about whether Ken had stabbed Denis before the tendons in his fingers were severed or afterwards.

The judge retired for exactly thirty minutes.

On his return Judge Watt delivered a surprisingly lengthy decision, given the time lapse, but one that undoubtedly took into consideration the Crown's protest about his handling of the first trial. Towards the end of his remarks, he observed, "It is incumbent upon the prosecution to establish, beyond a reasonable doubt, that the assault [on Denis Woods] must have occurred at a time when the accused was not in a somnambulistic state, hence acting consciously and voluntarily.... Ms. Mocha submits that the evidence establishes that the accused awakened in the television room after stabbing the deceased to death and thereafter returned to the bedroom, there to attempt to murder the complainant."

After stating the points of law involved, the judge continued, "It would be the height of speculation to conclude that such an event in fact occurred. It does not lie proven in the evidence of Denis Woods, the statements or the testimony of the accused, nor in any combination thereof."

He concluded, "I find the accused not guilty. Mr. Parks, you're free to go."

It was over just before eleven o'clock that morning.

Ten minutes later Ken stood in a courtroom downstairs from the first one. District Court Judge Ted Wren listened as the same Crown lawyer read the charge of fraud. To this Ken said, "Guilty."

The judge gave Cathy Mocha an inquiring look and she jumped up. "Your Honour, the Crown is suggesting a suspended sentence in this case." She explained the circumstances and then sat down. The judge considered while Ken held his breath.

"All right," he said. He then pronounced a three-year suspended sentence and required that Ken Parks attend meetings of Gamblers Anonymous and continue taking medication for his sleep disorder.

The comment current after the Parks acquittal was, "It opens the floodgates."

Marlys fumed. "I keep hearing about floodgates. People seem to think that everyone will claim to have been sleepwalking. That's nonsense. Sleepwalking is one of the hardest defences in the world to prove. It all has to fit. The jury brings an amount of suspicion to a sleepwalking defence. You have to produce an enormous body of evidence and expert testimony in order to win with it."

Indeed, almost a year later a sleepwalking defence was attempted and failed. William Wade, 58, a man from Brampton, Ontario, bashed his wife's head repeatedly on the curb outside their home. The attack was witnessed by many neighbours, despite the hour—four in the morning—because of the woman's screams. At the trial in the fall of 1989, the defence case rested on the evidence of a sleep-disorder specialist from Toronto Western Hospital who testified to William Wade's family and personal history of sleepwalking. The accused said he had no memory of the attack, had never struck his wife before, and loved her dearly.

"The only thing I can recall after going to bed was waking up in the Metro West Detention Centre," he testified.

The jury didn't believe him. He was convicted of second-degree murder and sentenced to life imprisonment, with no eligibility for parole for ten years.

On the other hand, there was the case of a sleepwalker in Brampton, Ontario, a night-shift worker who strolled naked out of his house one afternoon while masturbating. Neighbours summoned a police officer, who questioned the man and charged him with performing an indecent act. He was defended successfully by a young criminal lawyer, Tom Carey, who produced an affidavit from a neurologist who gave his opinion that the man was sleepwalking.

After a year behind bars, Ken was slow to shake his jail habits. He had looked forward to being able to walk outdoors whenever he liked, in any direction, but he found it made him nervous to be in the open. He preferred to stay inside in a small room. Crowds made him uneasy; like all prison inmates, he had a custom of watching his back. He found it difficult to concentrate. When he accompanied Karen to hunt for housing, he couldn't get as engrossed as she was in the project. In fact, it was hard to get interested in anything.

It was almost two months after his release before the couple felt they were ready to live together again. Ken moved back into the Pickering townhouse, and they renewed conjugal relations by courtship stages, beginning by holding hands and hugging, then progressing to kisses.

"He had to get to know me, he had to get to know Melissa," Karen says, taking a deep breath. "He had missed a lot of time."

Karen and Ken resumed sexual relations in July and Karen became pregnant at once.

"It wasn't planned that way. I had the pills and everything, but I get pregnant so easy it's ridiculous." She grinned. "Like my mum."

It was most untimely. Ken was unemployed and Karen was waiting to hear if she was accepted in nursing school. They discussed abortion. Ken said it would be all right with him if that's what Karen wanted. Karen gave it only brief consideration.

"I can't do that," she decided. "Considering the circumstances, that we were married and everything, I don't think I have a right to do that just because it was inconvenient for me. That's my view anyway. I can't make up my mind what I think about abortion, but right now I can't have one."

"Okay with me," he replied.

Ken agreed that Oshawa was a good place for them to move. He saw the need to get away from the Pickering-Ajax area where they were known and shunned. The presence of General Motors, the colossus that generates most of the jobs in Oshawa, raised Ken's chances of finding employment. Besides, his mother and Tyrone lived there—Ken's family, and now Karen's family, her only family. In July they had an additional reason to go to Oshawa: Karen was accepted at Durham College's registered nursing school.

Their financial situation was desperate. Because of Ken's fraud charge, the couple had no credit rating, Ken didn't have a job, and Karen was living on welfare.

Rough estimates of their legal costs to date were in the dizzying neighbourhood of $180,000, although Marlys Edwardh had reduced her fee from her normal $250 an hour to $150 an hour and waived collecting any of it. The money Ken's family had given her went to the experts whose testimony had formed the bulwark of the defence case. Grandma Hodge had paid a substantial amount—about $50,000, she estimates—by selling stock from her investments, and Ken's uncle, Glen Hodge, unhesitatingly put in a few thousand of his own savings. Others in the family contributed what they could. Even with this level of loyalty and generosity, Ken and Karen would owe Marlys close to $90,000 after they gave her some of the house sale money. They also had to return money to Revere.

To add to their woes, Gary McNeely, the lawyer Ken had retained on his fraud charge, sued them in small claims court for his fee. The judge ruled against Karen and Ken and ordered them to pay McNeely and court costs as well. That came out of the house sale money too.

The cash they received from the sale of their Pickering house was about $66,000. All Ken's half, approximately $33,000, went to Marlys, and Karen paid the $15,000 Ken owed Revere out of her half. Another $5,000 went to settle with the finance company from which Ken had borrowed against the household appliances and to his Visa creditor, the Canadian Imperial Bank of Commerce.

The amount that was left was so small it wouldn't be sufficient for them to buy another house, even if someone would give them a mortgage. They looked for something to rent, but Oshawa was in a boom period and rents were horrendously high. Finding nothing they could afford, they turned desperately to the real-estate market, looking for a break on their mortgage qualifications. The situation was reaching the point of crisis. If they didn't find a house by August 1, they would have to move in with Ken's family.

Luck was with them. A house at 311 Athol Street in Oshawa had been illegally subdivided to make it a triplex, and the real-estate agent who owned it was anxious to unload. He would take a small sum down on an agreement of sale, with the deal to be consummated in a year when the couple might have built up a credit rating sufficient to allow them to obtain a mortgage. All he asked was a co-signer on the agreement.

"He wanted to get rid of the property, and he wanted the money we had," Karen explains. "So we were lucky. But he wasn't taking a big risk, because he still held the mortgages."

For the necessary co-signer Ken turned to his brother Rob Parks, who had a good job at General Motors. He invited Rob to move into the triplex and share the mortgage payments of $1,400 a month. While Rob had no cash to put into a down payment or the legal costs of the purchase, he was earning a steady income and could manage the payments.

Over a two-year period, Rob would pay Karen and Ken $200 a month to cover his half of the down payment and legal costs, all of which they had provided, and at that point he would be fully the co-owner. Rob would have one apartment, Karen, Ken, and Melissa another, and the bachelor apartment on the third floor would be rented.

After the trial, Karen waited a few days to call her father. Out of respect for his situation, she wanted to give him time for the shock of Ken's acquittal to abate. She had no doubt that the conversation would be friendly.

"In his eyes I'm his daughter," she explains simply, "and that's that."

Her assumption that Denis would not reject her is a reflection of her own views about family loyalty. Karen's attitude towards Ken is, essentially, "He's my husband, and that's that."

She had not misjudged the situation. Denis said, in his fair-minded way, that he could understand the verdict. "I don't think the police did a very good job and I wasn't impressed by the Crown but, that aside, it is easy to see why the jury decided the way it did."

She thought that was an uncommonly generous remark, but what she said was, "Thanks, dad."

"I'm only concerned that it could happen again," he said slowly. "Your brothers and sisters are quite frightened that Ken will come back."

"He's taking medication so he won't sleep so deeply, you know," Karen reminded him. "That episode was associated with a lot of stress and sleeplessness. The doctors say that it was a fluke, a once-in-a-lifetime thing."

"I hope so," her father said quietly.

"Your brothers and sisters are having a hard time with the verdict," he went on. "They can't understand it at all. I think it will be a while before they get over feeling angry."

"I understand," Karen said, realizing with a sinking heart that he was telling her that they didn't want to see her. "I can appreciate how they feel."

Denis paused. "We'll keep in touch, of course," he told his daughter, "but I don't want to see Ken and I don't want to even talk to him on the telephone. If I call you, I'll let it ring twice and then I'll hang up and dial again. If Ken's there, please ask him to not pick up the phone when I call back."

"That's a good plan," Karen said, her voice under control.

Her friend Connie Sullivan dropped out of her life. "She's scared," Karen explains. "She has this big issue about Ken doing it again."

Ken started job-hunting immediately after the two trials on June 27, but the results were disheartening.

"I didn't know whether to tell the truth on the application or not," he confesses.

"At first you did," Karen reminds him.

"Yeah," he drawls. "They ask where you've worked and I had this missing year, the one when I was in jail. For a while I didn't lie about it, but that meant no one would interview me. Then I started to lie and I got interviews."

Even so, no one would hire him. Some told him that he'd be getting a call, but the call didn't come. Ken applied for unemployment insurance. After a grim wait, his application was accepted. Even with that income, they were living seriously below the poverty line; sometimes the household was scant on food. Once, welfare helped with an emergency cheque.

As months wore on, Ken's discouragement was profound. He continued to search for work, but the unrelenting rejections were hard on his always shaky confidence. Karen meanwhile obtained an Ontario government student loan and started classes at Durham College, at the same time working on Saturdays at the supermarket. She bubbled with enthusiasm about what she was learning. Nursing was *wonderful*, she told Ken. Though she found little time to concentrate on study, her marks were consistently in the nineties.

In November, almost five months after his release, Ken finally got employment. He was jubilant. He told his employer the truth about his past, but the man gave him a job anyway.

The company, Canadian Protective Products, produced salt and chemicals to spread on roads and sidewalks in winter. The pay, however, was $8.50 an hour, which left the family still pinched for money. Two months later Ken quit for something better, $11.05 an hour with Lear Siegler, supplier of car seats for General Motors.

A week after he started he had a phone call.

"Don't come in," he was told. "You're fired. We found out about your record and the guys on the line are afraid of you."

"How can you do that?" Ken protested.

"Easy," he was told. "You didn't tell us the truth on your application, so you were hired under false pretences."

Frantic, Ken counted himself fortunate to land a temporary job with a plastics company at $8.00 an hour. A few weeks later, he found a permanent job, at $9.75 an hour, with Greif Containers, makers of giant cardboard cores.

For about five months, Ken went regularly to Gamblers Anonymous. The group in Toronto, he found, was a vast improvement over the one in prison but not different in style and content. He gained understanding of the nature of compulsive gambling but saw himself as somewhat different from the others. For him, gambling had never been a thrill. Asked why he gambled, his answer was, "So I could buy my wife a trip to Australia." Like the others, though, he had dreamed of the big win; like them he had stolen money; like them he lied to people he loved.

"You become a compulsive liar because you always want to look good," Ken explained. "The big-shot attitude is the main thing with compulsive gamblers. I had that. I wanted everyone to like me."

"He was *just* like that," Karen interposed. "When we went out to dinner with my parents, Ken always wanted to get the cheque. He always wanted to pay for everything. All the time, not just once in a while. I used to try and hold him back. I didn't think we should pay for everyone's meal every time we went out, but that's what Ken wanted to do. When my mom wanted to buy him a drink he wouldn't let her. He wouldn't take anything from anyone."

Ken listened to Karen in a manner that suggested he wasn't taking her comments personally. She was talking about a person they both knew a long time ago, someone who isn't around any more.

Nevertheless Karen wasn't willing to take a chance that he wouldn't gamble again. They talked about her concerns and he agreed to the restrictions she asked.

"I don't carry any money, not more than I need for little expenses," he explained. "Anyway, I have no urge to go back to the track."

"I protect myself from him," Karen commented calmly. "I keep the accounts. We have just one bank account in both our names. I question any Visa things that I don't recognize. I still haven't got back the trust in him that I once had. I don't think he's going to start gambling, but I keep an eye on him just in case. He's become a good liar and I can't always tell when he's lying, so I question him a lot and try to catch his slips."

"Not lately," Ken protested.

She gave him a quick look. "No, not now. But I did for a long time."

Ken wanted the subject changed.

"Your cooking is better," he grinned winningly.

She laughed with delight. "That's true."

"She's getting a lot better," he beamed.

"Why don't *you* learn to cook?" he was asked.

"I don't have to," Ken replied, deadpan. "I'm a man."

Laughter pealed from Karen. "He's teasing," she said, her face full of delight. "That's what he used to do with my mom all the time. My dad's the same way, a tease."

One night shortly before Melissa's second birthday Karen woke in the night to go to the bathroom. As always when she's up, she checked on Melissa, but the child wasn't in her bed.

Frightened, Karen searched the house. Turning on the lights downstairs, she found the child in the living-room, placidly sitting on the couch with her doll.

"What are you doing here, Melissa?" Karen asked. The toddler looked at her with a dazed expression.

Getting back into bed later, Karen said to Ken, "Guess what. Your daughter sleepwalks."

The relationship with Rob Parks started to break down almost immediately after the move to 311 Athol. Each brother was supposed to put $850 a month into a joint bank account, out of which the mortgage and utilities were to be paid, but Karen discovered that Rob wasn't keen to make his deposit. Each month she had to chase him and patiently endure his procrastination. He progressed from refusing to pay for the utilities to lateness in making the mortgage payments. In November he was only a few days late, but he missed the December mortgage payment entirely. The household was in trouble.

"I'll pay it next week," he promised, but didn't. Karen fumed. Rob, who earned twice as much as she and Ken combined, was blowing his wages at the race track.

Though it left Ken and Karen in a serious financial situation, they made up the entire December mortgage themselves to avoid the risk of losing the house.

Karen did not expect to receive Christmas gifts from her sisters and brothers but she resolutely shopped for gifts for everyone in her family anyway. She was determined not to lose contact with them. She went regularly to see her father, taking Melissa with her, and always by an appointment made well in advance. She was careful not to arrive early. Warned, her sisters and brothers would absent themselves. Always, Denis was alone in the house. Karen asked no questions and he offered no apology.

In December she gave notice as usual and said she planned to deliver the Christmas gifts. To her surprise Jonny and Nicky were at home. Karen had not seen her brothers for seven months, not since the emotional scene in the courtroom when Ken was acquitted. She noted that Nicky, the baby of the family, had grown. He greeted her shyly but Jonny turned his back and wouldn't speak. Karen, disconcerted and hurt, made the visit a brief one.

"Nicky has totally forgiven me," she said that spring. "He doesn't hold anything against me, but Jonny was slow to come around. Now he'll say 'Hi,' and 'How are you, Karen?' My sisters still feel very strongly. They just clear out when they know I'm coming."

"It's strange," Ken commented tersely. "Instead of blaming me, they're blaming Karen."

She flashed to their defence. "They can't blame Ken," she said, "because the court says he can't be blamed. So they have no one left to blame but me."

The problems with Ken's unruly brother Rob continued. Though Rob eventually repaid them his share of the December mortgage, he then missed the January payment. Though her pregnancy already was making her weary, Karen stolidly attended nursing school and worked Saturdays at the supermarket. Ken's salary wouldn't stretch to carry the house alone, even when his sister, Tammy, moved in for a few months.

The real-estate agent called about Rob's missed payment and demanded a certified cheque immediately for the missing $704. By stripping their savings, Ken and Karen managed to put the money together.

"We can't go on this way," Karen said firmly. It was agreed that Ken would tell Rob that he had to move out so they could rent his apartment. Rob protested that he would make it good. By the end of the month he had repaid them, but in February he missed the mortgage payment again.

The argument between the brothers was heated. Karen stayed out of it, believing that families should resolve their problems internally. Rob finally agreed to leave but by that time Ken and Karen had realized that they couldn't afford to stay either, even with someone dependable in the house. Karen started to look for cheap rented space. She was more familiar with Oshawa by this time, so it was easier. She quickly located a three-bedroom townhouse renting for $675.

Karen was seven months pregnant when they moved in the middle of March to a townhouse located in a row that overlooks a bleak, littered parking lot. Access from the busy street, one of Oshawa's main arteries, is obtained by a rutted driveway between an animal hospital and a Kentucky Fried Chicken outlet.

The townhouses sit in the midst of a dejected strip of automotive and fast-food outlets.

Ken and Karen made a decision to rent the triplex on Athol until they could manage to unload it. The agreement of sale with the real-estate agent would lapse at the end of August, and both were anxious to be free of the arrangement with Rob. The house needed work to prepare it for tenants. Fortunately, April was approaching, and Karen and Ken could expect refunds from the income tax deducted from their pay. When the money came, $500, it was spent on repairs.

The house on Athol went on the market in the middle of March, just as Karen finished the second-term examinations for her first year at Durham College. Her average was 90 per cent, even though she'd had to study for the exams on the same weekend that the family moved from the triplex into the rented townhouse.

Their new tenants moved into the triplex. The upstairs rooms were rented to three tenants, the bachelor apartment to Ken's half sister, Tammy, and the downstairs to a fifth tenant. Ken and Karen felt no confidence in the arrangement but hoped it would tide them over, and that the triplex could be sold quickly.

No one would meet their first price, $175,900, so they became less ambitious. Tenant problems were driving them crazy. A month later they had an offer of $163,000. The real-estate agent, as anxious as they to get new owners, urged them to accept and sweetened the deal by offering to take a reduced commission—5 per cent instead of 6. They accepted. When the dust settled, they found they made their money back, plus $1,700 profit. To Karen's disgust, Rob Parks also got $1,000.

It was a bad time for Karen. Trying to study and at the same time cope with the pressure of the move, their complex financial situation, her pregnancy and the dispute with Rob had a disastrous effect on her health. Her blood pressure rose dangerously, and her obstetrician ordered her to bed. That put an end to nursing school for a while. Ken was also undergoing stress. The conditions of sale were that they were to get the tenants out, move an abandoned car, and clean up the place, which had been left a shambles. All of this fell to Ken, since

Karen was confined to her bed and Rob Parks wasn't interested in helping. On top of caring for Melissa and working at his full-time job, Ken undertook the chores of collecting rents from the tenants and easing them out, changing locks, and making repairs.

His psychiatrist, Ron Billings, advised him to have a check-up at the sleep laboratory in Sunnybrook Hospital. An appointment was made for May 1, but Karen asked Ken to cancel. The date was uncomfortably close to the new baby's arrival and she didn't want to be alone overnight.

Karen pined for her mother, who would have swooped in and taken her troubles away. Her pregnancy opened up fresh wells of grief. Every day stirred tormenting memories of her first pregnancy, when she and her mother had drawn so close. As the new baby's birth approached, Karen swam in pain. Her thoughts dwelt on her mother's sweetness and laughter, on the good times together when they went to England, and on how protected and safe she felt in her mother's love. When Ken was away, she wept; she felt it unkind to cry for her mother in front of him.

All she says of that period is, "My pregnancy was a very depressed time."

She longed for her father, but recognized that it wasn't fair for her to lean on him. Denis had shown no pleasure at the news that she was having another baby but he seemed aware of her isolation and saddened by it. Neither ever referred to Barbara. Karen would have liked to see him more often, but he proffered no invitations. He did promise, however, to visit her in hospital after the baby was born.

The baby arrived on May 4, a girl. When no one was around to see, Karen wept with loneliness for her mother.

Her father's promise to visit her in hospital assumed enormous proportions. She realized that he wouldn't want to encounter Ken or Ken's family, so she constructed a visiting schedule to avoid an encounter that would distress him. She asked Ken and his family to stay away, or to visit her only at those times when she could be sure her father would not appear.

Denis, however, wasn't aware of the elaborate precautions on his behalf. He was travelling and arrived back the day after Karen left the hospital.

Karen picked the new baby's name, Brittany Barbara Parks. Both names are in honour of her mother, the Brittany because Barbara loved England. "I know she would approve," Karen said. "I haven't even told my father. I don't know how he would react. If we'd called her Barbara, a lot of people would see that in the wrong way."

"We didn't want to call her Barbara," Ken said quietly, his voice morose. "It wouldn't be good for the family constantly to be reminded because of her name."

"Brittany Barbara sounds good," Karen agreed wistfully. "It hurts to think that my mother will never know my kids and they have missed knowing her."

Watching her children grow, Karen often wonders how she's going to tell them what happened. She thinks she'll start gradually and perhaps give them the whole story when they reach their teens.

"If we tell them sooner they might tell their friends," Karen explains. "You know, kids confide in their friends. I used to. It might affect the way their friends treat them. People might not let their children play with Melissa, and that kind of stuff."

She drew a ragged breath. "In the meantime we'll just answer questions truthfully as much as will satisfy her curiosity. We can't hide it from her. I don't think we have the right to hide it from her." Ken nodded agreement. "But right now we won't say more than we have to."

If Melissa asks why Ken never sees her grandfather, for instance, the plan is to tell her there has been a family disagreement. "And I hope as time goes by my brothers and sisters will come around. You can't hate someone for ever, at least I don't think you can. That's not the way we've been brought up to behave. Meanwhile, it hurts."

She received no gifts for Brittany from her brothers and sisters. She wept with pleasure when her grandmother in England sent a money order for twenty pounds for the baby. "She still cares," Karen says gratefully.

Karen, depressed and stubborn, would not push for reconciliation with her sisters and brothers, though Ken urged her to pay a surprise visit and open up relations. "They just need to get over the first awkwardness," he told her. "After that, they'll be all right."

Karen wouldn't do that. She counted on time being on her side. Routinely, she arranged with her father to visit with the children; routinely, he was the only one at home.

"I'm not going to let them keep me away from my dad, or my kids away from their grandfather," she said. "You have to make tough decisions in life, and you have to do what you think is right. And that's what I'm doing. This is the way I want to be. I don't want to be in a fight with them. I couldn't live with myself. I'll continue to think of their birthdays and their Christmases. I'll continue to ask dad about them. I'm still their sister no matter what. I'm going to make it as hard as possible for them to go on hating me."

She paused. "The one important value my mom always put on us was that the family should stick together, no matter what. I live by that. This is my family," she continued, with a wave of her hand that included Ken and the toys scattered in the living-room, "and I have to stick with them."

She has no recent pictures of her father or siblings. Old ones are mounted in a photograph album, along with her wedding pictures. Of the eleven photographs in her living-room, all are of Ken and Melissa and Brittany.

Karen took Brittany home from the hospital, devastated that no one from her family had come to see the baby. Heartsick for the baby's sake, she decided to drop in unexpectedly, bringing Brittany. Jonny, Nicky, and Emma were there. Karen and Emma hadn't seen one another for a year. Emma gave Karen a startled, blistering look and ran up the stairs to her room, slamming the door. Clearing her throat, Karen said, "How've you been, Nicky?"

He grinned at her. "Fine, Karen. And you?"

A few minutes later Pru came in the door. Karen tensed. Pru was disconcerted to see Karen, but her behaviour was polite. She was pleasant and even held the baby. Denis took his tiny grandchild in his arms and studied her small face. Brittany has her father's colouring.

"She's lovely," he said, handing her back to Karen. "What's her name?"

Karen hesitated, but decided her decision was the right one. She would not to tell him that the second name was Barbara.

"Brittany," she told him. "Just Brittany."

Her heart is heavy when she thinks of her brothers and sisters. She isn't invited to graduations. She doesn't expect to be asked to a wedding either. She misses those family occasions intensely; she misses being *in* her family. She's bitter only when she considers that her children, too, are deprived of a family: grandfather, uncles, and aunts.

Of her relationship with her father she says: "He's my dad and I love him, but I know he isn't the same with me as with the other kids. He's very good to me and he's concerned, but we can't ever be as close as we used to be. He's scared that Ken might come back again...."

Ken looks at her, his face soft and vulnerable, but says nothing.

"I was really hurt when my family ignored Melissa's birthday," she adds. "She's innocent in all of this. She had nothing to do with all this. She didn't ask for this. It isn't fair."

The closing date for the sale of their house was June 15. Ken was frantic when the tenants were slow to move. He spent every spare minute in the triplex cleaning up the mess as they reluctantly departed, one at a time.

Karen, up through the night with the infant Brittany, noticed that Ken was muttering in his sleep. He seemed to be dreaming about work. Most of what he said was unintelligible, but sometimes she picked out a word or a phrase.

"Could you turn the machine off," he said pleasantly one night.

"Pardon me?" asked Karen. Then she realized he was asleep.

One night in May 1989, Ken suddenly sat almost upright in bed beside Karen and called out, "Melissa, no!" Then he clenched his fists and said loudly, "Melissa, *no!*"

Remembering her instructions not to touch him, Karen called out his name until Ken awoke. Ken was baffled when she told him what he had said. He had no memory of dreaming about Melissa, or anything else.

"That scared me," Karen relates with a puckered forehead. "Sleeptalking is related to sleepwalking. So I called Marlys."

The lawyer urged Karen to call Dr. Billings. His first questions were about stress and the amount of sleep Ken was getting. "Sleep deprivation by itself can cause sleepwalking or sleeptalking," he reminded her. Karen described the ordeal of selling the house and how the new baby kept them awake. Ken was exhausted, she said. The doctor thought the solution might be to see that Ken got more rest.

For a few weeks Ken rationed his time in the house as best he could and tried to get to bed early. It seemed that Ron Billings was right. Ken sometimes muttered in his sleep, but the sharp movements didn't happen again.

He went to the sleep specialist at Sunnybrook, but didn't like him. He found him too cautious and thought the doctor seemed uncomfortable at having him for a patient. When Ken mentioned that Karen had overheard him talking in his sleep, the doctor, apparently horrified, said, "She sleeps with you?"

Ken decided he preferred Roger Broughton. If he had any more sleeptalking, he thought he'd talk to the specialist in Ottawa instead.

The last tenant left the Athol triplex at midnight on June 15, the date of closure. Ken had been wild with worry that the deal would collapse. He was feeling pulled from all sides, with Brittany keeping them both awake nights and Melissa, two and a half, demanding attention. Karen was still very weak, needing Ken's assistance, and his boss at work was criticizing him mercilessly. Despite Ken's best intentions, he realized that he was getting no more than five hours' sleep a night.

The night, June 15, when the last tenant was out and the house sale was finalized, both felt enormous relief. Karen was breast-feeding Brittany at about four-thirty that morning when she heard the sound of a car being revved outside the open bedroom window. Ken, who was sleeping soundly beside her, suddenly sprang up and walked rapidly to the window.

He put his hands on the window-sill and leaned out, his body tense. "I thought there was a car," he said loudly. Then he went briskly back to bed, covered himself up, and resumed sleeping.

321

"It was kind of weird how he did it," she relates. "Sort of wound up and tense, almost as if he was scared. I wondered if a car outside had wakened him, but he wouldn't have been so energetic. It would have taken him a while to go to the window and look out." In fact, Ken always is lethargic and slow when he first wakens.

The next morning when she told him about it, he had no recollection of the incident. They looked at each other with fear in their eyes.

"I'd better call Dr. Broughton," he said quietly.

"Are you under stress?" Roger Broughton asked. "Have you been missing sleep?"

"Well, yes," he answered. "Both things."

"You'd better come to Ottawa and we'll put you in the sleep lab," the specialist said. Meanwhile he increased Ken's medication, Rivotril, upping the dose from one to two pills.

"That should help," he said. "We'll make an appointment for you right away."

Ken anxiously queried Karen every morning. "Did I talk last night?" She assured him that the strengthened medicine was working: he had been silent.

Both of them like Roger Broughton very much. They're awed by his credentials, which Karen described as "taking a half hour to read in court", and grateful that the doctor is soft-spoken and not intimidating.

Ken had a week's vacation in July, so the couple planned to spend part of it in a rented cottage on Shadow Lake. After that, they would drive to Ottawa. They returned one lovely Saturday afternoon from their time at the cottage to prepare for the trip to Ottawa on Monday. They were appalled to discover that in their absence they had been robbed. Their furniture was pushed out of place, showing signs of a rapid search, and their television and VCR were unplugged, as if someone had considered removing them and then rejected the idea. Something better had come along. The thief or thieves had found one thousand dollars in cash hidden in the box of a board game. Karen had been hoarding it for their Ottawa expenses.

"It's typical of the way things go for us," Karen said flatly, shrugging.

On Monday, Ken and Karen packed up their children and drove to Ottawa, where they checked into a cheap motel. That night Ken met Roger Broughton at the sleep lab in the Ottawa General Hospital. He undressed to his underwear and stretched out on a cot. A mesh cover was spread on his chest, and technicians attached to it a transmitter to magnify the weak signals from ten electrodes glued at various places to his face, scalp, chest, and leg.

He was placed in a room so dark that he couldn't see his hand in front of his face. He knew that he was being watched and photographed by ultra-wave camera and observers behind glass. He composed himself for sleep but found the situation too unnatural. By morning he had slept so little that the results were not helpful. He was asked to schedule more appointments for the following Thursday.

This time the procedures went better. Ken was more relaxed and dropped off to sleep without difficulty. Through the night the electrodes sent their messages about Ken's level of sleep and counted the number of arousals. The troubling results found in the sleep test done in Metro East Detention Centre were still present. Even with the slow-wave-sleep–suppressing medication, Ken still had more deep sleep and more abrupt arousal from such sleep than are found in the normal adult person. Broughton re-emphasized with him the necessity to avoid sleep deprivation and unnecessary stress and continued the medication.

Karen was curiously serene about the return of Ken's sleep-walking. "We didn't know that he had a sleepwalking problem two years ago, so it escalated to the point where it was disastrous. It's different now, we're aware of it. I think we can keep a handle on it."

Ken wasn't so sanguine. "It scares me," he admitted, "when I sleeptalk and start wandering. I'm scared something will happen when I can't control it. The doctors assure me it won't happen, but still I'm scared."

"The doctors said it was a good sign that when he sleepwalked there was no violence in it at all," Karen added.

"A few people are violent every time they sleepwalk," Ken continued. "I don't mean they attack people, but they throw their arms around a lot. Apparently that isn't the kind of sleepwalker I am."

Karen and Ken had many talks with Dr. Broughton and with the Chicago expert, Dr. Rosalind Cartwright, about the nature of sleepwalking. Karen feels more confident than Ken does, but both are aware that whatever problems might arise will occur only if Ken is disturbed while sleepwalking.

"I've been instructed not to try to wake him, just to get out of his way and let him go," Karen said calmly.

In the silence that fell, she seemed concerned at the direction the conversation had taken.

"Basically," she said briskly, "he's over it. In the year he's been out of prison, he's only sleepwalked one time. He's done some sleeptalking, but very little. I don't think anything will happen again."

His face showed that he wished he could believe that too.

The couple began to experience difficulties in their relationship. Karen sometimes was impatient with Ken, and sometimes he woke in a grumpy state, nagging her about the way she made Brittany's formula or how the living-room looked.

Karen dismisses the clashes as "typical married stuff". None the less, they started to talk about seeing a marriage counsellor.

On August 17, 1989, Ken suddenly quit his job—simply walked out. His boss was an erratic man, caustic and fault-finding in the mornings, though pleasant and smooth in the afternoons. Ken was amused at first by the midday switch in personality, but he began to find the mornings hard to take. The man was particularly difficult when Ken worked nights. The next morning the boss would complain that he had done nothing, that he was a lazy bum. Ken, stung, showed him on production records that he really had done the work, sometimes even more than his quota, but his boss angrily brushed aside his protests.

Ken's fragile self-esteem withered under the rain of criticism. He began to fear that he might lose control and hit the man. He went to work with growing reluctance, dreading what lay ahead. The Thursday night he quit, two others who were equally affronted went with him. Later they reconsidered and returned.

"I'll give Ken his due," says Karen stoutly. "The first thing Friday morning he went out job-hunting and he registered with the unemployment office."

In a burst of bitterness that is rare in her, she added, "But if he was really a responsible person he would have looked for work before he quit. It's not good for us, money-wise."

A few days later, he had a new job as shipper in a warehouse that handles two-ton motors. The pay, $11 an hour, was slightly better than the job he had left, but it still scarcely met the needs of a family of four.

Always thrifty when they shop, they became almost fanatical in their search for bargains. Karen grinned, "Ken is always taking things out of my shopping cart. 'Why do we need this?' he says. He's become worse than I am about spending."

In the summer of 1989, after a delay of more than a year, Marlys Edwardh advised them that the appeal would be heard in October. They had been waiting for the report of the trial judge, she explained.

"David Watt is one of the best judges on the bench," she told Ken, "so this is unusual. For some reason or other he still hasn't written his reasons for not putting insanity to the jury. Those reasons probably will help us at the appeal and I don't want to proceed until we get them. But he promised to have them ready soon, and we're pretty sure of the October date."

"The more delay, the better," Ken told her.

"We're hoping the trial will be put over until winter," Karen explained. "Then people aren't around as much. It would give us a few months to be by ourselves while the neighbours got used to it. Maybe by spring, when children start to go out to play, the situation will have calmed down."

Ken and Karen didn't like to think of the consequences of losing the appeal. In both their minds was the spectre of police arriving at the door to take him away in handcuffs. If the appeal court ordered a new trial and removed sleepwalking as a defence, Ken might be convicted, or he might be found innocent by reason of insanity. Either way, he could face years in prison or the mental institution at Penetanguishene.

They shuddered to think of the costs. The family simply wouldn't be able to pay for the same expert witnesses again. Lil Hodge regretfully gave Ken notice that she could pay no more.

"It isn't fair to my other grandchildren," she explained, "if I spend everything I have on Kenneth. If there is a new trial, where is that money going to come from?"

She cries to think of it. She isn't at all sure that, without the weight of five psychiatrists testifying, a jury would again find Ken innocent. "I feel very bothered by all this. I'm so worried about the appeal."

The prospects were too sickening to contemplate. Instead the couple worried about something more immediate. They fretted that the appeal would draw media attention, exposing Ken's identity to the neighbours and his employer. Ken expected to be fired, and Karen shuddered to think what would happen if the neighbours became unpleasant.

The October date for the appeal came and went. Judge Watt still had not written his reasons. They were released on January 5, 1990. Obviously, the judge had laboured hard. "Supplementary reasons *re* instructions to the jury on defence of non-insane automatism" came to 112 pages.

Mr. Justice Watt opened by reviewing the trial. He noted that the Crown counsel had adduced no evidence to contradict the defence case of sleepwalking.

"The authorities," he wrote, "understandably without analysis, as none was compelled by the evidence adduced at the trial, have viewed somnambulism as paradigmatic of non-insane automatism."

In other words, the judge relied on the expertise of the five doctors. Further, he stated, he viewed somnambulism as an exception to the states of mind classified in legal precedents as insane or "a disease of the mind" within the statutes of the Criminal Code.

"Crown counsel," he repeated, "adduced no evidence to the contrary, although a well-known forensic psychiatrist and, it would appear, a sleep-disorder expert, were seated at the counsel table during the testimony of the defence experts."

He concluded: "It would seem passing strange to a reasonable person that one who committed what otherwise would be a crime in a somnambulistic state should be stigmatized as insane and subjected, theoretically at least, to indefinite confinement in a psychiatric institution, there to receive instruction in good sleep hygiene....

"For these reasons the jury will be instructed on the defence of non-insane automatism and not insanity or insane automatism."

CHAPTER FOURTEEN
The Appeal

The Ontario Court of Appeal sits in great dignity in one of the most beautiful buildings in Canada, the imposing and graceful Osgoode Hall, which looks down the gullet of Toronto's York Street from a landscaped garden protected for almost two centuries by wrought-iron cow-gates. Begun in 1829, Osgoode Hall was described by the late architect and archivist Eric Arthur as the finest building in Toronto, "a scholarly piece of classic architecture" whose spirit, he wrote, will never be dominated by the soaring glass towers that have sprung up around it.

On Monday morning, March 12, 1990, with a false spring delighting grateful Canadians, Ken Parks sat alone in one of the courtrooms, wiping his palms on his blue herring-bone suit to keep them dry. It was the same suit he had worn almost two years earlier for his trial; he has no other. Eczema, always a sign of stress in him, could be seen on his face, though partially concealed by a new beard, a surprising shade of bright orange in contrast to his blond hair.

Karen was writing a nursing examination and would join him later.

To get time off work, Ken had no option but to explain to his employer that he was the sleepwalker who had been acquitted of killing his mother-in-law. To his relief, the woman's response was sympathetic.

"If I didn't know you, that story would be hard to swallow," she told Ken. "But knowing you, I can believe it. If you need someone to testify for you, I'll come."

"Appeals aren't like that," Ken explained. "It's all, like, law."

The law to be argued that day, the next, and part of a third was new ground that puzzled even the judges. They were not certain whether they could replace a simple acquittal by another kind of acquittal—not guilty by reason of insanity—or whether, if they didn't like the idea of homicidal sleepwalkers, they should order a new trial.

The actors assembled. Marlys Edwardh and Delmar Doucette, dressed in flowing black robes and the traditional white winged collars of lawyers appearing before a high court, sat at a long polished table on the left side of the courtroom. The Crown's two lawyers, similarly gowned, were on the right. In front, beside, and behind them were piled red-covered transcripts, case-books bristling with tabs, Judge Watt's reasons bound in beige, and the factum each of them had prepared. While they waited for the judges, the counsel chatted easily together. Opposing lawyers do that.

Three judges swept in to a cry of "All rise!" and took their places behind an elevated desk on which could be seen the same transcripts, case-books, reasons, and factums. They proved to be three of the appeal court's best: John Brooke, a man with a quick mind and a neatly turned down mouth; Horace Krever, who has a lugubrious mien and is noted for his expertise on legal issues related to health and insanity; and sunny, white-haired Patrick Galligan, who contented himself in the main with droll asides.

The Crown, as the appellate, had the floor. He was Gary Trotter, a young man with thinning sandy hair and a pale peaked face. Not long out of law school, he had a firm manner despite his relative inexperience. His argument rested on a recital of all the sleepwalking trials known in English common-law courts, every one of which—without exception—viewed sleepwalking as non-insane automatism and therefore granted the accused a simple acquittal. The Crown's choice of ground was a curious one, seemingly self-defeating, but he persisted. The point he intended to make was that every previous judge and jury had erred because scientific knowledge about sleepwalking was lacking when those cases were tried.

"Are you saying," asked Mr. Justice Brooke, leaning his head on his hand and closing his eyes, "that the judge [in Parks] should have instructed the jury that sleepwalking is a disease of the mind?"

Gary Trotter wasn't disturbed by the judge's challenge. "If it was sleepwalking, then the jury must return a verdict that it is a disease of the mind."

"Schizophrenia is a disease of the mind," observed Mr. Justice Krever patiently. "If you find that the accused was suffering from schizophrenia, then you find disease of the mind."

"Yes, my lord," said Trotter.

"All the medical evidence goes one way," continued Mr. Justice Krever, "that sleepwalking is not a disease. The forensic psychiatrists said that it wasn't a disease of the mind, that it wasn't within the legal territory of disease of the mind."

"The trial judge was wrong in following what the medical evidence said," Trotter responded.

"Maybe there are degrees," said Mr. Justice Brooke, sitting up sharply. This, indeed, seemed to be what the judges wanted to know. "Maybe there is a state of sleepwalking that is so extreme it would amount to a disease of the mind, or so mild as not to." He closed his eyes again. "In this man's case, was his state such as to amount to disease of the mind?"

"It's not clear in the medical evidence," Trotter admitted. "But this *is* an extreme state of somnambulism."

Mr. Justice Krever raised his heavy brows. "What's the bottom line?" he inquired. "The result was an acquittal. What you're seeking is also an acquittal, subject to the lieutenant-governor's Board of Review. So the Board of Review would immediately release him, since the man is not suffering a disease of the mind. What is the practical result?"

Judge Krever sits on the Ontario lieutenant-governor's Board of Review, so this was ground he knew well.

"Is it that he's a time bomb walking around?" asked Mr. Justice Galligan.

Reporters in the courtroom bent their heads over notebooks and simultaneously wrote *time bomb*.

Trotter replied hastily, "I agree that this individual should not be incarcerated for any length of time, it should be a very short period of time, but the lieutenant-governor's warrant has power to monitor...."

Mr. Justice Galligan asked, "How are we going to watch him every night when he goes to bed?"

The Crown counsel, his agenda thoroughly trashed, tried to rally. He spoke about predisposition to sleepwalk, triggering factors, and precipitating factors. Ken Parks could be monitored, he said, "to cut down on the likelihood of this happening again...it's reasonable to protect the public."

Ken wiped his hands on his trousers again. He was sitting very still.

Mr. Justice Krever asked with an edge of irritation, "What is the point of putting this man in hospital?"

Trotter said hastily, "I agree that's not appropriate. I didn't say that. I did say that given the gravity of the conduct in this case, to have a regime of monitoring is not over-intrusive....We have in *Rabey* a definition of disease of the mind. This is a *legal* question. Whether expert witnesses thought it was not a disease of the mind is of no moment."

"No moment!" commented Mr. Justice Krever in mock astonishment.

"Are there cases of comparable violence associated with somnambulism?" asked Mr. Justice Brooke.

That put Trotter back on schedule. "Yes, m'lords," he said gratefully. With some interruptions from the impatient judges, he went solemnly through them. The first mention of sleepwalking in legal history occurred in 1878 in Scotland when a man named Fraser caused the death of his baby son while sleeping. The jury decided that the man wasn't conscious at the time of the death. Fraser was discharged with the requirement that he never again sleep with someone else in the room.

In Australia, Trotter continued, a man sleeping in the same room as a two-year-old child picked up the child and killed her by swinging her like a club against walls and floor. The man was acquitted of non-insane automatism.

"But he didn't drive miles and miles in a car," Trotter said. "The case is very different. He dreamed he was being attacked by a wild beast."

Mr. Justice Galligan was reminded of his amazement to read in the trial transcript that Ken was sleepwalking while he drove twenty-three kilometres. "He's stopping at stop streets, he's putting his foot on the brake, he's accelerating from a stopped position...."

Hunching his shoulders like an eagle on the nest, the lanky Judge Krever leaned forward. "Memory *must* be working. It's not all automation. It's difficult for a lay person to accept this."

The Crown lawyer couldn't agree more. The next example concerned an American case in 1879 when the accused fell asleep in a hotel lobby. When a porter tried to rouse him, the man shot the porter several times and killed him. The defence of sleepwalking was not allowed by the trial judge, but the case was appealed to the state Supreme Court, which ordered a new trial. This time the man was freed on the grounds that "somnambulism is more or less an unconscious state".

The sound of clicking high heels was heard on the echoing tile floor in the corridor outside the courtroom. Ken murmured, "There's Karen." A moment later, she slipped into the seat beside him.

In the court recess, Marlys Edwardh and Del Doucette stepped into the corridor where Marlys produced cigarettes and lit one. Taking long grateful puffs, she asked Karen, "How did the exam go?"

Ken responded for his wife with a slow smile, "She always gets nineties."

"It was okay," said Karen, with a nervous laugh.

Marlys turned to Del. "The Crown missed it," she said, as Ken and Karen listened quietly. "The judges were inviting him to argue that this is a degree of somnambulism which raises issues that wouldn't be found in most sleepwalking. He missed it, and now the bench is resigned to let him present his case his own way."

This proved an accurate reading. The interruptions dropped markedly as Gary Trotter proceeded through his litany of sleep-walking cases. From time to time, as the issue of recurrence loomed, the judges rained questions on him. At one point they digressed to mull over whether an abnormality of sleep is an abnormality of mind, hence a disease of the mind. Getting no comfort from the Crown, they turned to Marlys Edwardh, who rose and answered promptly.

"M'lords, for one hundred and twenty-five years sleepwalking has been regarded as automatism of a non-psychotic state. It is a disorder of sleep, not a disorder of the mind."

Trotter, leafing hurriedly through a document in front of him and then abandoning the search, insisted that there were "pockets of doubt".

Soon after, the judges recessed for lunch.

The defence lawyers lunched with Ken and Karen Parks in the great dining-hall of Osgoode Hall at a long table rainbowed with sunlight falling through stained-glass windows. Marlys discussed her strategy. Her first objective in the appeal was to have the simple acquittal upheld. Failing that, she hoped that the judges would not change the jury's unadorned "not guilty" to "not guilty by reason of insanity". If that happened, she planned to appeal the decision at once to the Supreme Court of Canada, and the court could not deny her right to be heard.

If the judges ordered a new trial, she intended to ask that the trial be restricted to an examination of whether somnambulism can be, in some degree, insane. She would fight to avoid putting Ken through another complete trial. Expense was not mentioned as a compelling reason, though she knew the Parks family could give little more help. Pinched resources might limit the number of expert witnesses she could call. What she stressed instead was that she wanted to avoid giving the Crown "another bite at the same apple".

She ordered a salad plate and explained, "If it goes back for a new trial we want to confine it to the issue of whether somnambulism can be described as a disease of the mind."

Ken, scarcely touching his food, asked, "Would that mean I would have to wait a year in Penetang before the case is heard?"

"Absolutely not," Marlys assured him quickly. "You won't even go to Penetang. We can expedite your release in two weeks."

Karen was silent, abiding by a promise to Ken that she would not talk about the case, but her face was stricken.

Catching her expression, Marlys said, "What you're facing is minimal compared to a new trial and the possibility of a new verdict."

Ken stopped eating altogether.

"If he goes back into custody," Karen asked slowly, "what will happen? Will the police come to the door to arrest him? That would freak out Melissa."

"That would freak out everyone," Marlys said. "That won't happen, never will happen."

Walking back to the courtroom, Karen looked miserable. "It brings it all back," she said unhappily. "Usually I blot it out, but this brings it all back. People talking about us as if we aren't there, as if we aren't even real."

That afternoon Gary Trotter continued with his accounts of acquittals relating to sleepwalking. He reached the case in Kentucky of Tibbs, who fell asleep in a whorehouse in a drunken state and stabbed someone in the eye. The Crown said, his voice trailing off, "but the court thought it was drunkenness rather than somnambulism".

"That doesn't help us very much, does it?" said Judge Brooke with an ominous edge to his voice.

"Ah, well no," agreed Trotter, moving to another American case of a man named Bradley, who, fearful of being attacked, kept a gun under his pillow and woke up to find he had shot the woman beside him. Bradley also was acquitted, because sleepwalking was found to be non-insane automatism.

The judges were growing irritated. Said Judge Brooke, "*Bradley* is not recognized in English courts or in our own courts or in the medical jurisprudence here. I don't know how this case helps you, Mr. Trotter."

"You need evidence of the medical component of the legal definition of insanity," Mr. Justice Krever explained in the exasperated tone of one teaching simple addition for the tenth time. "And you don't have it."

This indeed proved to be the insurmountable problem. In the trial of Kenneth James Parks, the Crown didn't ask any of the expert witnesses the clear question: Is there an extreme degree of sleepwalking that falls into the category of insanity? The answer might be no—Marlys Edwardh is convinced it would have been—but the problem for the Ontario Court of Appeal was that the question had not been asked.

Gary Trotter struggled on before three monumentally restive judges. "In the House of Lords in *Regina* v. *Sullivan*," he said, "Lord Diplock commented that in the future sleepwalking might find itself in the category of insanity." The context was that epilepsy, the situation in the Sullivan case, might fit into the legal definition of a "disease of the mind" if Parliament so decided.

Said Mr. Justice Krever gruffly, "What you're suggesting, Mr. Trotter, is something more appropriate for the legislature than the courts."

Gary Trotter gamely produced the comments of Canadian judges who have attempted to pin down the elusive legal definition of insanity. Chief Justice Dickson, in *Regina* v. *Cooper*, observed that in the legal sense disease of the mind "embraces any illness, disorder or abnormal condition which impairs the human mind and its functioning", but he excluded transitory states such as hysteria or concussion and said that "somnambulism *may* be unaccompanied by any abnormality of the mind", and, also, that "the defence of automatism...in the past has generally covered acts done while sleepwalking", leaving the matter maddeningly unresolved.

The courtroom was uncomfortably warm and the pitchers of ice-water placed on tables for the lawyers were nearly empty. Gary Trotter continued to parade through acquittals for sleepwalking, all of which described it as non-insane automatism. Sensing he was losing his audience, he declared that he wouldn't bother mentioning the South African and Zimbabwean cases referenced in his factum.

The judges were ready to adjourn for the day.

"How long will you be tomorrow, Ms. Edwardee?" asked Mr. Justice Brooke. He always pronounces her name that way.

"About three or four hours, m'lord," she replied.

In the corridor outside, Ken Parks observed with a bemused smile, "I don't know which lawyer I should be paying."

The next morning had the feel of an interminable theatre performance that had been interrupted by an intermission. The only noticeable change from the end of the first act was that the pitchers of ice-water had been freshened and Ken Parks was wearing a different tie. Gary Trotter, for the Crown, picked up his narrative with a flurry of some English jurisprudence that consistently found somnambulism to be non-insane.

Mr. Justice Brooke glared at him. "Why should we escalate sleepwalking into insanity here if England doesn't do that?" he asked.

"In *Sullivan*," Mr. Justice Krever pointed out, "that was a prediction which hasn't been borne out. In the English courts somnambulism has been consistently classed as non-insane automatism. I have not yet been persuaded that the medical evidence in this case supports a notion of a pathological condition. Doesn't your whole argument depend on our being persuaded that there is medical evidence for deciding this is a disease of the mind?"

"Well, yes," said Gary Trotter, sounding winded.

"The whole case turns on that," Mr. Justice Krever continued relentlessly. "All the rest is secondary. The principal interest is that one."

Krever and Brooke teamed to worry through the matter of whether sleepwalking in Ken Parks' case indicated an underlying emotional state that might be described as a disease of the mind by judicial extrapolation. Commented Judge Brooke, as though musing aloud, "If this man responded to a certain set of circumstances that caused him to respond, then is there something the matter with his psychological and social make-up, the same as in *Rabey*?"

Ken began cracking his knuckles, working methodically across the fingers of his left hand and then his right. His face was shining with sweat. Karen, sitting erect beside him, fixed a hard glare on Mr. Justice Brooke.

"But then this is a sleep disorder," Mr. Justice Brooke continued, closing his eyes. "It doesn't have anything to do with his mind. Medical people who testified didn't put it in that category. Unless you want to say that somnambulism generally is a disease of the mind, I would have thought that you would show that in this specific case it is."

"The law has been applied in a certain way for a long time," Mr. Justice Krever reminded the unhappy Crown lawyer. "Clearly the legislature finds it satisfactory."

"It might not be easy for the court to turn its back on a long line of authority," Trotter began bravely, "but...."

The court recessed at a quarter to twelve. Karen Parks had a copy of the *Toronto Star* article about the previous day's hearing. "It mentions the fraud," she said bitterly. "There goes Ken's job. He told them about the sleepwalking but he didn't mention the embezzlement."

"Maybe it will be all right," Ken consoled her.

"Why don't you call them right now?" she asked.

"Later," he assured her. "Later, I will."

At two minutes after twelve, the hearing resumed and it was the turn of the respondent, Marlys Edwardh. Delmar Doucette, sitting beside her, found the references she needed in the stack of transcripts and had them ready to her hand as she moved through her arguments.

She had been hoping from the tone of the judges' reactions to the appellant lawyer that the court might even dismiss the appeal without asking her to present her case for the respondent. This proved overly optimistic. She was to have no easier ride than Gary Trotter.

Marlys first wanted to knock out the argument that an underlying pathological state contributed to Ken's sleepwalking. To this end, she took the judges through Roger Broughton's testimony. Then she addressed the Martin decision in *Rabey*.

"Martin says that sleepwalking is a separate category, it is *not* insane," she said, her voice crackling with energy and her diction sharp. "The Dickson dissent is clear on this point, that sleepwalking is non-insane automatism. Chief Justice Dickson was concerned that Martin went too far, that it went beyond the category of what properly can be called disease of the mind. Let's not forget that's what we are talking about here."

The judges were not so sure. "What's a disorder in relation to an illness?" Mr. Justice Brooke asked her, looking pensively into the distance.

Marlys replied at some length, emphasizing that in sleepwalking the cerebral cortex, the thinking brain, is in a coma. "It's *not there*."

Mr. Justice Brooke protested. "His body did a series of acts directed by something....What directs a body to stop at a red light? This involves a long series of body activities that are directed. I think the psychiatrists should have been cross-examined on that."

A small silence fell. The judges longed for a crack at the expert witnesses themselves.

"The point, my lords," said Marlys softly, "is that they were not."

"I know that," Mr. Justice Brooke said testily.

"There is nothing abnormal about sleep," Marlys declared.

Later, the matter still on his mind, Mr. Justice Brooke returned to the same bone. "What *directs* the body to do these acts?"

"We have no answer," Marlys told him. "There is no evidence that it is driven by any impulse."

"So it doesn't fall into impairment of the mind," Mr. Justice Brooke sighed. "But what *is* directing his body? Something internal is directing the activities of driving the car, for instance. The only thing internal that could be directing him is his mind. Is he functioning while impaired or is it that he doesn't have any mind at all?"

"Nothing is directing his mind," Marlys replied. "All the evidence shows that is not the case. Parts of the brain are functioning, but the mind is not functioning."

Mr. Justice Krever looked perplexed. "We need a definition of the mind. What is the mind?"

"Reason, memory, and understanding," said Marlys promptly.

"It's like a computer," Mr. Justice Brooke said with a bitter smile. "Only this time someone stuck the wrong program in it."

"Sleepwalking is truly automatic behaviour," Marlys insisted. "It represents the possibilities of the human brain...."

"Let's have lunch," said Mr. Justice Brooke.

In the clatter of the Osgoode Hall dining-hall, Del and Marlys conferred. Both were worried.

"They cannot understand how someone can do something automatically that's complex," Del said, looking up from the menu he was studying. "Brooke's difficulty isn't that someone does something that's automatic, but that it goes from the simple to the complex. While most somnambulistic episodes will be simple, ah, you can go along a continuum from sitting up in bed, to peeing in the corner, to cooking. There's nothing to suggest that anything is different along that continuum, that the mind ever engages."

Marlys listened intently, buttering a roll.

"What has to be pounded into him is that things can be done automatically. We have no explanation, except that the behaviour is something familiar to the subject. For instance, it would be quite different if Ken had never driven that route before, if his in-laws had just moved and he found his way to their new house."

"I don't want to suggest that there are residual thoughts directing the sleeper," Marlys protested, "because that gets you into underlying psychological disturbance. The fact is, you can't plan to do something when you're awake and then carry it out in your sleep."

"Driving over to your parents-in-law when you've driven there many, many times before is not totally random," Del insisted.

Ken was feeling better. He ordered grilled breast of chicken and ate it all.

"The brain does not function in deep sleep and sleepwalking," Del continued, sipping his milk. "So that's why there is no mind. None of those attributes of thinking that come from the cortex, the attributes that *Sullivan* defines, they aren't there. You can do routine things like cooking, like driving to a place you've been before...."

Marlys interrupted. "You can't get around the fact that the sleepwalker is different from the sleeper. Not in terms of the human cortex, but in terms of those functions of the brain that permit motor action."

Karen and Ken continued to eat stoically. Karen's face bore an expression of deep sadness.

"Both the shift and the state are non-pathological," Del agreed. "Non-disease. Not abnormal. Just one of the potentials that the brain can go into."

"I've gone as far as I can by indicating that the shift in the brain is not pathological," Marlys said vehemently.

A silence fell. Del said, "Well, I just feel it's something we shouldn't have to overcome. It's not a legal issue. Brooke has it in his mind that there must be some mind function to drive that route. I think that has to be addressed."

"The problem is, if you say there is brain function, then are you necessarily saying there is mind function?" Marlys wondered.

More silence. "The answer is no," said Del. "You've read him the passage from Ervin's testimony. That explains how it could happen."

She nodded. "I've read them that. I'd rather go on and then come back to it when he comes back at me. They're having a visceral, gut reaction."

"We've somehow got to get the aura of those expert witnesses into the Court of Appeal," Del said with a grin.

"The judges are troubled," Marlys observed sympathetically. "They're saying he was sleepwalking, but they don't want to give it full force and effect. They would have got the answer they want from our expert witnesses that the mind is not engaged. There is no malfunction of the mind. It isn't there."

"Isn't the answer, in part, that the automatic behaviour is no more explainable after a concussion than it is in sleepwalking?" observed Doucette. "To say that the behaviour looks directed and therefore we should make it a disease of the mind would mean that *all* non-insane automatism would disappear. It would swallow the whole thing."

Court resumed promptly at two-thirty. Marlys was on her feet again, drawing the judges' attention to a page in Judge

Watt's reasons where he declared that "the authorities viewed somnambulism as paradigmatic of non-insane automatism."

She said, "It is the position of the respondent that there are no reasons in law, science, or common sense which warrant reclassifying the respondent's somnambulistic state as a disease of the mind. Jurisprudentially, somnambulism was and still is paradigmatic of the defence of non-insane automatism. The body of jurisprudence dealing with somnambulism, which stretches back decades and continues into the present day, cannot be characterized in the manner the appellant seeks as ill-considered, non-persuasive, and of mere historical interest."

She referred to the Martin decision in *Rabey*, in which he said that "sleepwalking appears to fall into a separate category". She reminded the appeal judges that Martin's principles had been upheld by the Supreme Court of Canada.

"We shouldn't widen the net so broad as to include those who do not suffer disease of the mind," she declared, "or those from whom there is no need to protect the community."

Judge Krever looked at her severely. "There *is* a need to protect the community," he said. "A lieutenant-governor's warrant could exercise some control."

Marlys replied quickly, "The possibility of recurrence is improbable. There have been no examples of a recurrence. There is no history of anybody doing it twice. And how can we monitor sleepwalking?... I don't mean to undercut the behaviour, but no one knows a medical difference between benign sleepwalking and the aggressive sleepwalker."

Judge Krever said something about treatment.

"When we talk about treatment for sleepwalking we're talking about good health," Marlys responded. "It's a matter of not getting sleep deprived, of getting appropriate exercise, and so on. There's no fit with medical treatment as we know it."

The lawyer was concerned. The drift of questions, especially those from Mr. Justice Krever, suggested the judges were looking fondly on changing the verdict to insanity in order to get some kind of a handle on Ken Parks. She pointed out that such a decision would result in a period of incarceration in Penetanguishene.

"The system isn't designed to get people immediately out," she observed. "It would take six months to a year."

Judge Krever considered this. "Didn't Martin say that it is unthinkable to have any deprivation of liberty in these cases?"

Marlys nodded. "There is no statutory mechanism to do anything but commit him after an acquittal for reasons of insanity. You have to convene the Board of Review, for one thing, and this doesn't happen in a day."

Krever, who sits on the Ontario Board of Review, corrected her. "It *hasn't* happened in one day," he said. "It should."

"Indeed it should," she concurred.

A sense of weariness hung in the courtroom. It was almost time to adjourn, and Marlys had not finished her presentation. Clearly the case would have to resume the following day, pushing back a number of other appeals scheduled to be heard.

Marlys was nearing her conclusion. "Therefore it is respectfully submitted that the respondent's somnambulistic episode cannot be classified as a disease of the mind through the application of general principle. We don't have a disease....We don't have a problem of recurrence....The mind is asleep....The precipitating factors largely were external: the factors of stress, over-exertion earlier that day, and sleep deprivation."

"We'll adjourn," said Judge Brooke, "until ten-thirty tomorrow morning."

In the corridor outside the courtroom, Marlys hurriedly lit a cigarette and had a murmured conversation with Doucette, who was leaving by taxi to catch a flight to Florida, where he planned to do some bird-watching.

Karen, looking depressed, said, "I think a lot of the public would feel better about it if Ken was said to be insane. A lot of people are uncomfortable that he was just set free. From the public point of view, I can see what the Crown is trying to do."

"But Marlys says I'm likely to be released right away, two weeks or a month," Ken points out. "The public probably wouldn't think that's enough. I don't know what's enough."

Marlys caught the end of that. "They'll likely reserve judgment," she told Ken. "Later on when they're ready with it, I'll be warned if it goes against us. I'll go with you to the police station when you give yourself up and I'll start bail proceedings right away. You'll maybe be in custody twenty-four hours."

Southern Ontario continued to enjoy a March heat wave, proclaimed in the media as record breaking, and deeply appreciated by Torontonians strolling the sidewalks in shirt-sleeves. Ken arrived in the courtroom Wednesday, March 14, in a T-shirt and work pants. The courtroom was boiling with black-gowned lawyers, resigned to wait until the Parks appeal ran its course.

Marlys finished and asked the court to dismiss the appeal. Then she raised the matter of critical importance. If the appeal court decided to send Parks back for a new trial, she wanted the process confined to the issue of somnambulism and mental illness. The judges weren't sure they could do that.

"I'm concerned with what you ask us to do here," commented Judge Brooke. "*Can* we limit the issue to be tried?"

"You're entitled to make any order that justice requires," Marlys reminded him.

"Shouldn't we be able to ask the jury to reconsider the whole case and allow the Crown to lead fresh evidence on this issue?"

Marlys protested. "You can't put someone who has been acquitted in a worse position. Justice in this unique circumstance would be done by a restraining order."

"It might run into an entirely new case," Mr. Justice Brooke warned her, "on the question of whether this amounted to a disease of the mind."

She agreed. That could happen. To her relief, Gary Trotter rose to say he saw no reason why a second trial should address anything other than the issue of sleepwalking and insanity. He was willing to accept, he said, that it was appropriate in this situation.

Marlys, knowing the repercussions, then made herself unpopular with all three judges. She entered a motion to have the appeal struck down on the grounds of delay. Because Judge Watt had taken more than a year to write his reasons, there had been a delay of eighteen and a half months.

The judges were incensed at the implied criticism of their colleague. Mr. Justice Galligan fumed openly. "He wrote the reasons at the request of counsel," he said indignantly. "His ruling at the trial was very clear. If the parties wanted his reasons, they could have taken what they got at the trial.... He couldn't stop everything he was doing and produce a one-hundred-and-ten-page document."

Marlys weathered the storm, which she had expected. If the decision went against Ken Parks, one of the arguments she intended to put to the Supreme Court of Canada was unreasonable delay. She couldn't introduce the issue of delay unless it was part of the appeal court proceedings. Despite the ruffled feelings, she had to get her protest on the record.

Gary Trotter rose to present his formal motion that the court substitute a verdict of not guilty by reason of insanity for the original verdict, a simple "not guilty". He repeated some of the arguments he had made for a day and a half.

Judge Krever leaned his head on his hand. "If the premise is that it was a completely unconscious act, how could we?"

Trotter suggested that a new trial could be ordered.

"What is there to re-try?" asked Mr. Justice Brooke.

"Whether somnambulism is sane or insane," explained the Crown lawyer.

Judge Krever wanted to know, "If this court concludes that sleepwalking is insane automatism, would the trial judge have to direct the jury to find insanity?"

"Yes," said Trotter firmly.

Mr. Justice Brooke closed his eyes. "If we send it back for a new trial without any limitation, it would be wide open. Where do we go from there? You're really asking us to try the issue on the basis of the evidence."

"We would be asking the trial judge to do what we can't do," said Judge Krever, enlarging on his colleague's comments.

"Do we have the power to instruct a trial judge to direct a jury?" Judge Brooke wondered, opening his eyes.

The proceedings ended abruptly. As Marlys predicted, the decision was reserved.

"How long will they take?" Ken asked as Marlys packed the transcripts in a moving company's heavy cardboard box.

"Can't tell," she replied. "It could be a month, it could be six months. You never know."

"You never know," said Karen, looking up at Ken's tall, hunched figure. "That's how it always is. You never know."

CHAPTER FIFTEEN

The Decision

The decision of the Court of Appeal of the Supreme Court of Ontario on the matter of the acquittal of Kenneth James Parks was rendered suddenly and unanimously on June 1, 1990. As Marlys Edwardh was leaving the office that Friday afternoon, she was notified that the appeal had been dismissed. Unless the Crown chose to appeal the dismissal to the Supreme Court of Canada, the strange case of the sleepwalker homicide was over.

The trial judge, David Watt, had ruled that the jury could not consider sleepwalking to be a form of legal insanity. The sole issue before the appeal court, therefore, was the correctness of that ruling.

"After reading all of the testimony of the medical experts," wrote Mr. Justice Galligan, "it seems clear to me that while sleep-walking, a person's mind is functioning very abnormally in that the mind's ability to be aware of reality and to exercise voluntary control over physical acts is acutely impaired. However, it seems obvious in this case that the mind must have been functioning in some respects."

How to sort it out? The judges looked to the factor of mental impairment that Brian Dickson in the Supreme Court of Canada declared must exist for behaviour to be considered insanity in the legal sense. Such impairment must arise from illness, disorder, or abnormal condition—and sleepwalking was none of those.

"The thesis of the medical evidence was that the impairment of the respondent's faculties of reason, memory, and understanding was caused not by any disorder or abnormal condition but by a natural, normal condition—sleep," he wrote. "When asleep, no one reasons, remembers or understands. Medical experts do not understand exactly why those faculties do not function during sleep but it is accepted that they do not. In a very real sense, sleep impairs the human mind and its functioning. Sleep, however, can hardly be called an illness, disorder or abnormal condition. It is a perfectly normal condition."

The decision continues with the firm statement, "There was, therefore, no basis upon which the defence of insanity could have been left with the jury. The evidence required that the defence of sleepwalking, as a category of non-insane automatism, be left with it."

Mr. Justice Galligan added, "This case is extremely troubling. The facts are so extreme that it stretches credulity to think that a person could perform all of those apparently deliberate acts over such an extended period of time without volition or consciousness. [But] the wisdom of the jury's verdict cannot be the subject of review in this court."

Mr. Justice Brooke, in concurring with his colleague, added, "If the respondent's acts were not proved to be voluntary, he was not guilty. He is presumed to be sane and not suffering from a disease of the mind. Somnambulism is a disorder of sleep. It is not regarded medically as a disorder of the mind or a disease of the mind."

Marlys called Ken and Karen Parks at once. Karen said, "It's such a relief that it's over. To have the Supreme Court of Ontario agree with you makes this whole thing so much better. But I can't help worrying that the Crown will appeal to the Supreme Court of Canada. Where does that leave us? We're people. We aren't 'the Parks case'. We are two real people who have two children."

Her first year in nursing school had just ended and she was awaiting the results. "She always gets ninety," Ken observed, grinning at her. After two more years of school, she would be a registered nurse. When that happened, they thought they would move out of the province.

"I don't think it would be fair to either of them to have my dad and Ken meet," she explains. "It's better that we go away."

347

Karen no longer expected to be reconciled with her brothers and sisters—especially not with her sisters. In the spring, however, she began having healing times with her father. On a warm day a few weeks before the appeal court verdict, she and Denis went together with the children to the Metro Toronto Zoo, where he romped with Melissa and Brittany. She values a picture she took of him there with Melissa. The scars from the knife wounds are almost hidden by his hair, which has turned white prematurely. There is sadness in his eyes, but he holds the child lovingly and she's laughing.

"He's getting on with his life," Karen said quietly. "He and I can talk now about how much we both miss mum. You can't be angry for ever. He looks at her death now the same as I do. It was an accident. She could just as well have been killed crossing the street."

He was out of the country at the time of the appeal hearing, but she thought he might have read about the decision in the newspapers. "He would be glad for my sake," Karen said earnestly. "He knows how hard this is for me."

Ken looked at Karen, a lot going on in his face, but he said nothing. There was really nothing to say.

In the middle of June 1990, Ken and Karen had a double dose of bad news. The Crown appealed the decision of the Ontario Court of Appeal to the Supreme Court of Canada. The reasoning seemed to be that the degree of violence that accompanied Ken's sleepwalking required something more than a simple acquittal. The country's highest court would be asked to think about *Rabey* again, and think about Ken Parks.

The Parks marriage abruptly fell apart. Karen asked Ken to leave while they tried to sort out their problems with a marriage counsellor and a psychologist. In the anguish of the parting he made an admission torn from his heart.

"There's never a day goes by," he said, "that I don't think about your mother. I feel so bad."

As the summer wore on, with Karen on welfare again and waiting to return to nursing school, they waited for the Supreme Court to decide whether it would allow the appeal or not. Most evenings Ken went back to the townhouse to help Karen put the children to bed. He promised he'd be there to babysit when she needed to study.

There is sadness and weariness between them, but the caring continues too. "I don't know what will happen," Karen commented. "Our situation is really difficult, you know?"